Teaching Mathematics with Fathom™ Dynamic Data™ Software

Contributors Christian Aviles-Scott, Tim Erickson, Christopher David

Project Editor Heather Dever

Consulting Editor Elizabeth DeCarli

Editorial Assistants Aneesa Davenport, Aaron Madrigal, Kristin Burke

Software Development KCP Technologies

Accuracy Checker Dudley Brooks

Production Director McKinley Williams

Production Editor Kristin Ferraioli

Copyeditor Margaret Moore

Production Coordinator Ann Rothenbuhler

Compositors Charice Silverman, Jennifer Young

Art Editor Jason Luz

Design Supervisor Marilyn Perry

Cover Designer Keith Nguyen

Prepress and Printer STI Certified Products, Inc.

Executive Editor Casey FitzSimons

Publisher Steven Rasmussen

This material is based upon work supported by the National Science Foundation under award numbers III–9400091 and DMI–0131833. Any opinions, findings, and conclusions or recommendations expressed in this publication are those of the author(s) and do not necessarily reflect the views of the National Science Foundation.

Some of the activities in this book are adapted from *Data in Depth: Exploring Mathematics with Fathom* by Tim Erickson, originally published by Key Curriculum Press in 2001.

Key Curriculum Press
1150 65th Street
Emeryville, CA 94608
510-595-7000
editorial@keypress.com
www.keypress.com

10 9 8 7 6 5 4 3 2 1 09 08 07 06 05 ISBN 1-55953-687-X

CONTENTS

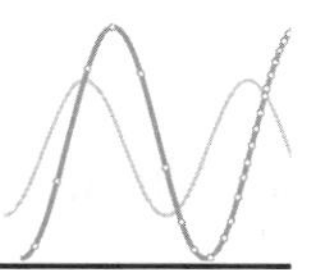

The pervasiveness of data and the importance of patterns in these data in all branches of mathematics make Fathom ideal for high school or college mathematics classrooms. Fathom can be used with algebra to provide tools for describing patterns in data, with geometry to explore data about spatial objects and relationships, with number theory to study the infinite data set of numbers, with probability and simulated data, and with topology's unending sources of data in its descriptions of spaces. Once you start seeing the data in mathematics, they will appear behind every equation, turn up under every integral, and lurk inside every proof.

Fathom is a data tool that becomes a dynamic environment whenever there exists a need to keep track of something, whether numeric or categorical. Creating a collection to record and systematize a mathematical object or relationship can lead to opportunities for exploring, conjecturing, and asking questions that lead to deep understanding. What starts as record keeping evolves into pattern recognition and model building.

Statistics, as it deals with variability and uncertainty, can hardly exist *without* data, and yet data, as often as not, get along without statistics. When the patterns in the data have sharp edges or represent mathematical relationships, the powerful tools of statistical inference have little place; but manipulation and visualization of the data remain central to understanding and describing the mathematics that underlies the data. By all means, rely on using Fathom for statistical situations, but expect to find ways to also use it in all of mathematics.

LEARNING MATHEMATICS WITH DATA

Working with data can make mathematics easier. Data make mathematics more concrete, because the data are often tied to the real world. Data make mathematics more connected, because data often come from contexts that have meaning outside the classroom.

On the other hand, working with data often makes mathematics more difficult because answers are often less definite. Data may have variability, which means that there is often no "correct" answer to a question. As you gain experience working with messy data, the underlying questions may become more conditional and hypothetical.

How can you, as an instructor, address the difficulties of working with messy data while benefiting from exploring in a connected and concrete dynamic environment?

- **Address variability head-on.** Develop a classroom culture that discourages the question "What's the answer?" and replaces it with "What do we know about the answer?" This begins informally, and gradually becomes more quantitative.
- **Be visual and use graphs often to answer questions about data.** This is especially useful when information isn't obvious from the numbers alone. Graphs make patterns (and deviations from patterns) clear, and good graphs are tools for prediction and inference.
- **Connect the areas of mathematics.** Use algebra—starting with very simple algebra—as you explore data and statistics, and connect geometric ideas to algebra through data.
- **Define terms and specify assumptions.** In any response, students should describe their assumptions and definitions; they should learn to habitually recognize their assumptions.
- **Predict, predict, predict.** Insist often that students make explicit written conjectures about the data, what the data will show, and what they might conclude. Do this before the students study the data. Then after the analysis, make a point of comparing the results to the predictions. Students need to work up to being inventive and tenacious about conjectures; don't expect them to be able to immediately articulate the details. Consistently challenge students to improve their conjectures.

The activities in this book take this approach. Some activities are quite challenging if completed to the fullest. But they all can be approached by students with varying levels of experience and tenacity.

USING THE ACTIVITIES

These activities provide a sample of what Fathom can do to deepen student understanding of algebra, geometry, precalculus, calculus, and statistics. Look for more activities for algebra and statistics from Key Curriculum Press.

Features of the Activities

A typical activity has three main sections: an introduction that describes the objectives of the activity and provides some motivation and context; a section titled Investigate, in which students follow steps to explore the data and answer questions; and a section titled Explore More, which lists possible extensions of the investigation. (Additionally Extensions sections are included in the Activity Notes.) Many activities also include a beginning section called Make a Conjecture, which helps students think about what they expect to see. Some activities have students experiment by manipulating the data or to explore the data using pencil and paper before investigating with Fathom. In all these sections, students are asked to write about what they are learning.

Some questions require simple answers (a number or an equation, perhaps), but others ask for more involved written responses. These questions attempt to guide students into expressing their ideas and hypotheses, reasoning about why certain things happen, and explaining their observations and conclusions. How can you encourage your students to engage in thoughtful writing? How can you reap the benefits of these questions without having to force every student to spend the required time and energy on each written response? This will depend on the particulars of your own classroom and students, but you might find these suggestions helpful:

- **Provide a why.** Mathematicians communicate with each other through writing to provide clear explanations or arguments or to convince each other of the truth of an argument. They also write to help them think through a problem. Some students may claim not to know where to start on a written response. You can ask them to describe what they do know, what they can observe, and what they don't understand.
- **Provide a model.** One way to encourage thoughtful writing is to provide models of written responses. You might provide a model answer for a question that is a variation of the one you would like the students to answer, and ask them to imitate the model. Or you might provide a response to a question, but one that has some flaws in it. Students can then critique the argument or provide a better response. Either of these approaches will give students a better idea of a good response.
- **Talk it through.** Students might benefit from working through questions in small groups, or even in a whole class discussion, since they will have to contend with other arguments or counterarguments. You can encourage the participation of classroom members by focusing not exclusively on the book's questions, but also on relevant "meta-questions" such as "What was difficult about this question?"; "Why did the writer think this question was important?"; "What question do you think would have been a better one?"

The Explore More suggestions at the end of an activity can be very challenging. Students who finish an activity early can get started on Explore More questions, but expect many of these questions, as well as the Extensions, to turn into long-term projects. Occasionally, you might want to prepare a demonstration of one of these questions as a class wrap-up.

The amount of specific Fathom instruction varies throughout the activities. In each chapter, the earlier activities assume no or limited familiarity with the software, while the later activities assume more. You may want to have a few copies of the *Quick Reference* card available to students as they work. As an instructor, you will probably want to be familiar with the basics of the software going into the activity. You might try the activity yourself, do a few tours from the *Learning Guide* that comes with Fathom, or read The Structure of Fathom, an overview provided in that book and in Fathom Help. (The *Quick Reference* card and the *Learning Guide* are installed with the software as PDFs.)

Activity Notes

Activity Notes are collected in the last chapter and contain answers to the questions posed in the activities, as well as stumbling blocks that students might encounter. They offer suggestions of how much class time to allow for activities, any prerequisite Fathom or mathematics ideas and terms the activity assumes, and the skills students will practice, as well as general notes on the activity and possible extensions. They also indicate which documents accompany the activity. All of the documents used in these activities come with Fathom; they are installed with the software and you can find them in the **Sample Documents | Teaching Math with Fathom** folder. The Activity Notes also include suggestions on other sample documents that you can use as extensions.

A CLASSROOM OF ENGAGED LEARNERS

Students learn best when they develop the concepts and tools they need to answer interesting questions. These suggestions about teaching with technology and using this book will help you include these activities as a meaningful part of your curriculum.

- **Think developmentally.** First, allow fooling-around time with new ideas and tools. Just as most first-graders need to play with pattern blocks before they start exploring symmetry, so do most of the rest of us need to play with computers and data before we are ready to buckle down and be systematic. Second, build ties to the concrete. Data analysis gets abstract fast. The more you can represent the data or their manipulation using physical materials, the better.
- **Have students work in pairs.** Students working in pairs solve many problems, especially those having to do with learning to use the program. But students who are talking to each other also stand a better chance of understanding the mathematics. Besides, pairs use only half as many computers.
- **Connect the activity to textbook topics.** Also help students compare and make analogies to other ideas as they work on the activity.
- **Observe students' work at computers.** The student sheets provide questions to answer, so you can look over students' work and listen to them as you circulate about the room. You can tell which pairs are on task and moving along, as well as where you may have to help students overcome problems. Do not hesitate to have students help each other.
- **Invite students to come up with their own ideas and methods.** For example, if students need a measure of spread, give them time to invent one that fills their need. Will they invent the standard deviation? No, but once they have their own measures, their first encounter with standard deviation will not be so traumatic. They will have already solved the question of why anyone would ever invent this.
- **Stretch the problem.** Encourage students to stretch their understanding of a situation by reframing it or examining its limiting cases. Look for alternate ways of representing the same problem, or consider changing one part of the question. Reinterpreting and reassessing a problem helps students better understand the core mathematics underlying the situation.
- **Look for opportunities to help students work backward.** Mathematics abounds with two-way processes such as adding and subtracting, simplifying and factoring, or differentiating and integrating. For some students, knowing how to undo something helps explain how to do it. Look for places where students can practice reverse-engineering a problem or mathematical idea.
- **Encourage "What if . . . ?" questions.** These types of questions can help students notice different properties of a situation and can also help launch them on their own investigations. Examining the types of questions they are asked by you or the book can make the questions seem less arbitrary. It can also help students become strong question posers.
- **Allow students time to reflect on things.** Allow time for students to make comments and exchange views about what they understand. Moderated classroom discussions are a good way of sharing insights and questions, and they can also lead to helpful debate and expose gaps in understanding.

USING FATHOM IN DIFFERENT CLASSROOM SETTINGS

Different schools have different classroom settings in which computers are used. Fathom was designed with this variety in mind, and you can optimize its display features for your own setting. You'll also need to adapt your teaching strategies to available resources. Here are some suggestions for teaching with Fathom in a classroom with one computer, one computer and a computer projection device, several computers, or in a computer lab.

A Classroom with One Computer

Perhaps the best use of a single computer is to have small groups of students take turns using it. Each group can investigate or confirm their conjectures while working at their desks with paper and pencil or graphing calculators. In this case, each group has the opportunity during a class period to use the computer for a short time. Alternatively, you can give each group a day on which to do an investigation on the computer while other groups are doing the same or different investigations at their desks.

A Classroom with One Computer and a Computer Projection Device

There are a variety of devices that plug into computers so that you can display screen output to a large group. You or a student can act as a sort of emcee for an investigation, asking the class questions: "What should we try next?"; "What kind of a table will best display these data?"; "How should we adjust the scale on this axis?" With a projection device, you and your students can prepare demonstrations, or students can make presentations. Watching you use Fathom as a demonstration tool is a good way for students to learn some fundamentals of the program before they go to the computer lab. You can also model good presentation techniques for students. Use large text in objects to make text and figures clearly visible from all corners of a classroom. (Choose font size in objects from **Preferences.**)

A Classroom with Several Computers

If you can divide your class into groups of three or four students and give each group access to a computer, you can plan whole lessons around computer investigations. Be sure to

- Introduce to the whole class what it is they're expected to do.
- Provide students with some kind of written explanation of the investigation or problem they will work on. You can leave room on the explanation sheet for students to record some of their findings. For some open-ended explorations you can simply write the problem or question on the chalkboard.
- Make sure students understand that everybody in a group needs the chance to operate the computer.
- Make sure that the students in a group who are not actually operating the computer contribute to the group discussion and give input to the student at the computer.
- Move among groups, posing questions, giving help if needed, and keeping students on task.
- Summarize students' findings in a whole-class discussion to bring closure to the lesson.

A Computer Lab

Instructors often find that even if enough computers are available for students to work individually, it's perhaps best to have students work in pairs. Students learn best when they communicate about what they're learning, and students working together can better stimulate ideas and help one another. If you do have students working at their own computers, encourage them to talk about what they're doing and to compare findings with their nearest neighbor—they should peek over each other's shoulders. The previous suggestions for students working in small groups apply to students working in pairs as well.

WHERE TO GO FROM HERE

The activities in this book are meant to get you and your students started exploring data and mathematics with Fathom. Here are some other resources:

- Fathom comes with over 300 sample documents. Some of these, located in the **Mathematics** and **Statistics** folders, are simulations or demonstrations that can aid students' understanding of abstract concepts. Most of the rest of the documents contain data taken from all areas of study, including science, social science, language and the arts, and sports. To open a sample document, choose **Open Sample Document** from the **Help** menu. To browse descriptions of these documents, choose **Sample Documents** from the **Help** menu.
- *Data Are Everywhere: Project Ideas for Fathom* is a book of project ideas that students can independently explore. This book comes with all editions of the software.
- At the Fathom Resource Center, you can share data and activities with instructors from all around the world. Choose **Fathom Resource Center** from the **Help** menu, or go to www.keypress.com/fathom.

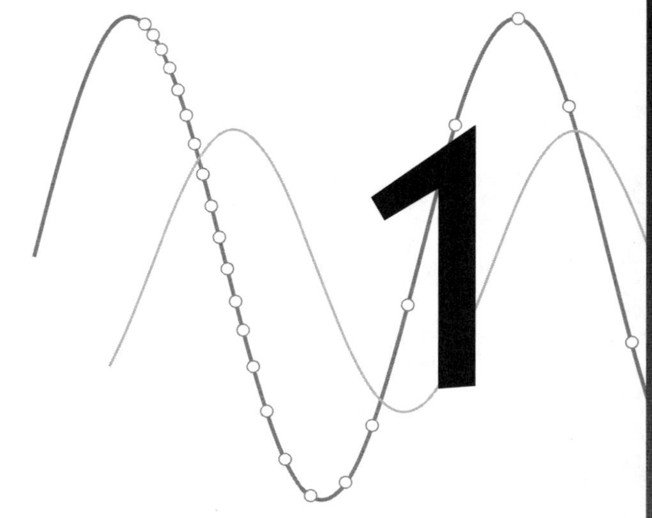
1

Algebra 1

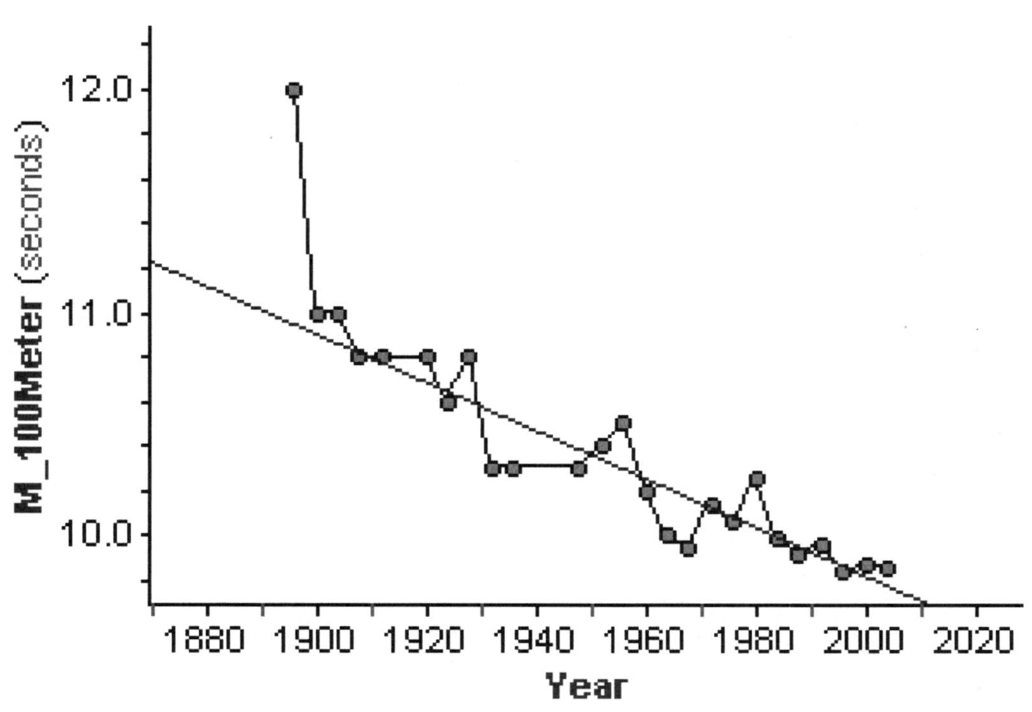
12.0
11.0
10.0
M_100Meter (seconds)
1880
1900
1920
1940
1960
1980
2000
2020
Year

Mammals' Brains

In this activity, you'll study the brain sizes of 62 mammals. You'll use Fathom to find the mammals with the largest and smallest brains. You'll see that your answers depend on how you define "largest" and "smallest."

MAKE A CONJECTURE

Before looking at the data, think about what you expect to see.

Q1 Assume that you could weigh the brains of the African elephant, mountain beaver, human, and rat. Predict their order from largest to smallest brain, based on brain weight. Explain your reasoning.

Q2 Assume that you could weigh these mammals' bodies, too. Would the four body weights go in the same order as the brain weights?

Q3 Assume that you calculate the ratio of brain weight to body weight for these four mammals. Predict their order from largest to smallest brain, based on brain-to-body ratio. Explain your reasoning.

INVESTIGATE

Now you'll use Fathom to look at the actual data.

1. Open the document **Mammals.ftm.** A box of gold balls appears. This is a *collection.* It stores the data.

2. Double-click the collection. The collection *inspector* opens. Click the **Cases** tab to show the data about one mammal. Each mammal is a *case.* Each piece of data, such as *Species, BodyWeight,* or *BrainWeight,* is an *attribute.* Use the arrows at the bottom to browse through the cases.

Inspect Mammals

Cases | Mea... | Com... | Dis... | Cat... | Imp...

Attribute	Value	Formula
Species	Donkey	
BodyWeight	187.1 kg	
BrainWeight	419 g	
Nondreami...		
DreamingS...		
TotalSleep	3.1 h	
LifeSpan	40 y	
Gestation	365 d	
Predation	5	
Exposure	5	
Danger	5	

14/62 Show Details

Q4 Find the brain weight (with units) of a human.

Q5 Find the body weight (with units) of a rat.

A *case table* is a good way to look at all of the data at once.

3. Select the collection by clicking it. Choose **New | Case Table** from the **Object** menu. A table appears that shows all of the data.

Q6 Which mammal has the brain that weighs the most? The least? (*Hint:* You can order the data by selecting an attribute's column and choosing **Sort Ascending** or **Sort Descending** from the **Table** menu.)

Q7 List the African elephant, mountain beaver, human, and rat in order from largest brain weight to smallest brain weight.

Q8 List these four mammals in order from largest body weight to smallest body weight. Is this the same order as for their brain weights?

Graphs are another convenient way to look at the data.

4. Drag a new graph from the object shelf into your document. An empty graph appears.

5. Drag the attribute name *BodyWeight* from the case table to the graph. Drop the attribute below the horizontal axis to create a dot plot. Point the cursor at one dot to see that body weight in the lower-left corner of the Fathom window. Click the dot to highlight the case everywhere and show that case in the inspector.

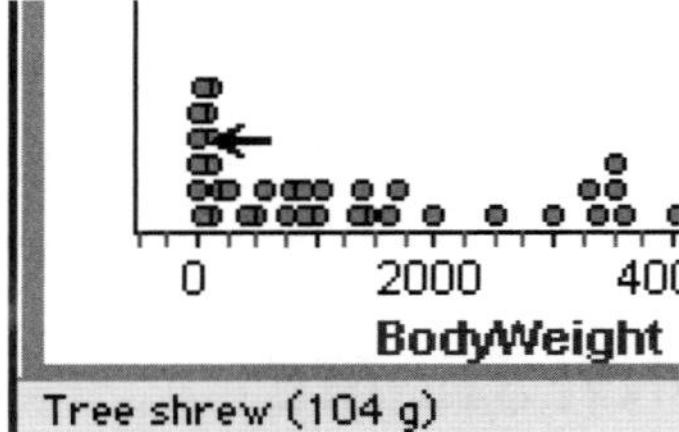

6. Make another dot plot of *BrainWeight.*

Q9 Using a dot plot, find the mammal whose brain weighs the most.

Q10 Are you able to use a dot plot to find the mammal whose brain weighs the least? Explain how you found it, or explain why you couldn't.

Q11 Do the brain weights of all 62 mammals go in the same order as their body weights? Explain how you found your answer, and compare this answer to your answer for Q8. What do the results mean?

7. Select the dot plot of *BrainWeight.* Use the pop-up menu in the upper-right corner to change to a histogram. A *histogram* shows the number (or *frequency*) of values that fall in certain intervals (or *bins*). Put your cursor over one of the bars to see the frequency of cases in that bin. Click a bar to highlight all of those cases everywhere.

Q12 Which mammals have a brain weight between 500 g and 1000 g?

You've found the mammals that have the largest and smallest brains, based on brain weight. Does that mean they have the largest and smallest brains for their overall size?

Q13 By hand or with a calculator, find the ratio of brain weight to body weight for the mountain beaver. What are the units of your ratio? What are some equivalent ways to write your ratio?

Next you'll create an attribute that finds each mammal's brain-to-body ratio.

8. In the case table, scroll to the far right. Click **<new>** in the last column, type `BrainToBody`, and press **Enter.** An empty column appears.

9. Select the *BrainToBody* column and choose **Edit Formula** from the **Edit** menu. The *formula editor* opens. Type `BrainWeight/BodyWeight` and click **OK.** The ratios appear.

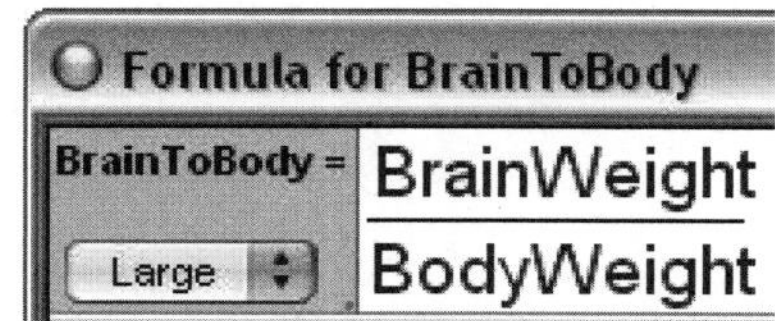

Q14 In the case table, find the brain-to-body ratio (with units) for the mountain beaver. Is this one of the answers you got for Q13?

Q15 Which mammal has the largest brain for its overall size? The smallest? What are the ratios? Are these the mammals with the brains that weigh the most and the least?

Q16 List the African elephant, mountain beaver, human, and rat in order from largest brain-to-body ratio to smallest brain-to-body ratio. Is this the same order that you predicted in Q3?

Q17 The order in Q16 should not be the same as the order in Q7. What does it mean about the sizes of these mammals' brains compared to the sizes of their bodies?

10. Make a graph of *BrainToBody* and change it to a box plot. A *box plot* shows how the data values divide into fourths (or *quartiles*). The upper and lower segments (or *whiskers*) each represent one-fourth of the values, and each half of the box represents one-fourth of the values. The vertical segment in the middle of the box is the *median*, and the distance between the ends of the box is the *interquartile range.*

Q18 Do more mammals have brain-to-body ratios above 0.01 or below 0.01?

Q19 Approximate the median and interquartile range for a mammal's brain-to-body ratio.

A *summary table* is a more precise way to find numerical statistics.

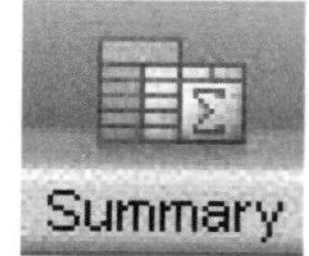

11. Drag a new summary table from the object shelf into your document. Drop the attribute *BrainToBody* in the row or column of the summary table. The mean appears automatically.
12. Select the summary table and choose **Add Five-Number Summary** from the **Summary** menu. The five number summary is added to the summary table.
13. Choose **Add Formula** from the **Summary** menu. Type `iqr()` and press **Enter.** The interquartile range is added to the summary table. You may have to resize the table to see all the formulas. If you click a formula, its value will be highlighted in the table.

Q20 What are the median and interquartile range? Round your answers to four decimal places.

Q21 What is a typical value for a mammal's brain-to-body ratio? Explain how you chose your answer.

EXPLORE MORE

1. Create a new attribute that gives each mammal's brain weight as a *percentage* of its body weight. What formula did you use? How do the brain-to-body percentages compare to the brain-to-body ratios? How does a graph of the percentages compare to a graph of the ratios? Does this make sense mathematically?
2. From the data that you have, discuss whether brain weight would be a good way to judge intelligence. Would brain-to-body ratio be better?

Reading the News

You will need

- newspaper
- centimeter ruler
- clock with a second hand or stopwatch

Somebody once said that listening to a half-hour news broadcast on the radio was the same as reading the front section of the newspaper. You're going to find out if that's true.

MAKE A CONJECTURE

You probably already have ideas about what will happen. Look through the front section of a newspaper and think about what you expect.

Q1 How long would it take you to read the front section of the newspaper aloud?

Q2 How many newspaper pages could you read in 30 minutes?

EXPERIMENT

First you'll choose a partner and collect data.

1. One person is the timer and the other is the reader. The reader picks a place to start reading. When the timer says "Go," the reader reads until the timer says "Stop." Read aloud as if you're a news announcer.
2. Measure and record the *vertical* distance of the column from your starting point to your stopping point. You'll read six different paragraphs, each for a different length of time. Use paragraphs in columns that are all the same width.

Name		
Time (s)	Vertical distance (cm)	Vertical distance(cm)
10		
20		
30		
40		
50		
60		

3. After one person reads six times, switch roles and repeat.

INVESTIGATE (BY HAND)

Q3 How many vertical centimeters of text are there on a typical page of your newspaper? Consider all columns, and exclude pictures and ads.

Q4 Use your data to approximate how long it would take each of you to read one page.

4. Make scatter plots of *vertical distance* versus *time.* Scale the vertical axes to match your data.

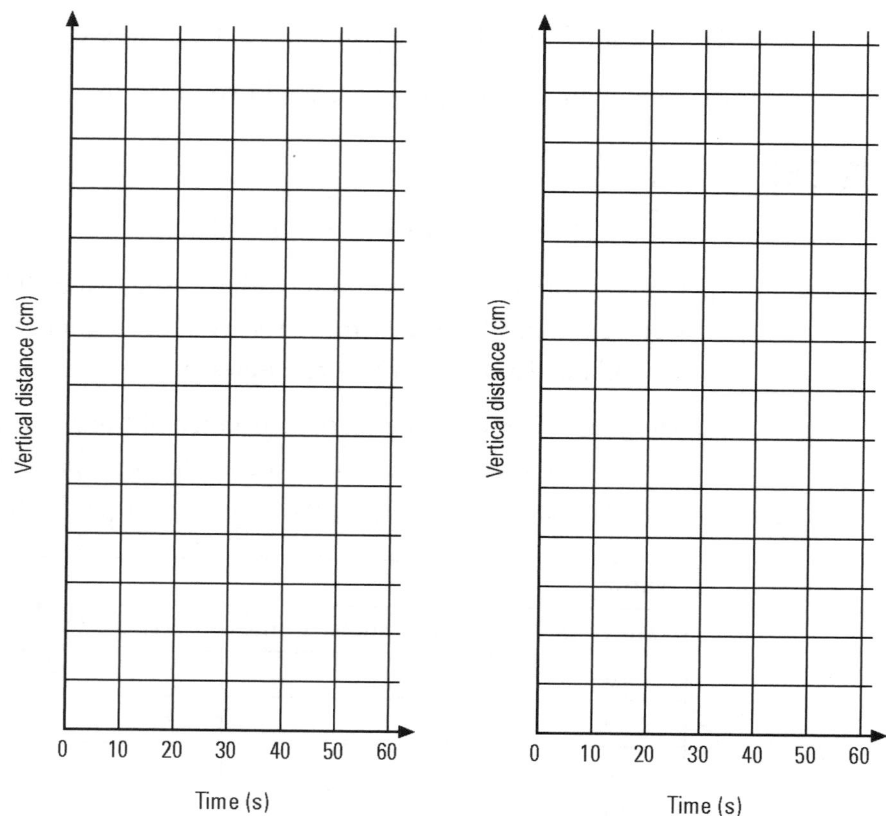

5. For each graph, draw a single straight line that approximates the data.

Q5 Do your lines go through the point (0, 0)? Should they? Explain.

Q6 Calculate the slope of both lines.

Q7 Your slopes' units are centimeters per second. That sounds like a speed. What does it mean in connection with reading?

Q8 Who reads faster? Explain how you can tell from the graphs. Explain how you can tell from the slopes.

Q9 Use your slopes to approximate how many centimeters you would each read in 100 seconds.

INVESTIGATE (WITH FATHOM)

Now you'll further analyze the data with Fathom.

6. Start Fathom. You'll have an empty document.
7. Drag a new case table from the object shelf into your document. Click <**new**> in the case table. Type `Time` and press **Enter** to make a new attribute. An empty collection appears.
8. Make two more attributes, *VertDist1* and *VertDist2,* for the vertical distances of you and your partner.
9. Enter the data from your table in step 2. Type the first value and its unit under each attribute. The unit will be applied to every value for that attribute.

	Time	VertDist1	VertDist2
units	seconds	centimeters	
1	10 s	20 cm	

10. Drag a new graph from the object shelf into your document. Drag the attribute *Time* from the case table and drop it below the horizontal axis. Drag *VertDist1* to the vertical axis. The graph changes to a scatter plot. Compare Fathom's scatter plot to the one you made.
11. Select the graph by clicking it. Now choose **Add Movable Line** from the **Graph** menu. A line and its equation appear. Choose **Lock Intercept at Zero** from the **Graph** menu to make the line pass through the origin.
12. Get comfortable with changing the line. Then move the line to best approximate the points. (*Hint:* When you try to move the line, you may accidentally grab a data point and change your data. If this happens, choose **Undo** from the **Edit** menu until everything is all right.)

Q10 What is the equation of the line that approximates the points? Write the equation exactly as Fathom shows it, including units.

Q11 The quantity multiplied by *Time* in the equation should be close to something you found before. What does this coefficient represent?

13. Select the graph and choose **Remove Movable Line** from the **Graph** menu. Now choose **Plot Function** from the **Graph** menu. In the formula editor, type the right side of the equation from Q10, including units, and click **OK.** This makes a fixed, unmovable line.

14. Drag *VertDist2* from the case table to your graph. When you are over the vertical axis, you'll notice a plus sign at the top of the axis. Drop the attribute on the plus sign, making a scatter plot of both sets of points.

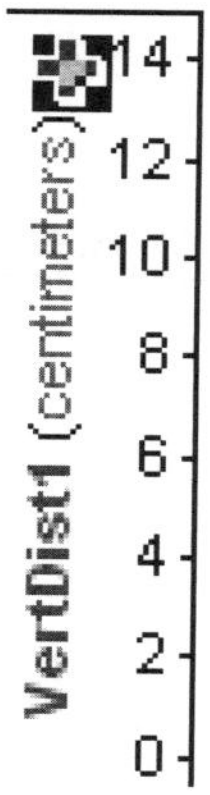

15. Repeat steps 11–13 to find a line that fits the new points.

Q12 How do the equations of the two lines compare? From the equations, how can you tell who reads faster?

16. Move the cursor over either line until you see a red point. Click and drag the red point to trace the line. The coordinates of the trace appear beside the point and in the lower-left corner of the Fathom window.

Q13 Use the lines and trace feature to answer these questions.

a. How many centimeters could each of you read in 100 seconds?

b. How long would it take each of you to read one page?

c. How long would it take each of you to read the front section of your newspaper? Compare this to your prediction in Q1.

d. How many pages could each of you read in 30 minutes? Compare this to your prediction in Q2. Did you overestimate or underestimate?

Q14 Is it true that listening to a half-hour news broadcast on the radio is the same as reading the front section of the newspaper? Explain.

Q15 What are some factors that would make reading the front section of the newspaper take more or less time than listening to a news broadcast? How might it be possible to make the timing about the same?

EXPLORE MORE

1. Make a graph with *VertDist* (1 or 2) on the horizontal axis and *Time* on the vertical axis. (*Hint:* You can swap the axes in a scatter plot by dragging the attribute on one axis and dropping it on the other axis.) Find a line to fit the points. What does the slope of this line mean? How is it related to the slope in Q6?

2. How would your results change if the newspaper columns were twice as wide? Half as wide?

Slope-Intercept Form

In this activity, you'll study data that fit perfectly on a line. By changing the data, you'll explore how the equation of the line changes.

INVESTIGATE

1. Open the document **SlopeIntercept.ftm.** You'll see a collection and case table of x- and y-coordinates. You'll also see a scatter plot of the coordinate pairs (x, y). Notice that the points form a perfect line.

Q1 Look for a pattern in the coordinates. What equation relates the x- and y-coordinates? Check your guess by selecting the graph and choosing **Median-Median Line** from the **Graph** menu. (*Note:* For this activity, you only need to know that a median-median line gives you a line that fits the points and shows you the equation of that line.)

You are now going to explore what happens when you add the same amount to every y-coordinate. You'll use a slider that allows you to easily explore the effect of adding different amounts.

2. Drag a new slider from the object shelf into your document. The slider will be called *V1*. Drag the slider and notice how the value of *V1* changes to different decimal values. Click the green "play" button to watch the slider change by itself; click the red "stop" button to stop it.

3. Double-click near the slider's axis to show the slider inspector. Enter the values shown here, which rename the slider b and limit its values to integers (multiples of 1) between -10 and $+10$. Close the inspector and drag the slider to test its behavior.

b = 5.00

-8 -6 -4 -2 0 2 4 6 8 1

Inspect Slider

Properties

Property	Value	Formula
b	5	
Max_updat...		
Lower	-10	
Upper	10	
Restrict_to...	1	
Reverse_s...	false	

4. In the case table, create a new attribute, *yPLUSb*. Define it with a formula that adds the value of slider b to each y-coordinate.

Q2 Set the value of b to 4. How do the coordinates *yPLUSb* compare to y? If you make a scatter plot of points $(x, yPLUSb)$, how do you think it will compare to the scatter plot of points (x, y)? You'll check your answer in the next few steps.

5. Select the scatter plot of (x, y) and choose **Duplicate Graph** from the **Object** menu.

6. Select the duplicate graph and choose **Show Axis Links** from the **Graph** menu. A broken chain link appears by each axis. Drag the broken chain link from the x-axis and drop it on the x-axis of the original graph. Do the same to link the y-axes. Now, if you change the axes in one graph, the axes change in the other graph, too.

7. Drag the attribute *yPLUSb* from the case table and drop it on the y-axis of the duplicate graph. You should have a scatter plot of (x, *yPLUSb*).

Q3 How does the scatter plot of (x, *yPLUSb*) compare to the scatter plot of (x, y)? How did the points change when you added b to each y-coordinate? Compare the results to your prediction in Q2. (*Hint:* If you select a point in one graph, its corresponding point will be selected in the other graph.)

Q4 How does the equation of the line for (x, *yPLUSb*) compare to the equation for (x, y)? How did the equation change when you added b to each y-coordinate?

Q5 An important aspect of any line is the place where it crosses the y-axis, or its *y-intercept.* What is the y-intercept for the line for (x, *yPLUSb*)?

Q6 Drag the slider to change the value of b. For several different values of b, notice how the points, the equation, and the y-intercept change. Write a few sentences that describe the general effects of b.

Q7 Use what you've learned to predict the equation of each line.

a.

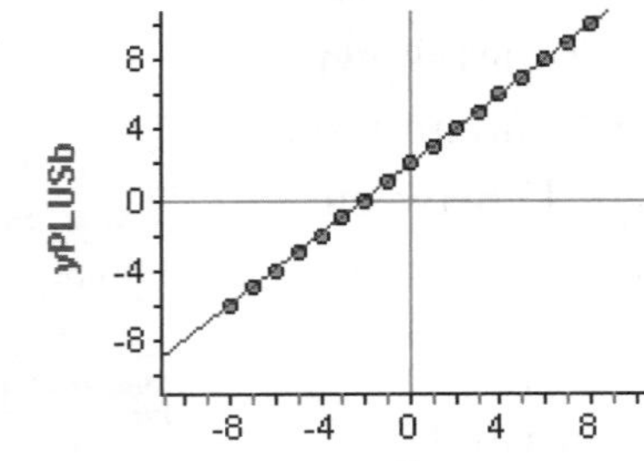

b.

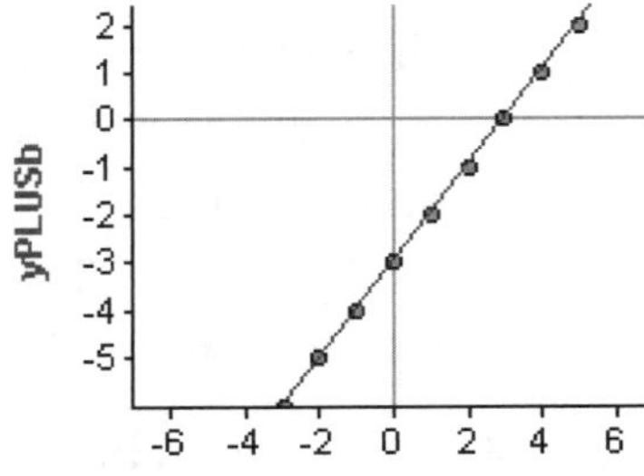

c.

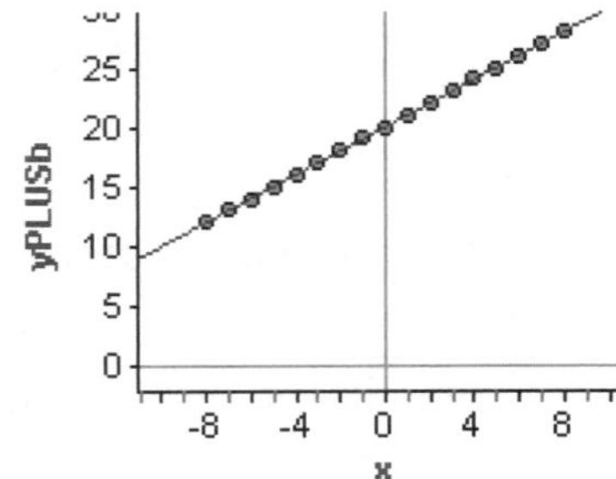

Now that you've created a slider for b and explored the effects of adding to the y-coordinate, it's time for you to explore the effects of multiplication.

8. Create a slider called m that goes from -10 to $+10$ by multiples of 0.25.

9. Create a new attribute called *mTIMESy*. Give it a formula that multiplies the value of m by the original y-coordinates.

10. Make a scatter plot of (x, *mTIMESy*). Use a duplicate graph with linked axes so that you can compare the points and equation for (x, *mTIMESy*) to the points and equation for (x, y).

11. Drag the slider for m and watch how the coordinates in the case table change, how the points on the graph change, and how the equation changes.

Q8 How does the scatter plot of (x, *mTIMESy*) compare to the scatter plot of (x, y)? How do the points change as the value of m changes? How does the equation of the line change? Write a few sentences that describe the general effects of m.

Q9 Another important aspect of any line is its *slope*. Write a few sentences explaining how m relates to the slope of the line.

Q10 Use what you've learned to predict the equation of each line.

a.

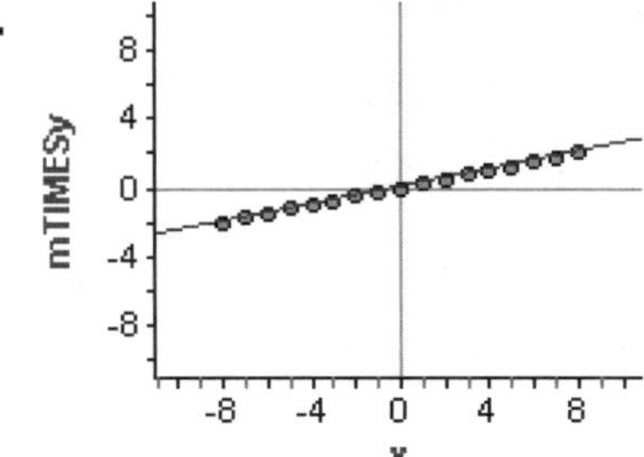

b.

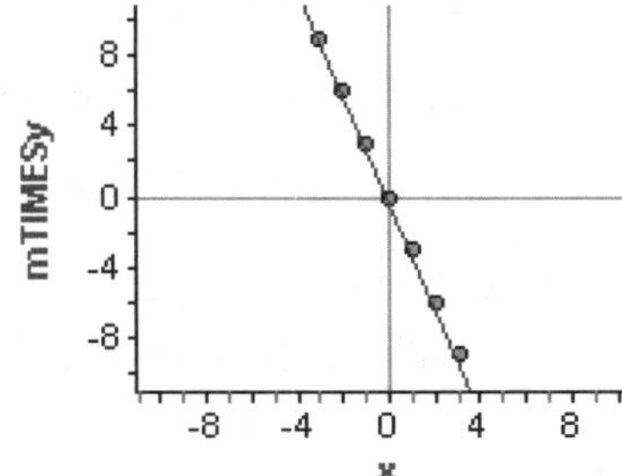

c.

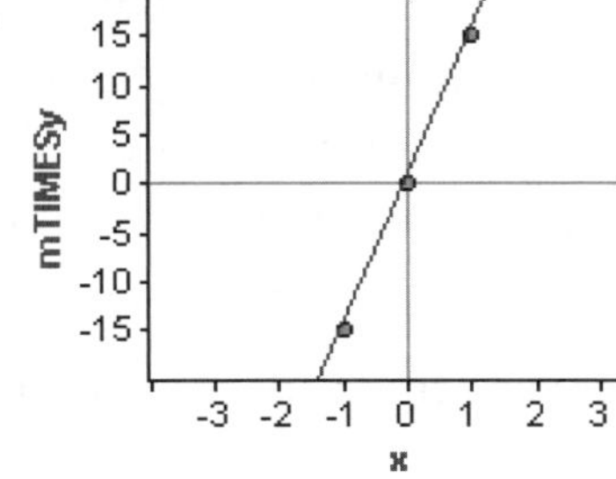

Now you'll explore the combined effects of multiplication and addition.

12. Create a new attribute, *mTIMESyPLUSb*. Give it a formula that multiplies the original y-coordinates by m and then adds b. Make a new scatter plot linked to the original plot. Explore as much as necessary for you to understand the combined effects of m and b.

Q11 Use what you've learned to predict the equation of each line shown or described here.

a.

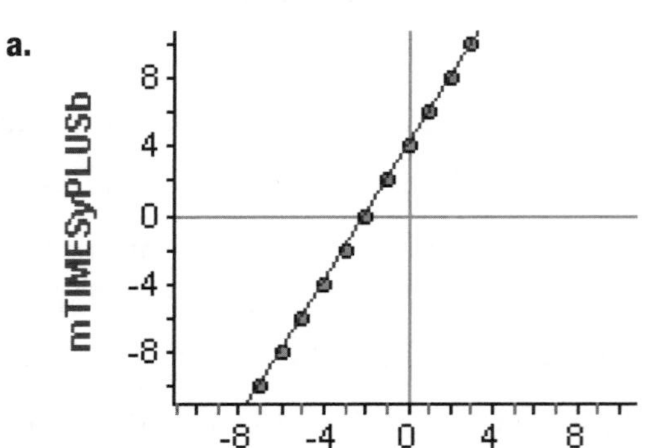

b.

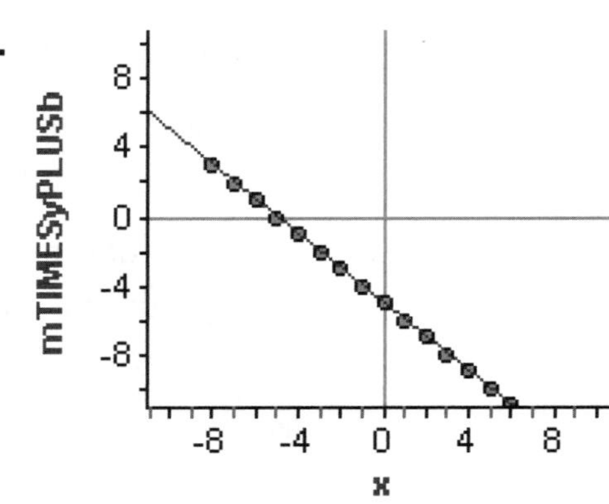

c. A line with slope 0.75 and y-intercept -9.

d. A line with y-intercept 0 and slope 12.

e. A line with slope 3.5 and y-intercept 2.

Q12 A linear equation in the form $y = mx + b$ is said to be in *slope-intercept form.* Why is this an appropriate name for this form?

EXPLORE MORE

1. Make a graph of (x, *mTIMESy*). Then add *mTIMESyPLUSb* as a second attribute to the y-axis by dropping it on the plus sign. You should see two sets of points and two lines. Adjust the sliders and watch how the lines change relative to each other. What geometric word describes the two lines?

2. Explore what happens if you change the x-coordinates instead of the y-coordinates. Look at scatter plots of (*xPLUSb*, y), (*mTIMESx*, y), and (*mTIMESxPLUSb*, y). Generalize the results and then explain how the results compare to the changes for the y-coordinates. When you change the x-coordinates, does b still relate to the y-intercept? Does m still relate to the slope? If yes, explain how. If not, explain what b and m do relate to.

The Ocean Train

You will need

- schedule for the Ocean train

In this activity, you'll study a passenger train called the Ocean, which runs from Halifax, Nova Scotia, through New Brunswick, to Montréal, Quebec. The trip takes place on parts of two days. If you leave Halifax Saturday afternoon, you get to Montréal Sunday morning.

How fast does the Ocean go? You'll use Fathom to find out.

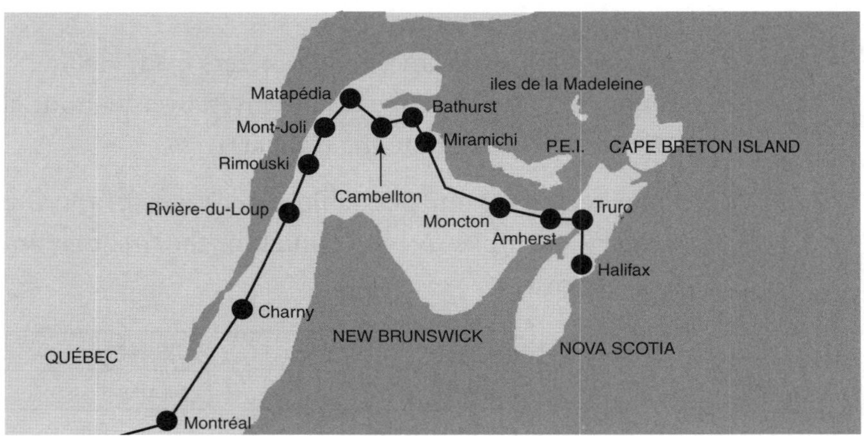

UNDERSTAND THE DATA

Train schedules can be confusing. You have part of the VIA Rail Canada timetables that shows information for two trains. Notice that the schedule uses a 24-hour clock, so 1920 means 7:20 P.M.

Assume that you'll travel from Halifax on a Thursday in next January. Work with a partner to understand the schedule.

Q1 What day of the week could you *not* leave Halifax?

Q2 When does the train leave Halifax in January?

Q3 How many kilometers is it from Halifax to Moncton?

Q4 What's the first city after midnight on the trip?

Q5 What's the next city the train stops at after Matapédia?

Q6 How many kilometers between Charlo and Montmagny?

INVESTIGATE

1. Start Fathom. In a new document, create a collection and case table for the data in the train schedule. You are interested in speed, so distance and time are important. The names of the stations are useful, too. At a minimum, you need these attributes:

   Station (the station name)
   Distance (the distance in kilometers from Halifax)
   Hour (the hour the train *arrives,* by a 24-hour clock)
   Minute (the minute the train arrives)

2. Once you have your case table, enter cases for the Ocean train's schedule in January. Use units to enter values for the first case and the units will be applied to every case.

	Station	Distance	Hour	Minute
units		kilometers	hours	minutes
1	Halifax	0 km	13 h	5 min
2	Truro	103 km	14 h	30 min
3	Springhill Junction	200 km	15 h	55 min
4	Amherst	227 km	16 h	20 min
5	Sackville	243 km	16 h	37 min
6	Moncton	304 km	17 h	25 min

Between Amherst and Sackville, the train goes 16 kilometers in 17 minutes, which is about 56.5 kilometers per hour. Is that a typical speed for this train? Next, you'll find a pattern for all of the cases.

3. Drag an empty graph from the object shelf into your document. Make a scatter plot of *Distance* versus *Hour.* You should see something like this graph.

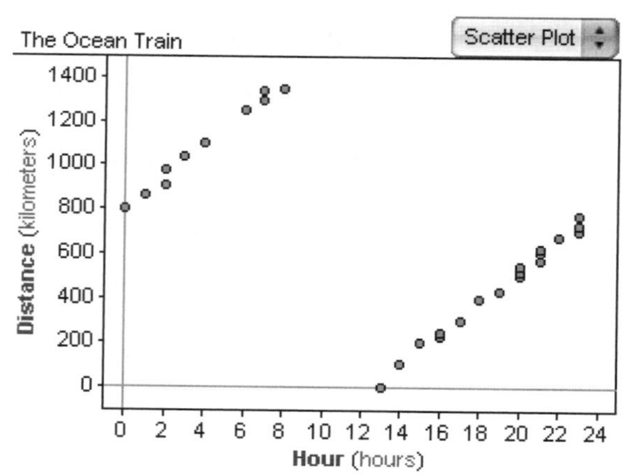

Q7 Why are there two "lines" of points? What does each group of points represent?

Q8 You need to "fix" the data to show only one line of points. Explain one way that you could manipulate the data to do that. (*Hint:* Think of ways to create and combine attributes so that you don't have to change the original data.)

4. Now follow your plan and fix the data to show only one line of points. Make a scatter plot with your new attribute(s) to verify that you have one line. Your graph should look something like this. If you don't get one line, try again. When you find a good fix, add it to your answer to Q8.

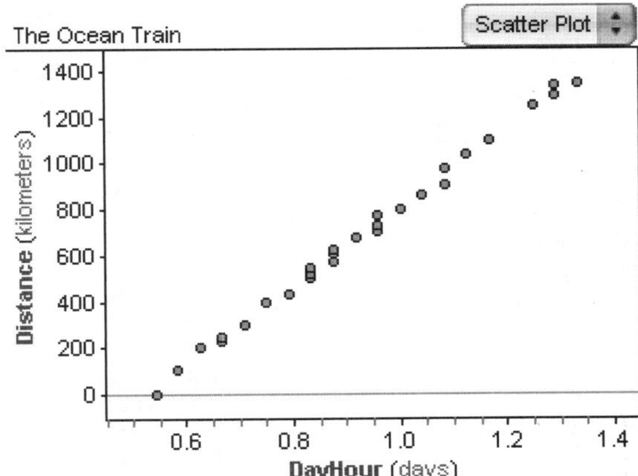

5. In some places, for example, between Bathurst and Jacquet River, the graph of points form a vertical line. What does that mean about the train's speed? Look back at the data and find another way to manipulate the data to fix this problem.

6. Select the graph and choose **Add Movable Line** from the **Graph** menu. Adjust the movable line to fit the points as best you can.

Q9 What is the equation of your line of fit?

Q10 What feature of your line represents the train's average speed? What is the average speed, including units? Does that seem like a reasonable speed for a passenger train?

Q11 What is the vertical intercept of your line? What are the units of the intercept? Explain the meaning of your intercept in relation to the train schedule.

EXPLORE MORE

1. If you look at the original schedule, you might notice an "error" between Campbellton and Matapédia. It appears that the train passes through Campbellton at 9:55 P.M., goes 19 kilometers, and then arrives at Matapédia at 9:53 P.M. But it's impossible for the train to gain 2 minutes. What is the problem here? Find a way to manipulate the data to fix this problem. Does fixing the data in this way change the average speed of the train? If so, by how much?

2. Try zooming in on smaller groups of points and readjust your line of fit for these points. Does the slope of the line become steeper or shallower? If so, what does that mean about the average speed of the train for these small parts of the trip?

The Via Rail Canada Schedules

HALIFAX • GASPÉ • MONTRÉAL

	TRAIN	KM	15	15	17	17
	NAME / NOM		Ocean Océan	Ocean Océan	Chaleur Chaleur	Chaleur Chaleur
	DAYS/JOURS		x2	ıı x2	1,4,6	ıı 1,4,6
DP	**Halifax, NS** AT/HA	0	1305	1245		
	Truro	103	1430	1415		
	Springhill Jct. ☆	200	1555	1540		
	Amherst, NS	227	1620	1605		
	Sackville, NB	243	1637	1623		
AR	**Moncton**	304	1725	1710		
DP			1745	1740		
	Rogersville ☆	397	1842	1842		
	Miramichi	433	1920	1920		
	Bathurst	504	2016	2016		
	Petit Rocher ☆	521	2031	2031		
	Jacquet River ☆	549	2051	2051		
	Charlo ☆	574	2111	2113		
	Campbellton, NB AT/HA	605	2155	2200		
AR	**Matapédia, QC** ET/HE	624	2153	2158		
DP	**Gaspé, QC** ET/HE	0	↓	↓	1445	1450
	Barachois	40			1527	1533
	Percé	63			1559	1604
	Grande Rivière	80			1622	1627
	Chandler	97			1639	1644
	Port-Daniel	130			1736	1741
	New Carlisle	167			1831	1836
	Bonaventure	182			1855	1850
	Caplan	200			1911	1916
	New Richmond	214			1928	1933
	Carleton	254			2012	2017
	Nouvelle ☆	269			2027	2032
AR	**Matapédia**	325	↓	↓	2125	2130
DP	**Matapédia**	624	2155	2200	2155	2200
	Causapscal ☆	681	2241	2246	2241	2246
	Amqui	703	2301	2306	2301	2306
	Sayabec ☆	727	2320	2325	2320	2325
	Mont-Joli	774	2359	0004	2359	0004
	Rimouski	803	0023	0029	0023	0029
	Trois-Pistoles	864	0106	0136	0106	0136
	Rivière-du-Loup	907	0201	0212	0201	0212
	La Pocatière	975	0241	0251	0241	0251
	Montmagny ☆	1035	0315	0324	0315	0324
	Charny	1099	0445	0447	0445	0447
	Drummondville	1246	0615	0625	0615	0625
	Saint-Hyacinthe	1292	0700	0700	0700	0700
	Saint-Lambert	1339	0742	0742	0742	0742
AR	**Montréal, QC** ET/HE (Central Stn./Gare Centrale)	1346	0800	0800	0800	0800

x3 x3 2,5,7 2,5,7

Days of operation		Jours où le train est en service
Monday	1	Lundi
Tuesday	2	Mardi
Wednesday	3	Mercredi
Thursday	4	Jeudi
Friday	5	Vendredi
Saturday	6	Samedi
Sunday	7	Dimanche
Except	x	Sauf
Except Saturday and Sunday	x6,7	Sauf les samedi et dimanche
Daily	Blank / Aucun symbole	Quotidien

HALIFAX • GASPÉ • MONTRÉAL

	TRAIN	KM	15	15	17	17
	NAME / NOM		Ocean Océan	Ocean Océan	Chaleur Chaleur	Chaleur Chaleur
	DAYS/JOURS		x2	ıı x2	1,4,6	ıı 1,4,6
DP	**Halifax, NS** AT/HA	0	1305	1245		
	Truro	103	1430	1415		
	Springhill Jct. ☆	200	1555	1540		
	Amherst, NS	227	1620	1605		
	Sackville, NB	243	1637	1623		
AR	**Moncton**	304	1725	1710		
DP			1745	1740		
	Rogersville ☆	397	1842	1842		
	Miramichi	433	1920	1920		
	Bathurst	504	2016	2016		
	Petit Rocher ☆	521	2031	2031		
	Jacquet River ☆	549	2051	2051		
	Charlo ☆	574	2111	2113		
	Campbellton, NB AT/HA	605	2155	2200		
AR	**Matapédia, QC** ET/HE	624	2153	2158		
DP	**Gaspé, QC** ET/HE	0	↓	↓	1445	1450
	Barachois	40			1527	1533
	Percé	63			1559	1604
	Grande Rivière	80			1622	1627
	Chandler	97			1639	1644
	Port-Daniel	130			1736	1741
	New Carlisle	167			1831	1836
	Bonaventure	182			1855	1850
	Caplan	200			1911	1916
	New Richmond	214			1928	1933
	Carleton	254			2012	2017
	Nouvelle ☆	269			2027	2032
AR	**Matapédia**	325	↓	↓	2125	2130
DP	**Matapédia**	624	2155	2200	2155	2200
	Causapscal ☆	681	2241	2246	2241	2246
	Amqui	703	2301	2306	2301	2306
	Sayabec ☆	727	2320	2325	2320	2325
	Mont-Joli	774	2359	0004	2359	0004
	Rimouski	803	0023	0029	0023	0029
	Trois-Pistoles	864	0106	0136	0106	0136
	Rivière-du-Loup	907	0201	0212	0201	0212
	La Pocatière	975	0241	0251	0241	0251
	Montmagny ☆	1035	0315	0324	0315	0324
	Charny	1099	0445	0447	0445	0447
	Drummondville	1246	0615	0625	0615	0625
	Saint-Hyacinthe	1292	0700	0700	0700	0700
	Saint-Lambert	1339	0742	0742	0742	0742
AR	**Montréal, QC** ET/HE (Central Stn./Gare Centrale)	1346	0800	0800	0800	0800

x3 x3 2,5,7 2,5,7

Days of operation		Jours où le train est en service
Monday	1	Lundi
Tuesday	2	Mardi
Wednesday	3	Mercredi
Thursday	4	Jeudi
Friday	5	Vendredi
Saturday	6	Samedi
Sunday	7	Dimanche
Except	x	Sauf
Except Saturday and Sunday	x6,7	Sauf les samedi et dimanche
Daily	Blank / Aucun symbole	Quotidien

Olympics

The first Olympic Games of modern times were held in Athens, Greece, in 1896. They have been held every four years since, with three exceptions—they were not held in 1916, 1940, or 1944 because of World Wars I and II.

In this activity, you'll explore the track-and-field gold-medal results from the Summer Olympic Games, 1896 to 2004. The data you'll use have the winning times or distances for several of the events that both men and women compete in.

MAKE A CONJECTURE

You probably already have some ideas about what the data look like. Think about what you expect to see.

Q1 In how many seconds do you think a male athlete can run the 100-meter dash?

Q2 From 1896 to 2004, do you think men's gold-medal times for the 100-meter dash have gotten longer, gotten shorter, or stayed the same? Explain your thinking.

Q3 How do you think the Olympic results for the 100-meter dash compare to the results for the 200-meter dash? Explain your thinking.

Q4 How do you think the men's results compare to the women's results for the 100-meter dash? If you think one gender's results are better, how much better do you think they are?

Q5 If there is a difference between men's and women's times for the 100-meter dash, do you think the difference has changed over time? Have the times gotten closer together, gotten farther apart, or stayed the same?

INVESTIGATE

Now you'll use Fathom to look at the Olympic data. You'll make several graphs and look for patterns and relationships. Keep questions Q1–Q5 in mind because you're going to see whether your predictions were correct.

1. Open the document **Olympics.ftm.** You'll see only a collection.
2. Use the collection inspector or a case table to look at the data. Be sure that you understand what each case and each attribute represent. You'll notice that some events (especially women's events) do not have values for every year. That's because more and more events have been added over time—not every event was held in 1896.

Question Q2 asked about changes in the men's gold-medal times for the 100-meter dash. You'll look at that event first.

3. Make a scatter plot of *M_100Meter* versus *Year*. Change the graph to a line scatter plot, which connects the points in order by year.

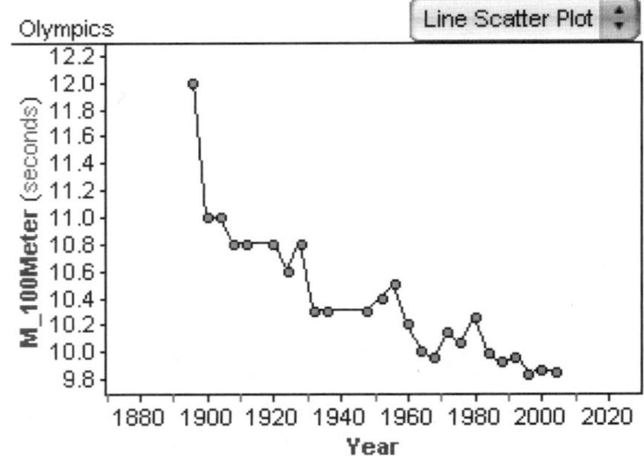

Q6 Based on your graph, have the times for the men's 100-meter dash gotten longer, gotten shorter, or stayed the same? Explain how you know.

Q7 Between which two years was there the greatest improvement? From the graph, how can you distinguish improvement from setback?

Q8 Are there any years for which the gold-medal result was unusual? If so, tell which years and explain why you picked those points.

4. Add a line of fit to your graph. You can use a movable line, median-median line, or least-squares line, whichever you think fits the best.

Q9 What is the meaning (if any) of your line's slope? What is the meaning (if any) of its *y*-intercept?

Q10 Use your line to predict the men's gold-medal time for the 100-meter dash in the next Olympics.

Question Q3 compared the results for the 100-meter dash and the 200-meter dash. Next you'll look at those two events.

5. Make a single scatter plot that compares the results for the 100-meter dash and the 200-meter dash over time. You can use either men or women, but use the same gender for both events.

Q11 Does your scatter plot support your prediction from Q3? If so, explain how. If not, describe the comparison that the graph does show. (*Hint:* You might want to adjust the graph's axes.)

Questions Q4 and Q5 compared the results for the men's 100-meter dash and the women's 100-meter dash. Now you'll look at those two events together.

6. Make a single scatter plot that compares the results for the men's 100-meter dash and the women's 100-meter dash over time. Look for patterns that help you understand how the data compare and change.

7. Add lines of fit to approximate the trends of each data set. Use median-median lines or least-squares lines because they'll give you a line for men and a line for women. Notice and interpret the slope and y-intercept of each line.

Q12 In general, how do the men's results compare to the women's results for the 100-meter dash? Are one gender's results better than the other's? If so, how much better?

Q13 The graphs definitely show a difference between the genders. Is this difference changing over time? Explain.

Q14 Based on your lines, will one gender ever "catch up" to the other gender? If so, when? How confident are you about this prediction?

EXPLORE MORE

1. In question Q8, you identified unusual results in the men's 100-meter dash. You probably did this by finding points that were very far from the general pattern of the data. When you add a line of fit, the line represents the general pattern of the data. You can then use *residuals* to measure how far each point is from the line.

Go back to your graph of *M_100Meter* versus *Year* and make sure you have a line of fit. Select the graph and choose **Make Residual Plot** from the **Graph** menu. Spend some time understanding what the residual plot shows you. How can you recognize points that are unusual for the pattern? How do you recognize points that fit the pattern almost perfectly? Really unusual points are sometimes called *outliers.* Try deleting one or two outlier cases from your collection and see whether the line of fit changes. After you've seen the effect of deleting the outliers, choose **Undo** from the **Edit** menu to bring back the cases.

2. Are there events for which there is no noticeable difference between the genders? Are there events for which the difference between the genders doesn't seem to be changing? Compare the data for other events and describe your findings.

Sequence of Squares

In this activity you'll explore the square numbers:

1   4   9   16   25   . . .

You'll use mental math to recognize a relationship between these numbers and then use Fathom to confirm or refute your conjecture.

MAKE A CONJECTURE

Without using Fathom or a calculator, look for a relationship between each square number and the one that follows it. Think about ways to use words, numbers, or algebra to make the conjecture as general as possible.

Q1 What is the relationship between any pair of square numbers? Be as specific as you can.

INVESTIGATE

Now use Fathom to test your conjecture. Make a collection in which one attribute contains the square numbers and another computes the relationship you predicted. Use any attributes or formulas that you want. In case you are stuck, here are some functions that you can research in Fathom Help: *caseIndex, prev, next.* You can also choose **New Cases** from the **Collection** menu to add cases.

Q2 List the formulas that you used and describe what happened.

Look at your results in Fathom and compare them to your original conjecture. Use the next questions to help summarize your findings.

Q3 Did your calculations match your conjecture? If not, explain why and write a revised conjecture.

Q4 Did your calculations reveal any other patterns in the sequence? If so, explain.

EXPLORE MORE

One of the problems with exploring data is that you don't know if your conjecture is *always* true. Even if your Fathom document has 5000 cases that show your conjecture to be true, you don't know for sure about case 5001. Make a convincing explanation (verbal, algebraic, or geometric) telling why your conjecture is true for all square numbers.

Geometry

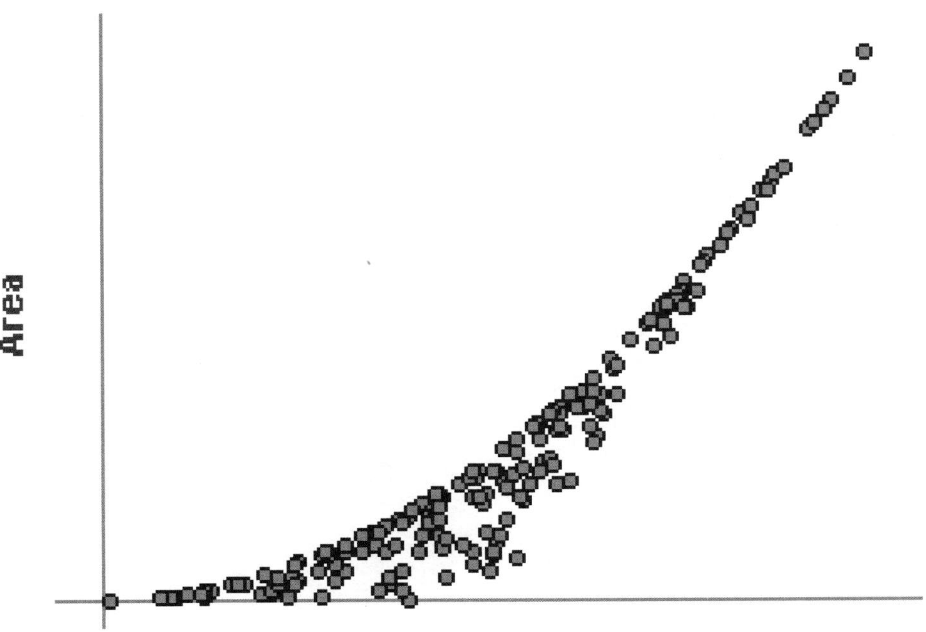

The Circumference Function

You will need

- circular objects of different sizes
- centimeter ruler or measuring tape
- string

What is the relationship between a circle's circumference and its diameter? In this activity, you'll discover (or, maybe, rediscover) this important relationship.

MAKE A CONJECTURE

You probably already have some ideas about what will happen. The relationship might even be familiar to you. Think about what you expect to see.

1. Take one of your circular objects. Imagine measuring its diameter and circumference and comparing the two quantities. Think about ways to use words, numbers, or algebra to describe the relationship as generally as possible.

Q1 What do you think the relationship between diameter and circumference is for any circle?

2. Now imagine measuring the diameter and circumference of many circles and making a graph of points in the form (*Diameter, Circumference*).

Q2 Sketch the way you think the graph of *Circumference* versus *Diameter* will look. Be sure to scale and label your axes.

EXPERIMENT

Now you'll actually measure the diameters and circumferences of your circular objects. Use centimeters for all measurements. Record your results in a table.

3. Measure each diameter by holding your ruler or measuring tape across the widest part of the circle.

4. Measure each circumference by wrapping your measuring tape or string around the outside of the circle. If you use string, unwrap the string and then lay it along your ruler to get the measurement.

Q3 How do your measurements compare to your conjecture in Q1?

INVESTIGATE

Next you'll put the data into Fathom and learn ways to analyze it.

5. Start Fathom. You'll have an empty document.
6. Choose **New | Case Table** from the **Object** menu. An empty case table appears.
7. Click the word <**new**> at the top of the column in the table. Type `Diameter` and press **Enter** to make a new attribute. Do the same to create an attribute for *Circumference.*
8. Enter your measurements in the case table. Type the first value and its unit under each attribute and the unit will be applied to every value under the attribute.

	Diameter	Circumference
units	centimeters	centimeters
1	4.0 cm	12.4 cm
2	8.0 cm	25.2 cm

When two quantities are related, a graph of points is a good way to see the relationship. You'll make a graph called a *scatter plot.*

9. Drag a new graph from the object shelf into your document. An empty graph appears.
10. Drag *Diameter* from the case table to the graph. Drop the attribute below the horizontal axis. Then drag *Circumference* to the vertical axis.

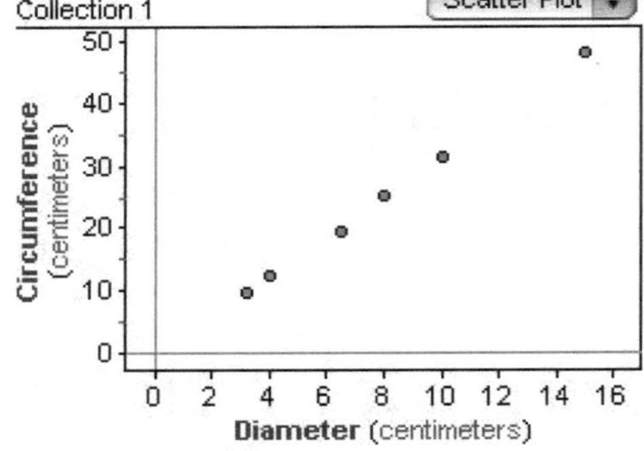

Q4 Sketch your scatter plot, with scaled and labeled axes. How does it compare to your conjecture in Q2?

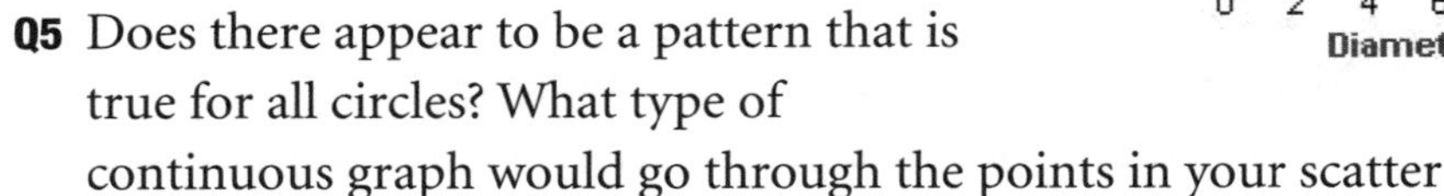

Q5 Does there appear to be a pattern that is true for all circles? What type of continuous graph would go through the points in your scatter plot?

Q6 Would the continuous graph go through the point (0, 0)? Should it? Explain.

You probably noticed a linear pattern in Q5. Fathom gives you several tools for making a line that fits your data. You'll use the simplest of them, a movable line.

11. Select the graph by clicking on it. Choose **Add Movable Line** from the **Graph** menu. A line and its equation appear. Choose **Lock Intercept at Zero** from the **Graph** menu to make the line pass through the origin.

12. Get comfortable with changing the line. Then move the line to best fit the points. (*Hint:* When you try to move the line, you may accidentally grab a data point and change your data. If this happens, choose **Undo** from the **Edit** menu until everything is all right.)

Q7 Add the line to your sketch of the scatter plot. What is the equation of your line? What number in the equation represents the relationship between the diameter and the circumference? How is this number represented by the graph of the line?

Q8 Your line indicates a linear relationship. But your points probably aren't all on the line, which means your measurements had some variability. Why would this be? Do you think the relationship between circumference and diameter is really linear? Explain.

The linear equation that you found indicates that the *ratio* of circumference to diameter remains the same. Calculating this ratio for each circle is another way to look at the relationship between diameter and circumference.

13. In the case table, create a new attribute *CircDiam.* This attribute will be the ratio of circumference to diameter.

14. Select the *CircDiam* column and choose **Edit Formula** from the **Edit** menu. The formula editor opens. Type `Circumference/Diameter` and click **OK.** The ratios appear.

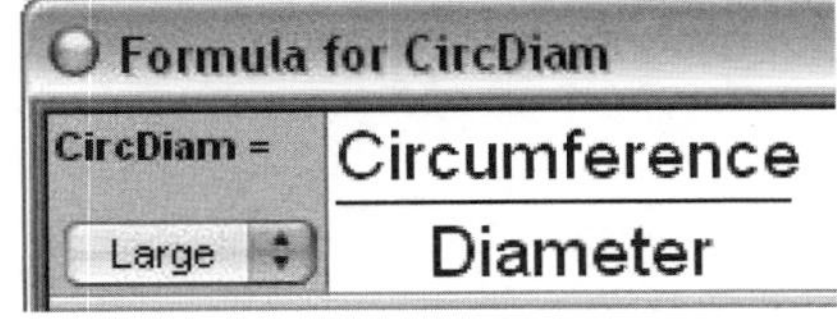

Q9 How do the ratios of circumference to diameter compare to the other work you have done in this activity? Does there seem to be an "average" ratio?

15. Drag a new summary table from the object shelf. Drop the attribute *CircDiam* in the row or column of the summary table. The mean is automatically calculated.

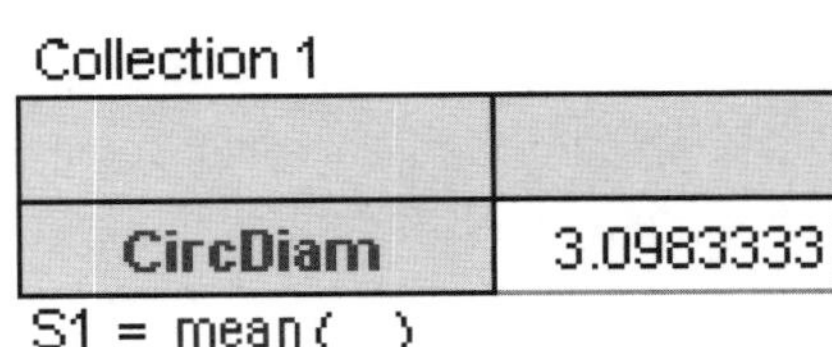

Q10 What is the mean value for the ratios?

Q11 Based on your work in Fathom, what is the relationship between diameter and circumference for any circle? Does this match your original conjecture from Q1? How well did your actual measurements conform to the relationship?

Q12 Did your work in Fathom reveal any surprises? Describe and explain.

EXPLORE MORE

1. In this activity, you used centimeters to measure both *Diameter* and *Circumference*. What happens if you measure everything in inches? What happens if you measure one attribute in centimeters and the other in inches? Make conjectures, collect revised data, and then analyze the data in Fathom.

2. Cut string into various lengths. For each string, measure the length to get an attribute *Length*. Using a simple knot, tie the ends of each string together to make a loop. Stretch each loop into a circle and measure the *Diameter*. Predict and then analyze the relationship between *Length* and *Diameter*. What relationship did you find? How is this relationship similar to or different from the relationship that you studied in the activity?

Area and Perimeter

How are the area and perimeter of a rectangle related? You probably know the formulas by heart:

$$Area = Length \cdot Width$$

$$Perimeter = 2(Length + Width)$$

But if you look at data for many different rectangles, would you notice any patterns? Are there relationships between area and perimeter? You'll use Fathom to explore these questions.

EXPERIMENT

The first step is to experiment with many different rectangles and gather data. You could get data by actually drawing or cutting out rectangles and measuring their lengths and widths, but that would get tiring. Instead, you'll use Fathom to generate random numbers for the lengths and widths. Using technology to randomly generate data for an experiment is one method of doing a *simulation.*

1. Open a new Fathom document and create a new case table.

2. Make two new attributes, *Length* and *Width.*

3. With the case table selected, choose **New Cases** from the **Collection** menu. Type `200` in the dialog box and click **OK.** The cases appear in your table, although they have no values.

For this activity, you'll assume that the length or width of a rectangle can be between 0 and 10 units.

4. Select the attribute *Length* and choose **Edit Formula** from the **Edit** menu. Type `random(10)` in the formula editor and click **OK.** The *Length* column fills with randomly generated numbers. If you want, choose **Rerandomize** from the **Collection** menu to see a different set of random numbers.

Q1 Look at the values of *Length.* What does the formula *random*(10) do? What would *random*(100) do? How about *random*()? (*Hint:* If you aren't sure, read about the *random* function in Fathom Help.)

5. Use the same formula to define *Width.*

6. Drag a new empty graph from the object shelf. Drag *Length* from the case table to the horizontal axis. You'll see a dot plot; you can change the graph to a histogram if you like. Make a dot plot or histogram of *Width*, too.

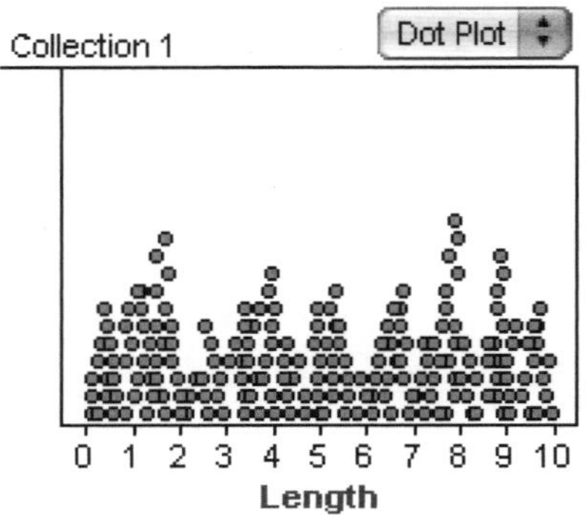

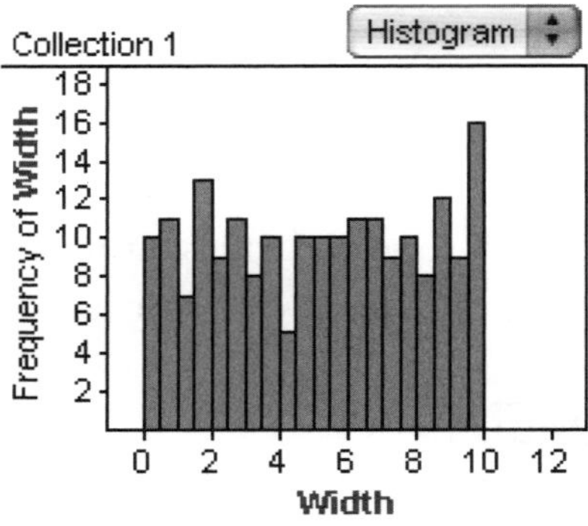

Q2 Describe the general "shape" of the graphs of *Length* and *Width*. If you want, rerandomize the data several times to get a better feel for the general shape. Why do these graphs have this shape?

7. Make another new graph. This time make a scatter plot with *Length* on one axis and *Width* on the other axis. Rerandomize the data a few times.

Q3 Describe any patterns in the scatter plot. Why does the scatter plot look the way it does?

Now that you have data that represent random rectangles, you need to find the perimeter and area of each. After all, you want to look for relationships between area and perimeter.

8. Make two new attributes, *Area* and *Perimeter*. Define each with a formula that uses *Length* and *Width*.

Q4 Copy on paper all of the values for the first two cases in your case table. Use by-hand calculations to verify that your formulas for *Area* and *Perimeter* are correct.

MAKE A CONJECTURE

So far, you've simulated many rectangles by randomly generating length and width, and you've calculated the area and perimeter. You've looked at graphs that help you see how length and width are related. Now, let's see how area and perimeter are related. But first, predict what you expect to find.

Q5 If you made a scatter plot of *Area* versus *Perimeter*, what do you think it would look like? Make a sketch of what you would expect to see or describe it thoroughly. Explain why you think it would look that way.

INVESTIGATE

9. In Fathom, actually make the scatter plot of *Area* versus *Perimeter*. Put *Perimeter* on the horizontal axis and *Area* on the vertical axis. You might want to rerandomize a few times to make sure you understand the general relationship.

Q6 Make a sketch of the actual graph or describe it thoroughly. Did the actual graph match your prediction? Is there anything about the graph that surprises you? Explain.

Q7 If everything went well, there should be no points in the upper-left part of the graph—a region bounded by a curve. Explain why there are no points in that region.

Now your goal is to figure out the function for that curved boundary. Because calculating area involves squaring, you might reason that the function is quadratic: $Area = Perimeter^2$.

10. Select the graph and choose **Plot Function** from the **Graph** menu. In the formula editor, type `Perimeter²` and click **OK.**

11. Unfortunately, the curve is too steep. Double-click the function equation at the bottom of the graph. Change the formula to divide $Perimeter^2$ by some number, such as $Perimeter^2/3$.

Q8 What equation did you try? What happened to the curve—did it get steeper or shallower? Do you think the divisor needs to be bigger or smaller than the number you used?

You can use a slider to try lots of divisors quickly.

12. Drag a new slider from the object shelf. The slider that appears looks like a number line with a pointer on it. It's probably called *V1* and has a value of 5.

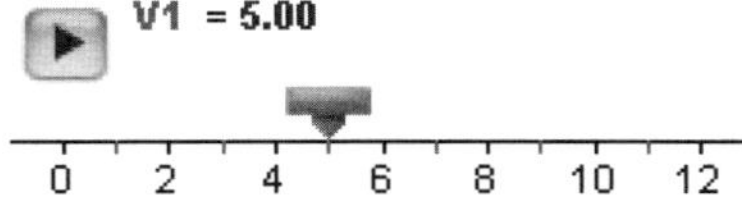

13. Double-click the function equation at the bottom of the graph and change it to use *V1* as the divisor. Now you can control the value of the divisor and change the function by dragging the slider. You will probably need to change the scale of the slider. The easiest way is to drag the numbers on the number line.

Q9 What value of *V1* makes the curve fit the boundary the best?

14. Double-click the collection (the box of gold balls) to show the collection inspector. Then go to the scatter plot of *Area* versus *Perimeter* and click any of the points nearest to the curved boundary. When you do, that case appears in the inspector. Do this for several of the points and notice the *Length* and *Width* of each point.

Q10 What do the cases near the boundary have in common? Why do all those rectangles have that relationship? What type of rectangles are they?

Q11 Use your observation from Q10 and the formulas for area and perimeter to find the boundary curve's function algebraically. Show that it is the same formula you got by using the slider to fit the curve.

EXPLORE MORE

1. There is another empty zone in the lower-right part of the scatter plot of *Area* versus *Perimeter*. Why are there no points in that region? What is the equation of that boundary? Why? Use this and your answer to Q11 to completely describe the relationships between area and perimeter.

2. Look at scatter plots of *Area* versus *Length* and *Perimeter* versus *Length*. Are there maximum and minimum relationships between these attributes? If so, find functions for the boundaries and explain why they exist.

3

Algebra 2

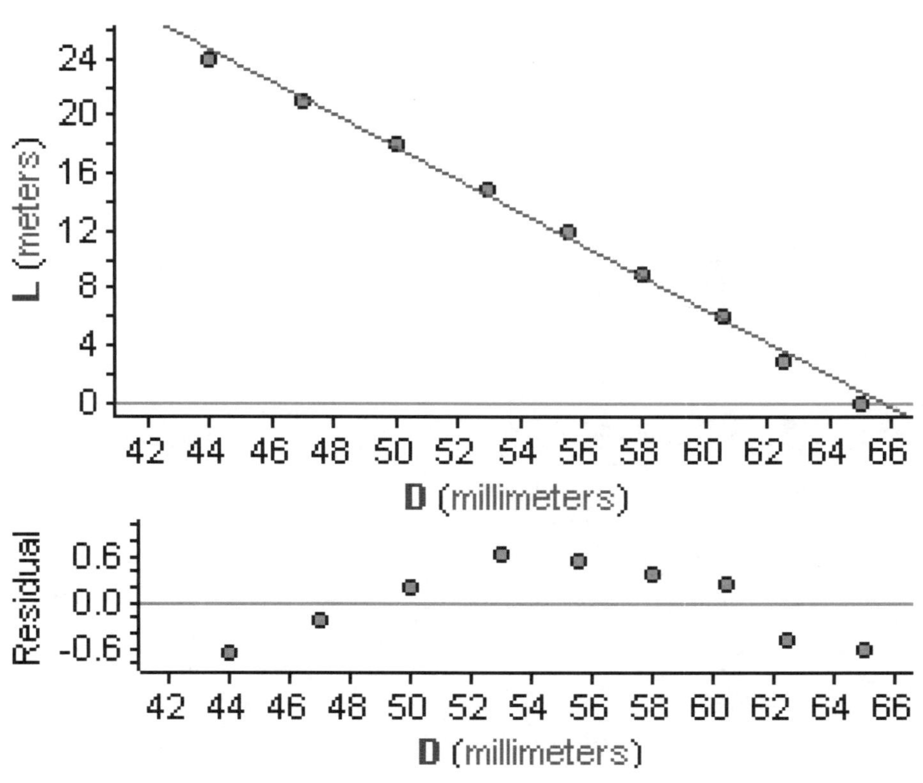
L (meters)
24
20
16
12
8
4
0
42 44 46 48 50 52 54 56 58 60 62 64 66
D (millimeters)
Residual
0.6
0.0
-0.6
42 44 46 48 50 52 54 56 58 60 62 64 66
D (millimeters)

Mauna Loa

Mauna Loa is a volcano on the island of Hawai'i. Since 1958, air samples have been continuously collected at the Mauna Loa Observatory and analyzed for carbon dioxide (CO_2) concentrations.

You may know that CO_2 is one of the "greenhouse gases" that scientists monitor in relation to global warming. The Mauna Loa Observatory is very important to the study of global warming. It is far removed from industry and other human activity, so any changes in CO_2 there are good indicators of global changes in the Earth's atmosphere.

In this activity, you'll look at the Mauna Loa data and see if there are any patterns.

MAKE A CONJECTURE

You probably already have some ideas about what the data look like, especially if you know anything about global warming. Before you begin, think about what you expect to see.

Q1 Since 1958, do you think the concentration of CO_2 at Mauna Loa has been increasing, decreasing, or staying the same?

Q2 If you think the concentration has been increasing or decreasing, what shape do you think the data will have? Will it be straight or curved?

INVESTIGATE

Now you'll use Fathom to look at the Mauna Loa data. Keep questions Q1 and Q2 in mind, because along the way you'll see whether your predictions were correct.

1. Open the document **MaunaLoa2003.ftm.** You'll see two *collections* of data that look like boxes of gold balls: Mauna Loa, Continuous and Mauna Loa, By Month. Both collections contain the average CO_2 concentrations in parts per million (ppm) for every month from 1958 to 2003, but they are organized differently. You'll also see two *case tables,* one for each collection, that help you view the data in the collections. Each row is a *case* and each column is an *attribute.*
2. Scroll through the case tables and make sure you understand how the data are organized. (*Note:* There are seven months that have no data: four in 1958 and three in 1964. You'll see these as empty cells.)

Q3 What was the CO_2 concentration in March 1970? How do you find the answer from Mauna Loa, Continuous? How do you find the answer from Mauna Loa, By Month?

Q4 From looking at the case tables, is the concentration of CO_2 increasing, decreasing, or staying the same? Explain your answer, as well as any difficulty you may have had.

Looking for patterns in a case table isn't very efficient when you have a lot of data. Graphs are sometimes a more efficient way to look at the data.

3. Drag a new graph from the shelf. An empty graph appears.

4. Go to the case table for Mauna Loa, Continuous and drag the attribute *Year* from the case table to the graph. Drop the attribute below the horizontal axis. Then drag *CarbonDioxide* to the vertical axis. The graph becomes a scatter plot that shows the concentration of CO_2 over time. If your graph of points is bunched up, drag the corner of the graph to make it larger.

Q5 From looking at the graph of *CarbonDioxide* versus *Year,* is the concentration of CO_2 increasing, decreasing, or staying the same?

You probably recognize a problem in your graph. Although the graph shows changes over time, you have big gaps between each year. The problem is that *Year* doesn't account for *Month.* You'll fix that in the next few steps.

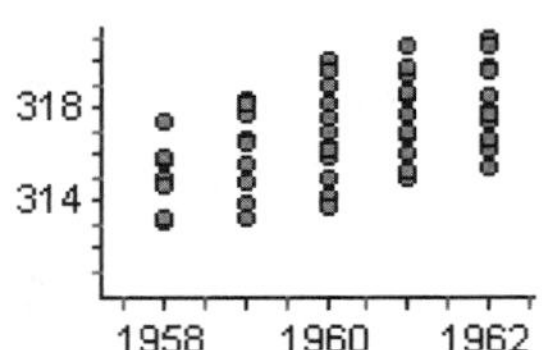

5. In the case table for Mauna Loa, Continuous, scroll to the far right. Click <*new*> in the last column, type `YearAndMonth`, and press Enter. This creates a new attribute.

6. Select the *YearAndMonth* column and choose **Edit Formula** from the **Edit** menu. The formula editor appears. Type a formula that appropriately combines *Year* and *Month* and click **OK.** The column fills with calculated values.

Q6 What formula did you use? Use at least one case in the case table to verify that the formula is working properly.

7. Drag *YearAndMonth* from the case table and drop it below the horizontal axis of the scatter plot. The new attribute should replace the old one.

Q7 From looking at the graph of *CarbonDioxide* versus *YearAndMonth,* is the concentration of CO_2 increasing, decreasing, or staying the same? Describe any other patterns that you see in the data. (You may need to make the graph larger to see a pattern.)

Q8 How would you describe the shape of the data? How does the shape compare to what you predicted in Q2?

Because linear equations are simple—they have only a slope and an intercept—lines are frequently used to "fit" data. Fathom gives you three ways to fit a line to your data: a movable line, a median-median line, and a least-squares line.

8. Select your graph and choose one of the lines of fit from the **Graph** menu. Try a movable line first because it allows you to adjust the line to the fit that you think is best. If you've learned about median-median lines or least-squares lines in class, your teacher may tell you to try those lines of fit, too.

Q9 How well does your line fit the data? What other mathematical curves do you think might fit the data better?

Q10 Based on your line of fit, approximate the rate at which the concentration of CO_2 is increasing or decreasing.

For these last two questions, you can use the graph that you've already made or make a new graph. You can use the data in either collection, and you can make new attributes if you want. Because different people will use different strategies, fully explain how you found each answer.

Q11 Predict the general CO_2 concentration at Mauna Loa this year. (*Hint:* If you used a median-median line or a least-squares line, you can trace it.)

Q12 Predict what the CO_2 concentration will be on your 21st birthday.

EXPLORE MORE

1. When you used the attribute *YearAndMonth*, you probably noticed that the data have seasonal fluctuations. And when you used a line of fit, you probably noticed that the general shape of the data is slightly curved. Use what you know about other functions, including periodic functions, to find curves that fit the data better. Once you have a better fit, answer Q11 and Q12 with your new function. (*Hint:* Use Fathom Help to learn about plotting functions. You may also want to learn about sliders.)

2. Focus on the seasonal fluctuations for each year. In general, during which month does the maximum CO_2 concentration occur? The minimum? Is the range of the fluctuations increasing, decreasing, or staying the same over time? Describe any other patterns that you see in the seasonal fluctuations.

Function Transformations

In this activity, you'll study data that perfectly fit a function. The functions you'll look at may already be familiar—quadratic, absolute value, exponential, square root, inverse variation, and linear. By changing the data, you'll explore how the equation of the function changes.

INVESTIGATE

1. Open the document **FunctionTransformations.ftm.** You'll see a collection and case table of x- and y-coordinates. You'll also see a scatter plot of the coordinate pairs (x, y). Notice that the points form a parabola.

You probably know that a parabola is formed by a quadratic equation. In fact, the y-coordinates are calculated by the formula $y = x^2$.

2. Select the graph and choose **Plot Function** from the **Graph** menu. In the formula editor, type x^2 and click **OK.** You should get a parabola that perfectly fits the points.

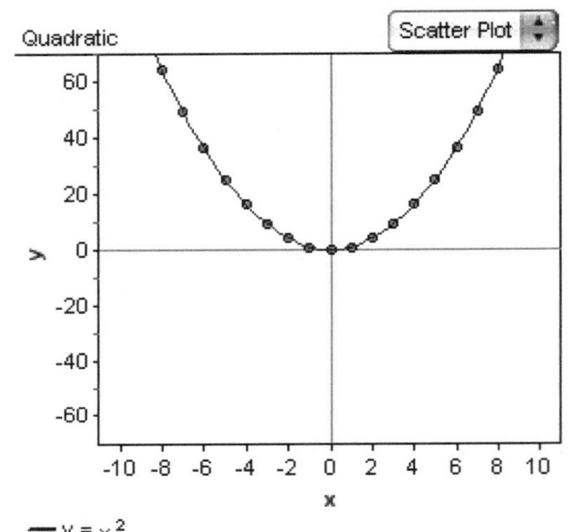

You are now going to explore what happens when you add the same amount to each x- or y-coordinate. You'll use a slider that allows you to easily explore the effect of adding different amounts.

3. Drag a new slider from the shelf. The slider will be called *V1*. Drag the slider thumb and notice how the value of *V1* changes to different decimal values. Click the green arrow button to animate the slider; click the button again to stop it.

4. Double-click near the slider's axis to show the slider's inspector. Enter the values shown here, which rename the slider h and limit its values to integers between –20 and 20. Close the inspector and drag the slider thumb to test its behavior.

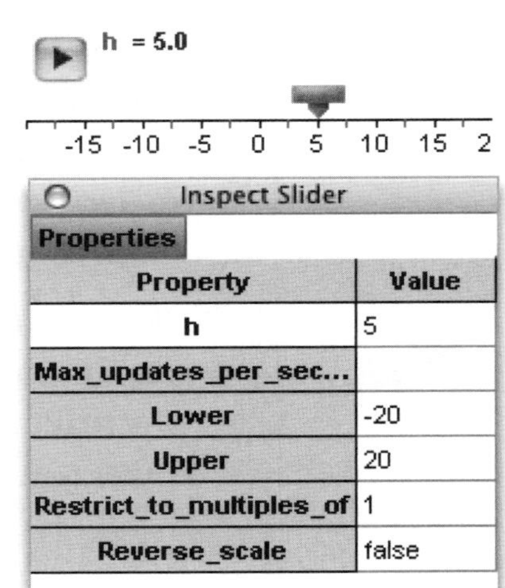

Property	Value
h	5
Max_updates_per_sec...	
Lower	-20
Upper	20
Restrict_to_multiples_of	1
Reverse_scale	false

5. Select slider *h* and choose **Duplicate Slider** from the **Object** menu. Rename this slider *k*, but keep it restricted to integers between –20 and 20.

6. In the case table, create a new attribute, *xPLUSh*. Define it with a formula that adds the value of *h* to each *x*-coordinate.

7. Make another new attribute, *yPLUSk*, that adds *k* to each *y*-coordinate.

8. Select the scatter plot of (x, y) and choose **Duplicate Graph** from the **Object** menu.

9. Select the duplicate graph and choose **Show Axis Links** from the **Graph** menu. A broken chain link will appear by each axis. Drag the broken chain link from the *x*-axis and drop it on the *x*-axis of the original graph. Do the same thing to link the *y*-axes. Now, if you change the axes in one graph, the axes change in the other graph, too.

10. So far, you have two identical scatter plots of (x, y). Drag the attribute *xPLUSh* from the case table and drop it on the *x*-axis of the duplicate graph. Drag *yPLUSk* to the *y*-axis. You now have a scatter plot of (*xPLUSh*, *yPLUSk*), but you still have the graph of $y = x^2$ for reference.

11. Because the names of your axes have changed, the function is now called $yPLUSk = x^2$. Double-click the function equation at the bottom of the graph and edit it to show *xPLUSh* rather than *x*.

Q1 Set the value of *k* to 0. Then drag slider *h* and watch the scatter plot change. How does the scatter plot of (*xPLUSh*, *yPLUSk*) compare to the scatter plot of (x, y)? How do the points change when you add *h* to each *x*-coordinate?

Q2 Set the value of *h* to 0. Then drag slider *k* and watch the scatter plot change. How does the scatter plot of (*xPLUSh*, *yPLUSk*) compare to the scatter plot of (x, y)? How do the points change when you add *k* to each *y*-coordinate?

Q3 Try changing both sliders and watch the scatter plot change. Use what you learn to predict what the scatter plot would look like for these values. After you write your prediction, use the sliders to check your work.

a. $h = 3, k = 5$

b. $h = -8, k = 0$

c. $h = 5, k = -20$

Q4 An important aspect of any parabola is its *vertex.* Set the sliders to any values and then point the cursor to the vertex. Look in the bottom-left corner of the Fathom window for the vertex's coordinates. How do the coordinates relate to the values of h and k?

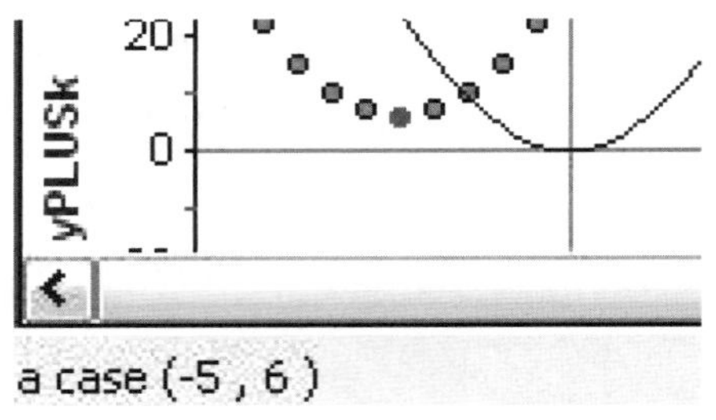

Q5 The original parabola is $y = x^2$. What parabola fits the points transformed by h and k? Make a guess and plot a new function. If it doesn't go through the points, double-click the equation and make changes in the formula editor. In general, what quadratic function fits the points (*xPLUSh, yPLUSk*)? (*Hint:* Try using h and k in the function equation and see whether the parabola moves with the points when you change the sliders.)

Q6 The transformations that you've just seen are called *translations.* You learned how to translate points and how to translate a quadratic function. Do the same rules apply to all functions? Below the case table are five other collections of points for $y = |x|$, $y = 2^x$, $y = \sqrt{x}$, $y = \frac{1}{x}$, and $y = x$. Create case tables, attributes, graphs, and functions to explore translations with these functions. Summarize your findings by answering questions Q1–Q5 for each function. Then explain how translations were similar or different for all of the functions. In general, if you are given any function $y = f(x)$, how would h and k affect it?

You've seen what happens when you add h and k. Now you'll see what happens when you multiply x or y by a constant.

12. Create two sliders, a and b, that each go from -10 to 10 by multiples of 0.25.
13. Create two new attributes, *aTIMESx* and *bTIMESy,* that multiply the values of the sliders by the coordinates.
14. Make a scatter plot of (*aTIMESx, bTIMESy*). Be sure that you can compare the transformed points to the graph of $y = x^2$.
15. Adjust the sliders for a and b and watch how the scatter plot changes.

Q7 How does the scatter plot change when you change a and b? Fully describe the effects, including anything special that happens.

Q8 What parabola fits the points transformed by a and b? In general, what quadratic function fits the points (*aTIMESx, bTIMESy*)?

Q9 The transformations that you've just seen are called *dilations.* Do the same dilation rules apply to all functions? Explore dilations with the other collections and summarize your findings. In general, if you are given any function $y = f(x)$, how would a and b affect it?

Q10 A special type of transformation occurs when $a = -1$ or $b = -1$. Explore these values for any (or all) of the functions and summarize your findings. What kind of transformation happens when $a = -1$? When $b = -1$?

EXPLORE MORE

1. Explore what happens when you combine translations and dilations. That is, look at scatter plots of (*aTIMESxPLUSh, bTIMESyPLUSk*). Summarize your findings. If you are given any function $y = f(x)$, how would *a, b, h,* and *k* affect it? If you see the graph of any parabola (or any absolute value function, or any exponential function, and so on), how could you use the points on the graph to determine the function's equation?
2. Another fundamental type of transformation is a *rotation.* Find ways to transform the coordinates to create rotations. How are rotations significantly different from the other function transformations that you've seen in this activity?

Moore's Law

Gordon Moore (b. 1929) is cofounder and past chief executive officer (CEO) of Intel Corporation, a company known for making computer central processing units (CPUs). In 1965, three years before founding Intel, Moore made a famous observation that computer processors would get more powerful exponentially. The press called his observation "Moore's Law," and different variations of it have been stated ever since.

One way to measure a CPU's power is to count the number of transistors on it. In this activity, you'll look at data about Intel's processors. You'll test Moore's Law by using an exponential function to model the data, determine how frequently the number of transistors doubles, and predict the future of CPUs.

INVESTIGATE

1. Open the document **MooresLaw2004.ftm.** You'll see a collection and case table. There is one case for each major Intel CPU from 1970 to 2004. The attributes tell you the name of the CPU, the year it was introduced, the number of transistors, and the number of years since 1970. (*Note:* The year 1970 was chosen as the nearest multiple of 10 before the year of the first Intel processor.)

2. Make a scatter plot of *Transistors* versus *Since1970.*

Q1 Sketch the graph and describe its shape in one or two sentences. What mathematical curve does the graph resemble? What does that mean about the number of transistors over time?

3. Moore's original observation was that "complexity . . . has increased at a rate of roughly a factor of two per year." If you assume that "complexity" can be measured by number of transistors, you get the function $Transistors = 2^{Since1970}$. Plot this function on your graph.

Q2 Describe how well the function fits the scatter plot. How could you transform the function to make it fit the data better?

4. Make sliders and use them as parameters to transform the function $Transistors = 2^{Since1970}$. Try any transformations that you think are necessary—translations, dilations, or reflections. Adjust your sliders to get the best fit possible. (*Hint:* You may want to zoom in to check your fit. Select the graph. Hold down Ctrl (Win) Option (Mac) and click in the graph. Hold down Shift as well to zoom out.)

Q3 List the sliders and transformations that you tried. Which ones helped you get the best fit? Are they the same transformations that you predicted in question Q2?

Q4 Add the curve to your sketch in Q1. Record the final function, inserting the values of the sliders where necessary.

Q5 According to your function, how many years does it take for the number of transistors to double? That is, what is the *doubling time*?

5. Move the cursor over the graph of your function. The arrow cursor changes to a red point. Click and drag to trace the graph with the red point. Notice that the coordinates appear beside the point and in the bottom-left corner of the Fathom window. This gives you a way to approximate how many transistors a CPU would have in future years, according to your function model.

Q6 Approximately how many transistors would a CPU have in 2005? In 2010?

A *residual* is the vertical distance between your function and an actual data point. A *residual plot* shows all of the residuals and helps you judge how well the function fits.

6. Select the graph and choose **Make Residual Plot** from the **Graph** menu. A residual plot appears below your original graph.

7. Adjust your sliders and watch how the residual plot changes as the function's fit changes.

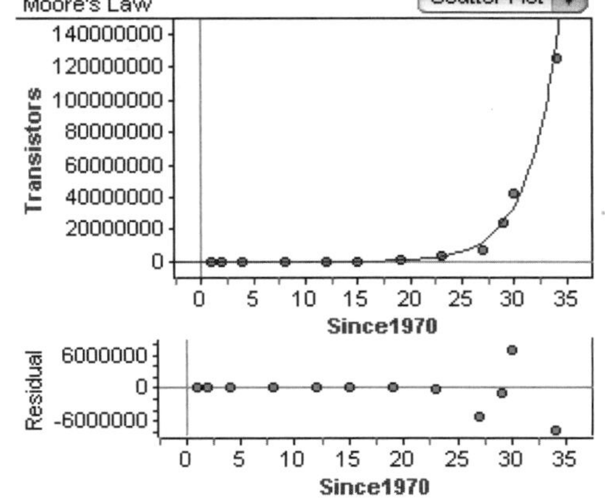

Q7 What happens to a residual when the function passes through the original data point? What happens when the function doesn't pass through the data point? What happens to the residual when the fit gets better? Gets worse?

Q8 Which data points in your original graph have the most problematic residuals? Why did you pick these points?

Q9 Use your sliders to find the best residual plot. Record this new function, inserting the values of the sliders where necessary. How does it compare to your function in Q4?

Q10 According to your function, was Gordon Moore correct to observe that computer processors get more "complex" exponentially? Was he correct that the complexity doubles each year? How would you state Moore's Law based on your function?

Q11 What do you think about using your Moore's Law function to make predictions for the future? Do you think transistors will continue to increase at the same exponential rate? Why or why not?

EXPLORE MORE

1. Research any new Intel processors that have been released since the Pentium 4. Compare the processor's actual number of transistors to the number of transistors that your function predicts for that year of release. How well did your model work?
2. You may have learned about logarithms. Create a new attribute that takes the logarithm of *Transistors*, and make a scatter plot of *logTransistors* versus *Since1970*. Describe what happens and find a function to fit this new graph. How can you use this new graph to predict values for the future? How can you use the equation of the function of fit to get something like the exponential function you used before?

Printing Paragraphs

You will need

- The Seven Paragraphs worksheet
- centimeter ruler

You have a handout with seven paragraphs on it. They're all exactly the same text, but they are set in columns of different widths. As you might expect, when the paragraph is really wide, it is also really short. Conversely, narrow paragraphs are really long.

Exactly how does the height of the paragraph depend on the width? In this activity, you'll find a function that models the data. Then you'll use a residual plot to improve your model.

MAKE A CONJECTURE

Before you begin, look at the seven paragraphs. Think about how the horizontal width and vertical length are related, and what you might see.

Q1 If you make a graph of length versus width, what would it look like? Fully describe your prediction or make a sketch.

Q2 Approximately what geometric shape is each paragraph?

Q3 Each paragraph takes up area on the page. What geometric formula could you use to find the area of each paragraph?

Q4 Do you think the area taken up by each paragraph is approximately the same? Explain your reasoning.

EXPERIMENT

Now measure the horizontal width and vertical length of each paragraph to the nearest centimeter. First, decide *how* you will measure. The width is going to be particularly tricky because some lines are long and some are short. Be as precise and consistent as you can.

1. Measure the width and length of each paragraph. Record your results in a table.

Q5 Describe how you measured width and length. Where did you begin and end each measurement? Why did you choose the beginning and end that you did?

INVESTIGATE

Next you'll analyze the data with Fathom.

2. Start Fathom and create a new case table with the attributes *Width* and *Length*. Enter your data into the case table. Don't use units with your measurements.

3. Make a scatter plot of *Length* versus *Width.*

Q6 Sketch the graph and describe its shape in one or two sentences. How does it compare to your prediction in question Q1?

For Q2, you and your classmates probably said that the paragraphs are rectangles. And, for Q3, you probably thought about *Length* • *Width* = *Area.* You can rewrite this formula as the inverse variation $Length = \frac{Area}{Width}$. If *Area* happens to be the same for all of the rectangles, then this gives you a functional relationship between *Length* and *Width.* You'll use a slider to explore *Area.*

4. Make a new slider. Name it *Area.*

5. Select the graph and plot the function $Length = \frac{Area}{Width}$. A curve appears but it probably doesn't fit the points at all.

6. Adjust the slider and try to make the curve fit the points. You'll probably need to adjust the slider's scale.

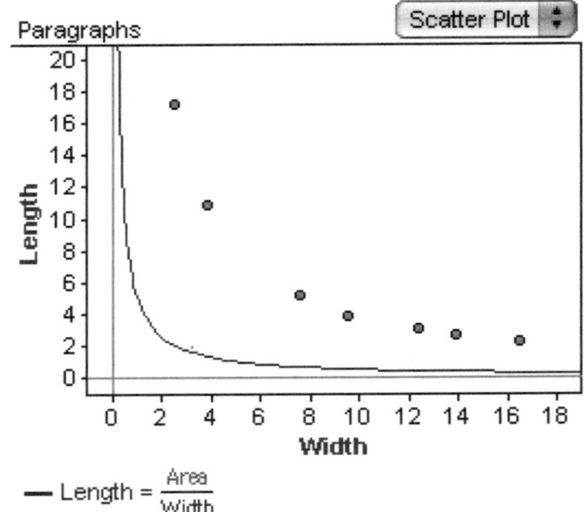

Q7 Describe any patterns that you notice while adjusting the slider. Explain why the patterns exist based on the printed paragraphs.

Q8 Do all of the paragraphs have exactly the same area? Do they have approximately the same area? Explain.

Q9 If you had to pick one value of *Area* that makes the curve fit the points best, what value would it be? Explain why you would select this value.

Q10 Adjust the slider to find the maximum and minimum values for *Area* that you think are reasonable. (*Hint:* To get finer control of the slider, you can zoom in to its axis by pressing Ctrl (Win) Option (Mac) while you click on the axis.)

7. In your case table, create a new attribute, *A* (for area), and define it with the formula *Length* • *Width.*

Q11 Do the values of *A* support the patterns that you saw in Q7? Do they support the range of values that you saw in Q10? Do you see any additional patterns in the areas?

Q12 How does your best value of *Area* from Q8 compare to the values of *A*?

A *residual* is the vertical distance between your function and an actual data point. A residual of zero means the function perfectly fits the point. A *residual plot* shows all of the residuals and can help you judge how well a function fits the data.

8. With the graph selected, choose **Make Residual Plot** from the **Graph** menu. A residual plot appears below your graph.

9. Adjust the slider and watch how the residual plot changes as the function's fit changes. Based on the residual plot, find one value of *Area* that makes the curve fit the best.

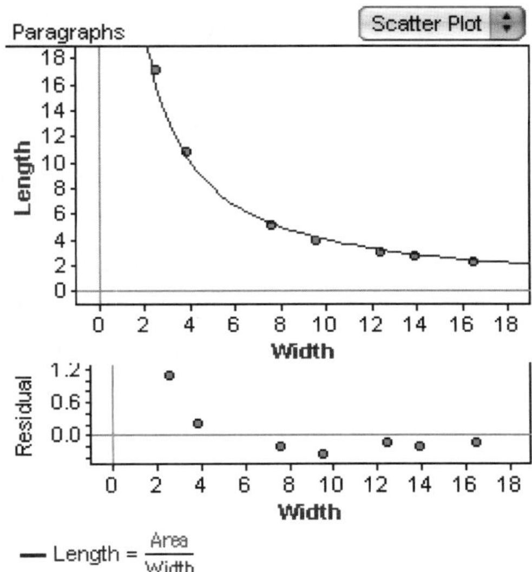

Q13 What value of *Area* did you get? Explain how you decided what value was best.

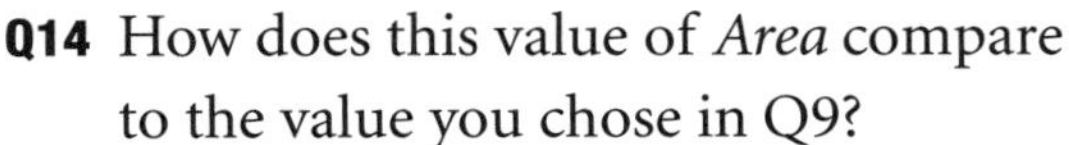

Q14 How does this value of *Area* compare to the value you chose in Q9?

Q15 From what you have done so far, how does the height of the paragraphs depend on the width? Do you think you've found the best model for this relationship? In what ways could it be improved, if any?

EXPLORE MORE

1. You probably noticed that it is impossible to fit the curve to all seven data points. The points that represent the narrowest two paragraphs are particularly problematic. That's because the paragraphs aren't perfect rectangles—a line may or may not have extra white space at the end because of words moving to the next line. Assume that the average amount of white space is the same for every line. Make a new slider called *White*. Then the area of the paragraph is *Area* = *Length* • (*Width* − *White*). Modify your inverse variation function accordingly and adjust the sliders to find the best fit now. Does *White* help reduce the residuals? Describe which residuals *White* impacts the most, and explain why this makes sense. Is your value for *Area* bigger or smaller than before you added *White*? Explain why the change in *Area* makes sense.

2. After finding the best fit with *Area* and *White,* adjust the sliders some more and watch how the graph of the inverse-variation curve and the residual plot change. What happens to the curve when you change *Area*? What happens to the residuals? What happens to the curve when you change *White*? What happens to the residuals? Try to explain mathematically why this happens.

3. When you first made a graph of *Length* versus *Width,* you may have thought that the relationship was exponential. That would have been a good guess, especially if you didn't know the geometric relationship. (Mathematicians don't always know what model is best. They usually have to try several to find the best fit.) Try fitting an exponential function to the data. Use sliders to help you adjust parameters in the function, and use residual plots to help you judge how well the function fits. After you've found the best fit that you can with an exponential function, compare its residual plot to the residual plot for the best fit with the inverse-variation function. Which residual plot implies the better fit?

THE SEVEN PARAGRAPHS

Some rational functions can create very different kinds of graphs from those you have studied previously. The graphs of these functions are often in two or more parts. This is because the denominator, a polynomial function, may be equal to zero at some point, so the function will be undefined at that point. Sometimes it's difficult to see the different parts of the graph because they may be separated by only one missing point, called a hole. At other times, you will see two parts that look very similar—one part may look like a reflection or rotation of the other part. Or you might get multiple parts that look totally different from each other.

Some rational functions can create very different kinds of graphs from those you have studied previously. The graphs of these functions are often in two or more parts. This is because the denominator, a polynomial function, may be equal to zero at some point, so the function will be undefined at that point. Sometimes it's difficult to see the different parts of the graph because they may be separated by only one missing point, called a hole. At other times, you will see two parts that look very similar—one part may look like a reflection or rotation of the other part. Or you might get multiple parts that look totally different from each other.

Some rational functions can create very different kinds of graphs from those you have studied previously. The graphs of these functions are often in two or more parts. This is because the denominator, a polynomial function, may be equal to zero at some point, so the function will be undefined at that point. Sometimes it's difficult to see the different parts of the graph because they may be separated by only one missing point, called a hole. At other times, you will see two parts that look very similar—one part may look like a reflection or rotation of the other part. Or you might get multiple parts that look totally different from each other.

Some rational functions can create very different kinds of graphs from those you have studied previously. The graphs of these functions are often in two or more parts. This is because the denominator, a polynomial function, may be equal to zero at some point, so the function will be undefined at that point. Sometimes it's difficult to see the different parts of the graph because they may be separated by only one missing point, called a hole. At other times, you will see two parts that look very similar—one part may look like a reflection or rotation of the other part. Or you might get multiple parts that look totally different from each other.

Some rational functions can create very different kinds of graphs from those you have studied previously. The graphs of these functions are often in two or more parts. This is because the denominator, a polynomial function, may be equal to zero at some point, so the function will be undefined at that point. Sometimes it's difficult to see the different parts of the graph because they may be separated by only one missing point, called a hole. At other times, you will see two parts that look very similar—one part may look like a reflection or rotation of the other part. Or you might get multiple parts that look totally different from each other.

Some rational functions can create very different kinds of graphs from those you have studied previously. The graphs of these functions are often in two or more parts. This is because the denominator, a polynomial function, may be equal to zero at some point, so the function will be undefined at that point. Sometimes it's difficult to see the different parts of the graph because they may be separated by only one missing point, called a hole. At other times, you will see two parts that look very similar—one part may look like a reflection or rotation of the other part. Or you might get multiple parts that look totally different from each other.

Some rational functions can create very different kinds of graphs from those you have studied previously. The graphs of these functions are often in two or more parts. This is because the denominator, a polynomial function, may be equal to zero at some point, so the function will be undefined at that point. Sometimes it's difficult to see the different parts of the graph because they may be separated by only one missing point, called a hole. At other times, you will see two parts that look very similar—one part may look like a reflection or rotation of the other part. Or you might get multiple parts that look totally different from each other.

from *Discovering Advanced Algebra* by Murdock, Kamischke, and Kamischke

How Much Paper Is Left?

You will need

- fulll roll of adding-machine paper
- millimeter ruler
- meterstick

You have a full roll of adding-machine paper. The question for this activity is "How much paper is on the roll?" The catch is that you can't find the length by unrolling the entire roll.

As you pull paper from the roll, the roll gets smaller. Because the roll is a circle (or a cylinder, to be exact), you can use the diameter as one way to measure the roll's size. This leads to a related question: "How does the diameter of the roll relate to how much paper you pull off?" Once you find a mathematical model for this relationship, you will be able to calculate the total length without unrolling it.

MAKE A CONJECTURE

Before you start unrolling, make a conjecture about what will happen. You already know that as the diameter gets smaller, it means you've pulled off more paper. But what is the functional relationship?

Q1 If you make a graph of the *cumulative* length pulled off (L) as a function of diameter (D), what would it look like? Is the function linear? Is it curved? If it's curved, how does it curve? Sketch your prediction.

EXPERIMENT

Now you'll collect data by measuring diameter and cumulative length pulled off. For each measurement, be as careful and precise as you can.

1. Use your ruler to measure the diameter of the full roll to the nearest half millimeter. You haven't pulled off any paper yet, so record this diameter for D along with 0 m for L in this table:

	D	L
units	millimeters	meters
1		0 m
2		
3		
4		
5		
6		
7		
8		
9		

diameter of core = _____ mm

2. Pull off a few meters of paper. Measure the length with your ruler or meterstick and record it for L. Precisely measure the new diameter and record it for D. Repeat this several times. Make sure that you record the *cumulative* length; that is, if you unroll about 3 meters each time, the values for L should be about 3, 6, 9, and so on. Stop when the roll is about half gone.

3. Measure the diameter of the core—the spool that the paper is wound on. Record this measurement below the table. You'll need it later.

INVESTIGATE

Next you'll analyze the data with Fathom.

4. Start Fathom and enter your data into a case table. Use the attributes *D* and *L*, and use units, as shown in the table.
5. Make a scatter plot of *L* versus *D*. The data probably look fairly linear.
6. With the graph selected, choose **Least-Squares Line** from the **Graph** menu.

You can use a residual plot to help you judge how well the function fits the data.

7. Choose **Make Residual Plot** from the **Graph** menu.

Q2 Describe what you see in the residual plot. Based on the residual plot, do you think the least-squares line is a good fit?

Q3 Compare what you have in your graph so far to your prediction in question Q1. Which aspects of the Fathom graph meet your expectations? Which do not?

Here's a sample graph from step 7. Your graph probably looks similar. Notice that even though the least-squares line has an r^2 close to 1.00, there is something wrong with the line as a model. The residuals form an obvious and consistent bow, which you can barely see in the top graph. When the residuals have an obvious pattern like this, it usually means that the function model is not correct.

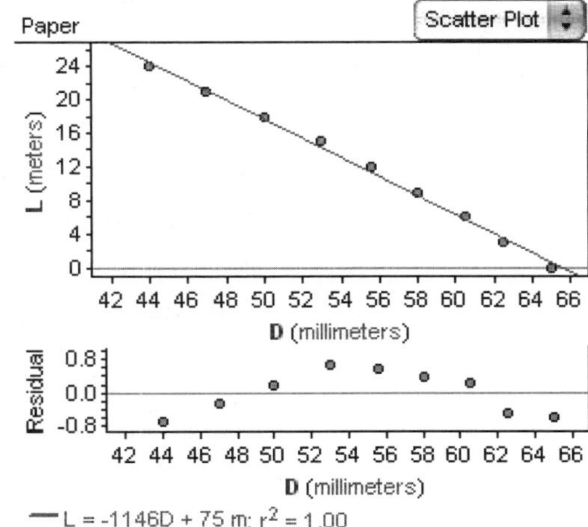

To find a better model, think about what aspects of the circular roll change as you remove paper. The diameter of the circle changes, but the area also changes—pulling off paper removes area from the outside of the circle. Area is a square dimension, so see whether squaring the variables helps make a better fit.

8. Make two new attributes, *DD* and *LL*, that are defined by the formulas D^2 and L^2, respectively.
9. Make scatter plots of all combinations of *L* or *LL* (vertical) versus *D* or *DD* (horizontal). Add a least-squares line and residual plot to each scatter plot.

Q4 Sketch the four possible graphs. Which graph is closest to a straight line?

Q5 Write the equation of the least-squares line for the graph in Q4 that was most linear.

Q6 When you're out of paper, *D* will be the diameter of the core. When you're out of paper, what value do you need to substitute into the equation in Q5? (*Hint:* Pay attention to units!)

Q7 Use your answers to Q5 and Q6 to substitute and calculate how much paper is on the roll.

Q8 Unroll the entire roll and measure the total length of paper. Or, if your teacher has the packaging from the adding-machine rolls, find out how much paper is supposed to be on each roll. How does your prediction in Q7 compare to the actual length of paper on the roll?

Q9 In step 5, the scatter plot of *L* versus *D* looked fairly linear even though the relationship is *not* linear. How can it be that the data looked so straight? If you had collected more data, do you think you would have recognized the curve more clearly? Explain why or why not.

EXPLORE MORE

1. Most adding-machine rolls have a band of red on the paper nearest the core. When you use the roll in an adding machine, calculator, or cash register, you know you are about to run out of paper when you see a red edge on the paper. Calculate how much paper is left on the roll when you first see the red edge.
2. The equation that you wrote in Q5 is the least-squares line for *transformed* data. Use algebra to turn the linear function into a curved function for the original data. What type of function do you get? Does that function make sense based on the geometry of this situation? Plot the curved function on your original graph of *L* versus *D*. How well does the curved function fit your data?

Compound Interest

Interest is a charge that you pay a bank for borrowing money, or that the bank pays you for keeping money in your bank account and letting the bank invest and earn interest on it. Interest rates are usually stated as annual, or yearly, rates. *Simple interest* is calculated by multiplying the initial investment (the *principal*) times the interest rate times the length of time. With simple interest, the interest earned does not become part of your principal. The interest is always calculated as a percentage of the original principal.

Most banks, however, use *compound interest.* This means the interest earned is added to your principal, so that interest is calculated on a growing amount of money. You probably already know that compound interest is an exponential function. For example, if you invest \$2000 at an annual interest rate of 7%, your *balance* over the years is

Year 0: \$2000

Year 1: $\$2000(1 + 0.07)$

Year 2: $[\$2000(1 + 0.07)]\,(1 + 0.07) = \$2000(1 + 0.07)^2$

Year 3: $\left[\$2000(1 + 0.07)^2\right](1 + 0.07) = \$2000(1 + 0.07)^3$

Year n: $\$2000(1 + 0.07)^n$

Many banks calculate interest on an account or a loan more frequently than once a year. In these cases, the annual interest rate is divided quarterly (by 4), monthly (by 12), or by another number that corresponds to the number of periods per year. This creates an exponential function, too. For example, if the annual rate of 7% is compounded monthly, then your balance over the months is

Month 0: \$2000

Month 1: $\$2000\left(1 + \frac{0.07}{12}\right)$

Month 2: $\$2000\left(1 + \frac{0.07}{12}\right)^2$

Month 3: $\$2000\left(1 + \frac{0.07}{12}\right)^3$

Month n: $\$2000\left(1 + \frac{0.07}{12}\right)^n$

When you add money to the account—or make *payments*—your interest is calculated from the previous month's balance plus the payment. Here's an example with a monthly payment of \$500:

Month 0: \$2000

Month 1: $\$2000\left(1 + \frac{0.07}{12}\right) + \$500$

Month 2: $\left[\$2000\left(1 + \frac{0.07}{12}\right) + \$500\right]\left(1 + \frac{0.07}{12}\right) + \$500$

Month 3: $\left[\left[\$2000\left(1 + \frac{0.07}{12}\right) + \$500\right]\left(1 + \frac{0.07}{12}\right) + \$500\right]\left(1 + \frac{0.07}{12}\right) + \$500$

Month n: $\$2000\left(1 + \frac{0.07}{12}\right)^n + \$500\left(1 + \frac{0.07}{12}\right)^{n-1} + \$500\left(1 + \frac{0.07}{12}\right)^{n-2} + \cdots + \$500$

In this activity, you'll use Fathom to explore compound interest. By watching the balance change as you adjust the parameters, you'll get a better understanding of compound interest.

INVESTIGATE

1. Open the document **CompoundInterest.ftm.**

The sliders in this document change the principal (*Principal*), the annual interest rate (*InterestRate*), the compounding periods (*PeriodsPerYear*), and the payment (*PaymentPerPeriod*). The case table uses formulas to show time in different formats, the current balance, the interest that *accrues* (is earned) during each period, and the payment that is made during each period. The graph shows *Balance* as a function of *TimeInYears.*

2. Play with the sliders, individually and in combination with each other. Get a feel for how each slider affects the values in the case table and the graph. If you use values that make points go off the graph, choose **Rescale Graph Axes** from the **Graph** menu to see the entire graph.

Q1 How does *Principal* affect the graph of *Balance* versus *TimeInYears*?

Q2 How does *InterestRate* affect the graph? What happens if you use a negative value of *InterestRate*? What would a negative interest rate mean in a real-world situation?

Q3 How does *PeriodsPerYear* affect the graph?

Q4 How does *PaymentPerPeriod* affect the graph? What happens if you use a negative value of *PaymentPerPeriod*? What would a negative payment mean in a real-world situation?

Now that you know how the sliders work, try using them to solve some specific problems.

Q5 Adjust the sliders to solve one or more of these problems. Along with your answer, briefly explain how you set the sliders and found the solution.

a. Suppose $3000 is invested in a retirement account that earns 2.5% annual interest, compounded quarterly. You make no additional contributions to the account. What is the balance after the 3rd quarter of the 5th year?

b. You enroll in an investment plan that deducts $100 from your monthly paycheck and deposits it into an account that earns 7%, compounded monthly. How much will you have invested after your 25th paycheck?

c. You borrow $1200 at 4.5% annual interest, compounded monthly. If you must pay off the loan within 3 years, how much will you need to pay each month? (*Hint:* For a loan, your payments *reduce* the balance.)

d. Kelly buys $2000 of furniture on her credit card. The card has an annual interest rate of 18%, compounded monthly. If Kelly makes only the minimum payment of $40 each month, when will she pay off the balance? How much will she have actually paid for the furniture, including all of the interest? (*Hint:* In order to find the answer, you'll need to add several months to your case table. Select the case table and choose **New Cases** from the **Collection** menu to do this.)

EXPLORE MORE

1. For a given principal and interest rate, how much more is the balance at the end of 3 years compounding once per year versus quarterly? How does monthly compare? How about weekly (52 times per year) and daily (usually taken as 360 times per year)? Complete this sentence: In the long run, if your interest is compounded more frequently, your balance will be . . . .

2. Investigate the relationship between interest rate and *doubling time*—the time it takes for your balance to be twice as much as your principal. First explore interest compounded yearly, then quarterly, and then monthly. Regardless of your principal, can you figure out doubling time based on the compound interest rate? Is it possible to figure out what compound interest rate is required to have the balance double after a certain amount of time, say, 3 years? (*Note:* Keep *PaymentPerYear* set to 0 for this exploration.)
3. Investigate the relationship between payment per period and the balance after 3 years. Be as quantitative as possible. Explore interest compounded yearly, then quarterly, and then monthly.

Precalculus and Calculus

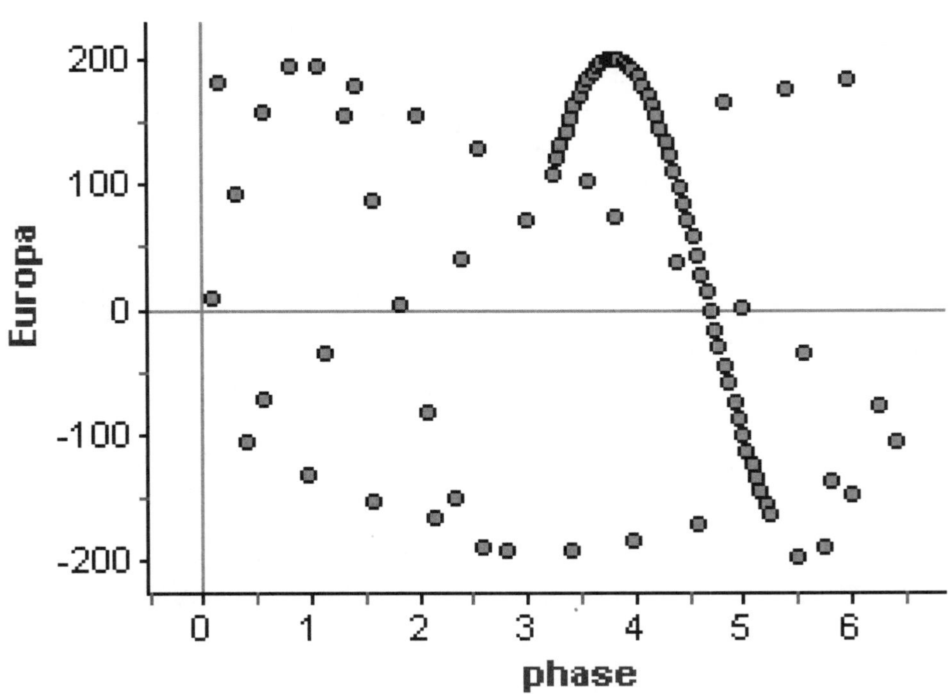

Jupiter's Moons

Astronomers have been able to model many parts of the universe to accurately predict where planets, stars, comets, and moons will be at any time. In this activity, you'll look at data about one of Jupiter's four largest moons and estimate how long it will take for the moon to complete one full revolution around the planet.

If you look at one of Jupiter's moons from night to night, it seems to be swinging back and forth. It's really going around the planet, of course, but you're seeing the moon's orbit edge-on.

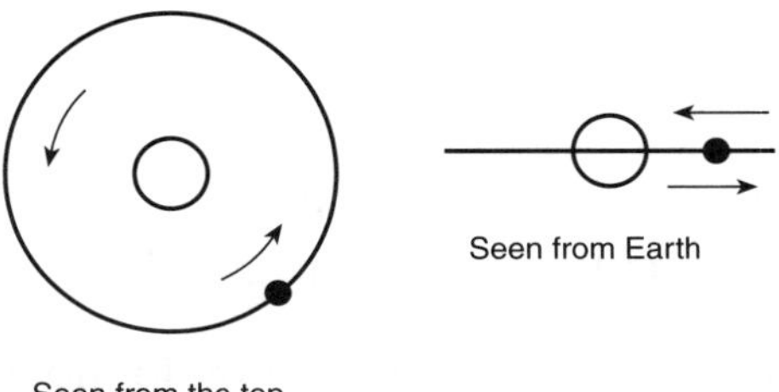

If you record the distance of the moon from Jupiter—positive to the west, negative to the east—as a function of time, you get a wavy curve. You will find the period of this curve.

INVESTIGATE

1. Open the document **JupiterMoons.ftm.** You should see a case table with ten attributes.

The attribute *mjd* stands for Modified Julian Date in decimal days. (The Modified Julian Date measures days since November 17, 1858.) The attributes for the four moons, *Io*, *Europa, Ganymede,* and *Callisto,* give the distance of the moon from Jupiter as seen from Earth, measured in arc seconds $\left(1 \text{ arc second} = \frac{1}{3600} \text{ degree}\right)$. Positive distances are to the west; negative distances are to the east.

2. Choose one of the moons to use in this activity. You'll be able to experiment with the other moons later. Create a graph of the distance of the moon you chose as a function of *mjd*. Examine the table to understand why the initial points in the graph are tightly clustered together.

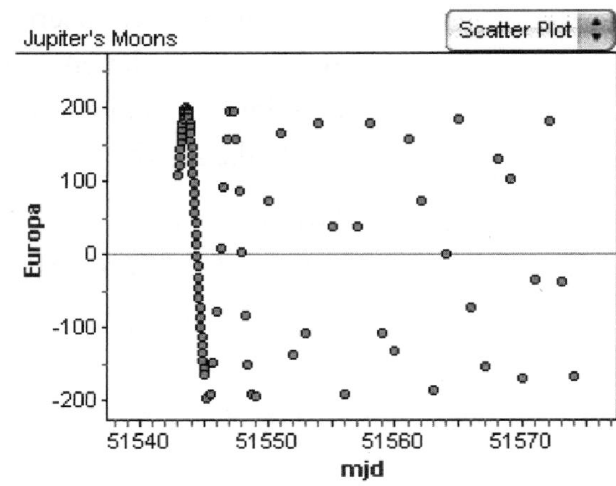

Q1 What specific kind of periodic function does this graph appear to be? Estimate the period of the graph.

Now you'll attempt to find a function to model this graph.

3. Create a new slider called *period*.

The *phase* of a periodic function is how far a function is into its current cycle.

4. In the case table, create a new attribute called *phase*. Enter a formula for *phase* that calculates the phase of the function using your slider for the period. (*Hint:* You want to find the time since the function has completed its last cycle. Use the *floor* function to help you find the number of whole cycles completed.)

Q2 What formula did you come up with?

5. Make a new graph that plots the distance of your moon as a function of *phase*.

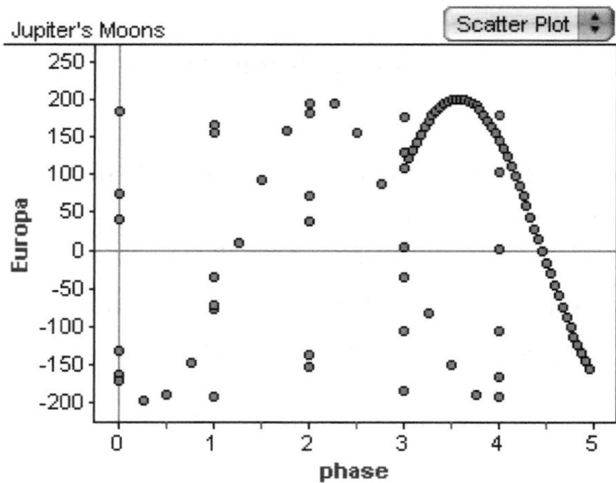

Q3 Adjust the *period* slider. Describe what you see in the graph. What period seems to best fit the data for your moon? How did you choose that period?

The *mjd* values are so large that any changes in the estimate for the period lead to a large change in the calculation of the *phase*.

6. Add a new attribute, *newjd*. Edit the formula for this attribute to be *mjd* − 51544.

Q4 What date does the number 51544 correspond to in your model?

7. Edit the *phase* formula to use *newjd* instead of *mjd*.

8. Adjust the *period* slider until the points line up and show just a single cycle. (You may have to rescale the graph axes to see the complete cycle.) Try to be as accurate as possible by shortening the range of values for the slider. Do this by double-clicking on the slider axis and changing the lower and upper values. You will probably want to adjust the slider several times as you get more and more accurate.

Q5 What value of *period* to three decimal places makes the points in the graph line up? How accurate do you think your estimate is?

You now have an estimate for the period. But your data cover only a few cycles. Next you'll test your estimate by using data from several months later.

9. Add these data to your case table.

Date	Modified Julian Date	Io	Europa	Ganymede	Callisto
July 1	51726.0	27.28	−26.23	−239.64	−196.76
July 2	51727.0	14.45	−152.89	−83.11	−34.57

10. Select the new points by holding down the Shift key as you click on the case number for each new point in your case table. The points should be highlighted red in the second graph.

11. Now adjust the value of *period* to make the two highlighted points in the *phase* graph fit the curve.

Q6 Does your estimate for *period* change due to adding the new points? If so, what is your new estimate and why do you think it changed? Which estimate do you think is more accurate?

Now you'll create a function that models the data. You already know the period of the function (although the true period requires a bit of manipulation of the period you've already found). You'll need to come up with values for amplitude and phase displacement and decide whether to use the sine or cosine function.

12. Use your graphs to make an estimate for the amplitude of the function. Try using the *max* and *min* functions of Fathom to create a formula for the amplitude.

Q7 State the formula and the value you found. Explain why this is a good starting point for estimation, but probably isn't the actual amplitude of the function.

13. Before you can find the phase displacement, you need to decide which function to use. Although you can use either sine or cosine, one may be easier than the other. Once you have chosen which function to use, estimate the phase displacement by inspecting the graph. (*Hint:* When you click on a point on the graph, the coordinates of the point are shown in the bottom-left corner of the Fathom window. Think of points that may be helpful in estimating the displacement.)

14. You may need to adjust the amplitude and phase displacement, because they are only estimates. To help with adjustment, create two sliders—*amplitude* and *displacement.*

15. Now you have all the information for the equation. Click on the *phase* graph and then choose **Plot Function** from the **Graph** menu. Enter a function for the graph, using *amplitude, displacement,* and *period* as constants in your equation. Adjust the sliders to improve your model.

Q8 State the function that best matched your data. Could you write a different function that would model the data equally well? Explain.

EXPLORE MORE

1. Plot your function on the first graph you created, replacing *phase* with *mjd.* Does the graph fit the data? Explain.
2. Predict the position of the moon you chose at midnight on your birthday in 2006. Remember to convert to the New Modified Julian Date.
3. Compare your findings with those of other members of the class. Compare your graphs. Which planet has the longest orbital period? Can you determine which moon is closest to Jupiter? Which moon is farthest away?

Population Growth

Most populations are subject to a number of factors that affect the rate at which the population grows or decays. The rate at which a human population grows often depends on limiting factors, such as the availability of housing, food, and other resources. In the first three parts of this activity, you'll model a population assuming no limiting factors. In the last part, you'll introduce a limiting factor and study how this affects the population.

EXPERIMENT

Suppose you are part of the swiftly growing community of Chelmsdale. When you first moved to Chelmsdale, there were 2000 inhabitants, but in each of the next 4 years, Chelmsdale has grown at a rate of approximately 25%.

1. Open the document **PopulationGrowth.ftm.** You should see a case table with the attributes *year, new,* and *pop* and a formula for each attribute.
2. Select the case table. From the **Collection** menu, choose **New Cases.** Create five new cases.

Q1 What do the three attributes represent?

Q2 What is the population of Chelmsdale after 4 years? What could be some of the causes for the rise in population?

3. Graph *pop* as a function of *year.*

Q3 What kind of function have you graphed?

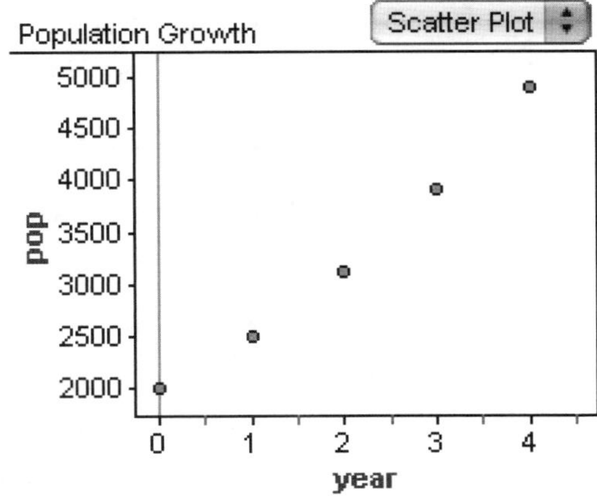

Now you will use your model to see how many people might live in Chelmsdale if the population continues to grow at this rate.

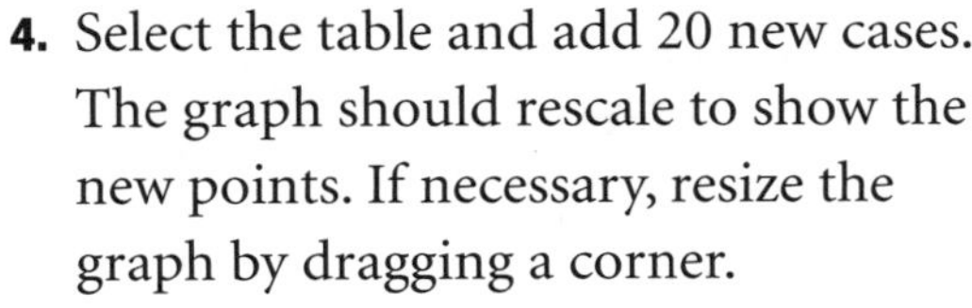

4. Select the table and add 20 new cases. The graph should rescale to show the new points. If necessary, resize the graph by dragging a corner.

Q4 After 24 years, how many people live in Chelmsdale? Does it seem reasonable for the population to have grown this much in 24 years? Why or why not? (You'll explore this idea more later.)

INVESTIGATE

Now you'll find an exponential function that fits these data. You'll experiment using sliders.

5. Drag two sliders from the shelf into your document. Rename them *A* and *B* by clicking on their names and typing new ones.

6. Select the graph and choose **Plot Function** from the **Graph** menu. Enter the formula `A*B^year` in the formula editor. A curve should appear on the graph.

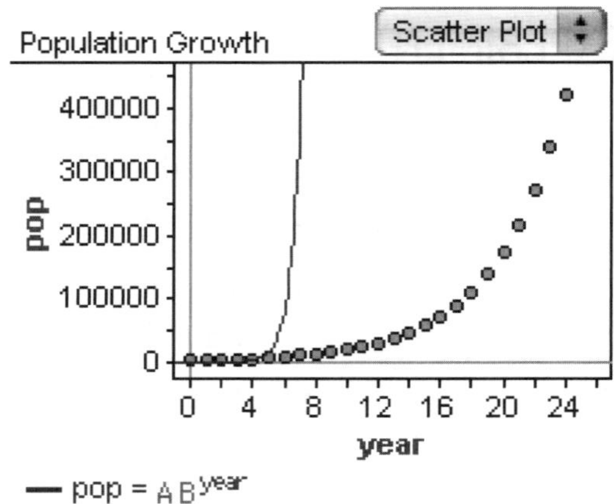

7. Adjust the *A* slider and watch how the curve changes. (You may want to change the bounds on the slider axis to bring larger numbers into view. Grab the right end of the axis and drag left.)

Q5 Describe the way the curve changes when you change the value of *A*.

8. Adjust the *B* slider. (The curve is very sensitive; you may want to restrict the values of *B* that you see. Double-click near the axis and enter new values for the *Lower* and *Upper* bounds.)

Q6 Describe the way the curve changes when you change the value of *B*.

The scale on the vertical axis is very large, and it's hard to see how well the function is fitting the smaller values.

9. Adjust the scale of the graph so that you can focus on the first 10 years. Double-click the graph to show its inspector. Change *xUpper* to 11. Pick values for *yLower* and *yUpper* that will show only the first 10 years in the graph.

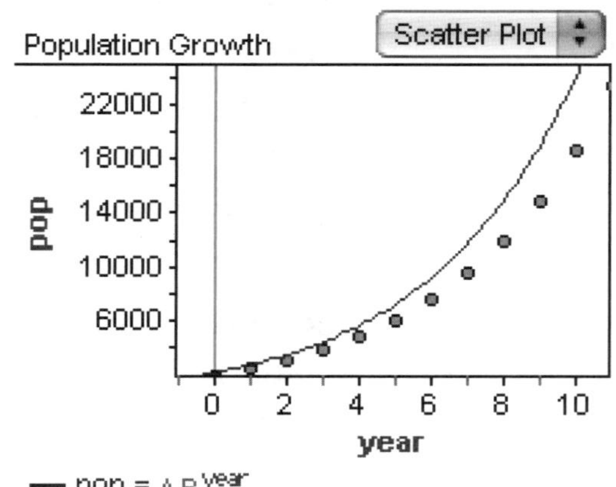

10. Move both sliders to fit the function to the data. (*Hint:* The values of *A* and *B* have something to do with the original data you were given.) After you have matched the function to the data for the first 10 years, select the graph and choose **Rescale Graph Axes** from the **Graph** menu. If your function doesn't fit the later points, adjust the sliders until it does.

Q7 What values of *A* and *B* fit the data best? How did you come to this conclusion? Explain as clearly as you can what *A* and *B* represent.

You may have noticed a flaw that makes this simulation unrealistic—for many of the years, there are non-integer values of people. Next you will update the model to use only integer values of people.

11. Change the original formula for *new* so that there are only integer values of new people coming into the community. (Try using the *floor* function in the formula editor.)

12. The original model also neglected to include the death rate. In the case table, create a new attribute called *deaths.* Assume that the death rate is constant at 2% per year. Enter the formula for *deaths.* Don't forget to use integer values.

Q8 You know the death rate is constant. But the percentage increase in the actual population of Chelmsdale is known to be 25% each year. How must you change the formula for *new* to take into account the addition of *deaths* to your model? Explain.

Q9 Now change the formula for *pop* to take into account these changes. What is the new formula? Does it still agree with your exponential equation for *pop*?

Q10 See if you can express *B* in terms of the rate of new inhabitants and the death rate. Create two new sliders, *newrate* and *deathrate,* to take the place of *B.* Change your exponential equation to reflect these changes. What is your new equation?

13. Update the formulas for *pop, new,* and *deaths* in the case table by inserting the three sliders in place of the constants. Experiment with different values for the rate of new inhabitants, death rate, and initial population by moving your sliders.

Real populations do not grow without limit. There are a number of factors that can limit the growth of a population. For example, a community has only a certain amount of land to build new homes. Also, water, food, and energy resources are limited, thereby limiting the number of people that can come in to a community. This phenomenon is often called the *crowding effect.*

To simulate the crowding effect, you'll increase the death rate as the population of the community becomes too large. There are several ways to do this. One of the most interesting ways is to change the formula so that the death rate gradually increases with the population. That's what you'll do.

14. Edit your formula for *deaths* by multiplying *deathrate* by $\frac{pop}{1000}$. That way there will be fewer deaths when *pop* < 1000 and more deaths when *pop* > 1000. Set the *A* slider to 2000 and set the *newrate* and *deathrate* sliders to their original values.

Q11 Graph *deaths* as a function of *pop*. Describe what happens.

Q12 Rescale your graph of *pop* as a function of *year* by choosing **Rescale Graph Axes** from the **Graph** menu. You should have just created a *logistic function.* Describe the graph. Add 50 new cases to your case table and scroll down. What number does *pop* appear to be approaching?

Q13 Increase *newrate* to 0.28. You can type the value directly into the slider by clicking its current value. What number does *pop* approach now? What about when *newrate* is 0.29? Do you see a pattern?

EXPLORE MORE

The logistic function has the form $y = \frac{c}{1 + a(b)^{-x}}$, where *a*, *b*, and *c* are constants. The function has two horizontal asymptotes at $y = 0$ and $y = c$. Create a logistic function that models the population growth including the limiting factor. The population limit for your graph can be modeled with a horizontal asymptote. Use this limit as your value for *c*. Choose two points from the case table to solve for the constants *a* and *b*. Does it matter which two points you choose? Solve for *a* and *b* and write the resulting equation. Graph the equation of the logistic function on your graph of *pop* as a function of *year*. Is the function a good model for the population? Explain.

Rates of Change

You may have learned that the connection between position (or distance), velocity, and acceleration has to do with derivatives. In this activity, you'll develop an initial understanding of the mathematical relationship between these concepts. You'll explore the difference between the average rate of change and instantaneous rate of change of a function.

EXPERIMENT

1. Open the document **RatesOfChange.ftm.** You should see an empty case table with attributes x, v, and a, two empty line scatter plots, and a slider, b. Attribute x stands for time, v stands for velocity, and a stands for acceleration.

2. Select the case table. Choose **New Cases** from the **Collection** menu, enter `50`, and click **OK.** You should see points on each of the graphs that look similar to the ones shown here.

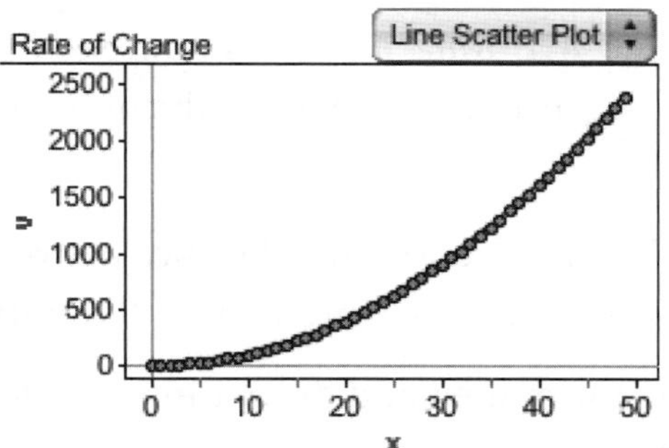

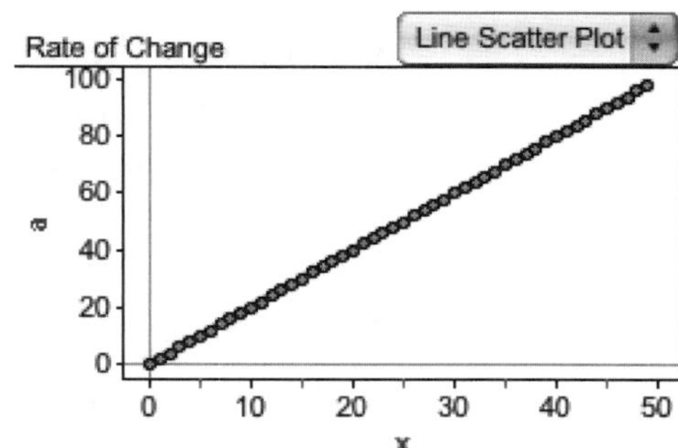

Q1 Describe attribute a in terms of the derivative of v. (*Hint:* The derivative of a power function decreases the exponent by one.) What motion in the real world might have this velocity and acceleration?

3. The slider b represents the exponent of the power function $v = x^b$. Move the slider back and forth and observe the change in the graph of v.

Q2 Set b to 1. (You can do this directly by clicking on the value of b and typing in the new value.) Rescale each graph by selecting the graph and choosing **Rescale Graph Axes** from the **Graph** menu. (You can also do this by choosing **Line Scatter Plot** again from the pop-up menu in the graph.) What kinds of functions are shown on each of the graphs now? Be as specific as you can.

The *average* rate of change of a function calculates the slope between two points of a function. Next you will calculate the average rate of change of v and explore how it relates to the derivative.

4. Set b to 3.00 and rescale the graphs. Create a new attribute by clicking on <*new*> in the case table and entering `Ave_Rate`.

5. Select *Ave_Rate* and choose **Edit Formula** from the **Edit** menu. Enter the formula

```
(v-prev(v,""))/(x-prev(x,""))
```

and click **OK.** ("") means that if there is no previous value of v and x, no value of *Ave_Rate* will be calculated.

INVESTIGATE

In question Q1, you should have answered that a is the derivative of v. Another way to say derivative is *instantaneous* rate of change. So, you know the instantaneous rate of change of v is a. We want to compare *Ave_Rate* to a.

Q3 Compare the values for a and *Ave_Rate.* Do you see a trend in the difference between a and *Ave_Rate* as x gets larger? Calculate the difference when $x = 5$, $x = 20$, and $x = 35$.

Now, let's see what happens when we decrease the distance between x-values. We'll do this using a slider that directly affects the increment of the x attribute.

6. Drag a new slider from the object shelf and drop it into the document. Name the slider n. (Click the slider name and type in the new name.)

7. Next, insert the value of the slider into the formula for x. Select the x attribute in the case table and choose **Edit Formula** from the **Edit** menu. Change the formula to `n(caseindex-1)`.

8. Finally, you want x-values to be a fraction of what they were, so you need to limit the values of the slider to account for this. Double-click the slider axis. Set the lower value to 0 and the upper value to 1, then close the inspector.

9. Check to make sure you have done this correctly by setting $n = 1$. The values for x should be the same as they were before you changed the function. If they aren't, go back and redo steps 6–8.

Q4 Set $n = 0.5$. Find the difference between a and *Ave_Rate* at $x = 5$. Is the difference less than when $n = 5$? Describe what you think will happen as you continue to decrease the value of n.

Q5 Repeat Q4 for $n = 0.2, 0.1, 0.05, 0.01$, and 0.001. (You will have to add more cases each time. To find the number of cases you need, calculate $\frac{5}{n}$.) Record the values you get for *Ave_Rate* and $a -$ *Ave_Rate* in a table. What conclusions do you draw?

Q6 Based on what you've just discovered, define the instantaneous rate of change at $x = 5$ in terms of the average rate of change. (*Hint:* Use the limit of the average rate.)

You've compared average and instantaneous rate of change numerically. Next, you'll approach the same problem graphically. You'll observe graphs of the derivative and the average rate of change as the increment of x decreases.

10. For a change of pace, set $b = 2.5$. Set $n = 1$. If you have more than 300 cases in your case table, delete the extra cases. To delete cases, select them and choose **Delete Cases** from the **Edit** menu.

11. Drag a new graph into the document. Drag attribute x from the case table and drop it below the horizontal axis of your new graph. Drag *Ave_Rate* to the vertical axis. A scatter plot should appear. Choose **Line Scatter Plot** from the pop-up menu on the graph.

12. You want to compare this to the derivative (or instantaneous rate of change), so let's put a graph of the derivative on the same graph. Select the a attribute in the case table and choose **Copy Formula** from the **Edit** menu. This is the formula for the derivative.

13. Now select the graph you just created and choose **Plot Function** from the **Graph** menu. Paste the formula here and click **OK.** The two curves should look almost identical.

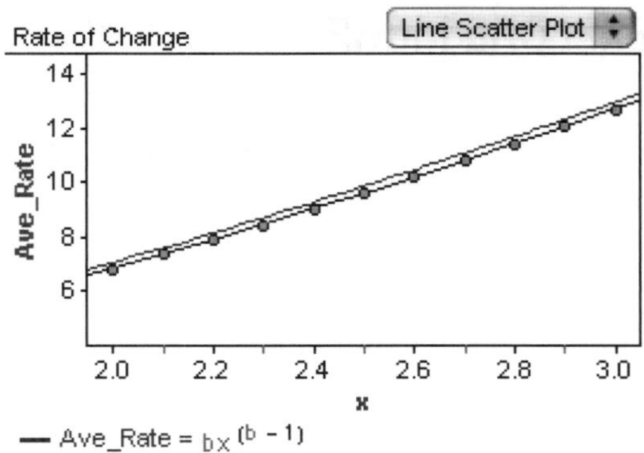

14. Let's zoom in on a small portion of the graph, to make it easier to see what happens as the increment between x-values gets smaller. To zoom in on a smaller portion of the graph, double-click the graph to show the graph inspector. Change the bounds to $1.95 \leq x \leq 3.05$ and $4 \leq y \leq 15$. Also, change *xAutoRescale* and *yAutoRescale* from true to false. (This keeps the scale of the axes the same as you change the data.) The graph should look similar to the one shown here.

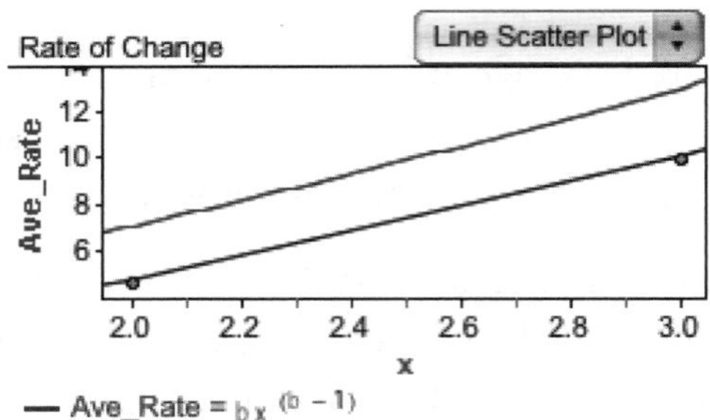

Q7 Experiment with different values of n. Try $n = 0.5, 0.1, 0.05$, and 0.01. (As n decreases, you may want to make the axes bounds smaller to see just how close they get.) Describe what happens on the graph as n gets smaller.

Q8 The formal definition of derivative of a function, $f(x)$, at point $x = c$ is the instantaneous rate of change of $f(x)$ with respect to x at $x = c$. Describe $f(x)$ and c in the context of this activity. Can you come up with a numerical definition of derivative?

EXPLORE MORE

Try repeating the activity with different values for b.

5

Statistics

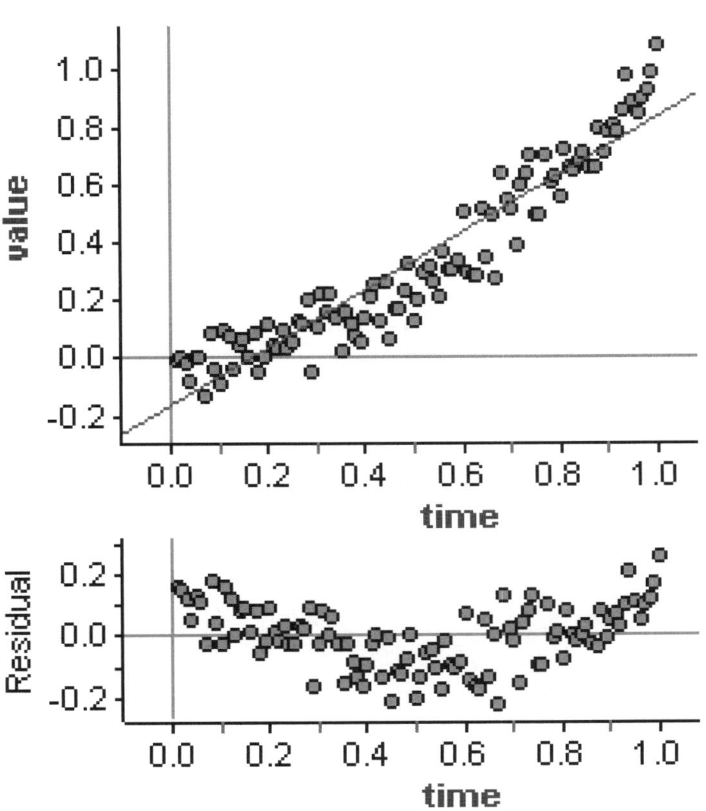
value
1.0
0.8
0.6
0.4
0.2
0.0
-0.2
0.0
0.2
0.4
0.6
0.8
1.0
time
Residual
0.2
0.0
-0.2
0.0
0.2
0.4
0.6
0.8
1.0
time

U.S. Census Data

Every ten years, the United States Census Bureau administers the U.S. Population Census. Every household in the country answers questions about topics such as their members' ages, races, and genders. About 6% of the households receive a longer version of the questionnaire that asks detailed questions about their commute to work, living conditions, and household expenses.

In this activity, you will look at data about individual people. You'll explore the range of ages, marital status, and incomes in your sample and see if they are related.

EXPERIMENT

1. Open the document **CensusData.ftm.** A *collection* appears—a box with gold balls.
2. Select the collection. Drag a case table from the shelf and drop it in your document. Stretch the corner to view some of the people in the collection.

Q1 What *attributes* are shown for each person in the case table?

INVESTIGATE

First you'll look at *Age.*

3. Drag a new graph from the shelf into your document. An empty graph appears.
4. Drag the column heading for *Age* from the case table and drop it below the horizontal axis of the graph. You get a dot plot of the ages of the people in your collection. If you click a dot, you can see the age of the person in the bottom-left corner of the window.

Q2 Describe the shape of the graph and any important features.

5. With such a large population, another type of graph may be better for viewing the data. Choose **Histogram** from the pop-up menu in the graph.

Q3 How many people in your data set are between 15 and 20 years old? (*Hint:* You can change the widths of the bars by dragging on their edges. If you select a bin, the number of cases appears in the bottom-left corner of the Fathom window.)

To answer the questions that follow, do not look up exact numbers in a table. Just read the graphs and estimate. You may want to change the type of graph to better view the data for the particular question. You can zoom in to a particular part of the graph by dragging the axis numbers. Choose the type of graph again (for example, box plot) to zoom back out.

Q4 How old is the oldest person in your file? What kind of graph did you use?

Q5 What is the median age of the people in your file? Again, what kind of graph did you use?

6. Drag the column label *Sex* from the case table to the vertical axis of your *Age* graph. It should split into two graphs, one for males and one for females.

Q6 What is the median age for males? For females?

7. Select the graph and choose **Plot Value** from the **Graph** menu. When the formula editor appears, enter `mean(Age)`. Click **OK.**

Q7 What are the mean ages for males and females in your file? What does the value of *mean*(*Age*) shown at the bottom of the graph represent?

Q8 For most communities, the mean age is greater than the median age. Why? Is that true for your data file?

8. Drag a new graph from the shelf. Drag the attribute *Marital_status* from the case table to the vertical axis of the new graph. A bar chart appears.

9. Click the "Never Married" bar to select it. Notice that red regions appear in the *Age* graph as well. You may also see cases in the collection or the case table that are highlighted. Whenever you *select* cases, those cases appear selected in all views of the data. Also, when you point at a bar in a graph, the status bar shows how many cases are in that bar.

Q9 What observations can you make about the people in your collection who have never married?

Q10 How many people in your data set are married?

10. Make a new graph of *Wage_and_salary_income.* Select all the really rich people—those few people who earn the most money. See who is selected in the other graphs.

Q11 Are the richest people predominantly from one group? That is, are they mostly male? Are they mostly old? Look for patterns. What do you find?

11. Decide how much income will define what you mean by *rich.* Don't make it too high; that is, you want more than just a few people to fall into that category.

Now you will create a new attribute for wealth. This attribute will divide the population into two groups: "rich" and "poor."

12. Click in the far-right column of the case table, where it says <*new*>. Type `Wealth` and press Enter.

13. Select the *Wealth* column by clicking its label and choose **Edit Formula** from the **Edit** menu. The formula editor appears. Enter a formula like the one shown here. This formula uses $50,000 for "rich." (*Note:* You don't have to type in *Wage_and_salary_income.* Open the Attributes list and double-click *Wage_and_salary_income* to add it to your formula. You will see that it comes up red because it is an existing attribute.)

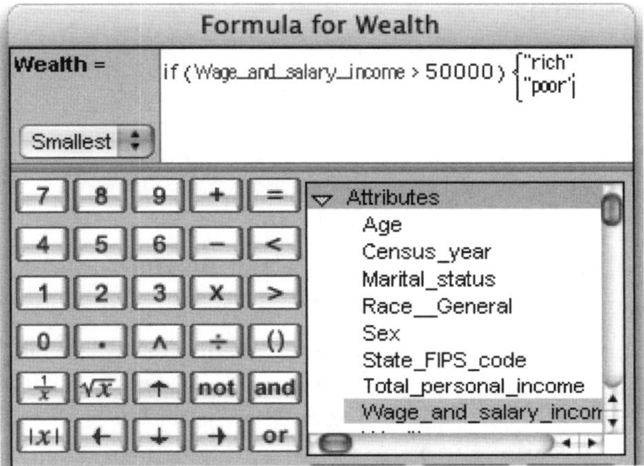

Q12 Describe how the formula works. Who will be considered "rich"? Who will be considered "poor"? Does it make sense to have only two categories for wealth? What categories would you add for a better description of wealth?

For now, we will keep our simple model with only "rich" and "poor." Later, you may want to explore adding more categories.

14. Make a new graph with *Wealth* on the horizontal axis.

Q13 Sketch the graph; be sure to label and scale your axes.

Q14 How many "rich" people are there in your data set? What percentage of the population is "rich"? How do you know?

15. Change the bar chart to a ribbon chart using the pop-up menu.

Q15 Which graph do you prefer for viewing the information? Explain why.

Your collection from the census includes data for children. It would be nice to exclude children from the graphs and look only at adults. To do this, you will add a filter. A *filter* is a formula that specifies which cases are kept in view.

16. Select the collection and choose **Add Filter** from the **Object** menu. Enter the formula `Age>18` and click **OK.**

Q16 Look at your graph of *Wage_and_salary_income.* Experiment with different types of graphs. What is the median *Wage_and_salary_income*? The mean *Wage_and_salary_income*? Remember that you can plot values on your graph.

17. To exclude retired people as well as children, you can change your filter. Double-click the filter (it's at the bottom of the collection). Edit the formula to *inRange*(*Age,* 18, 65). This will filter out people with an age less than 18 or greater than 65.

Q17 Describe the changes in your graphs. What are the new mean and median *Wage_and_salary_income*?

EXPLORE MORE

1. Write a new formula for *Wealth* that has more than two categories. One function that may be helpful is *switch.* Look in Fathom Help to get started using *switch.* Describe who fits into your new categories—married people? Young people?
2. Use a filter to find out how many teenagers are in the collection. How many of them are female? Find the mean and median *Wage_and_salary_income* of the teenagers.
3. You have been looking at *Wage_and_salary_income* to measure wealth. There is another income attribute, *Total_personal_income.* Examine the differences between these two attributes in the case table. What is each attribute measuring? Graph *Total_personal_income* as a function of *Wage_and_salary_income.* What do you observe? Double-click points that do not match the general trend of the graph to see their information. Are there any people with a large *Total_personal_income* but a small *Wage_and_salary_income*? Describe your observations.
4. Use a filter to look at the elderly people in the collection. (You will need to decide what *elderly* means.) Look at the incomes of elderly males and females. Remember that you can drag the *Sex* attribute to the vertical axis to split a graph by *Sex.* Does it make sense to look at the *Wage_and_salary_income* or the *Total_personal_income*? What is the mean income for elderly women? For elderly men?

Random Walk

A *random walk* is a process in which, for every step, you flip a coin. Heads, you step east. Tails, you step west. On the average, you'll wind up where you started—or will you? It depends on what you mean by *average*. In this activity, you will simulate and explore the random-walk situation.

MAKE A CONJECTURE

Before you build the simulation, try to predict what you will see. Imagine that you are standing on a number line at 0. You flip a coin to decide which way to walk. If the coin lands on heads, you take one step along the positive direction, as if you are adding 1. If the coin lands on tails, you take one step in the negative direction, as if you are adding −1.

Q1 Predict where you will be standing on the number line after 5 steps (this means 5 coin flips). Where will you be after 10 steps? After 100 steps? Explain your reasoning.

EXPERIMENT

Now you will build a simulation of a random walk in which you will start at 0 and take 10 random steps. Each step will be +1 or −1.

1. Open a new Fathom document. Create a new case table by dragging one off the shelf.
2. Make a new attribute, *distance*. To do this, click in the table header marked <*new*>. Type `distance` and press Enter. This attribute, *distance,* will record your distance from the start during your random walk.
3. Make 10 cases (these will be the steps in the walk). Choose **New Cases** from the **Collection** menu, enter `10`, and click **OK** to close the box. Ten (empty) cases appear in the table. You now have 10 cases for *distance,* but you need a formula to compute the values for *distance.*

Q2 Write the formula you will use to calculate the position of your next step based on your last step. If you aren't certain how to do this, write in words what the formula will do.

4. Select the *distance* column. Choose **Edit Formula** from the **Edit** menu. The formula editor appears.

5. Enter this formula: `prev(distance) + randomPick(-1,1)`. This formula takes your distance from the previous step and randomly adds either +1 or −1. Click **OK** to close the formula editor. Numbers appear in the table, representing your distance from 0 after each step.

6. Choose **Rerandomize** from the **Collection** menu. Do this a few times.

Q3 Describe what happens when you rerandomize. Update your conjecture from question Q1. Have you changed your mind about your prediction?

7. Create a new graph by dragging one off the shelf. Drag the attribute label for *distance* from the top of the column in the case table to the vertical axis of the graph. The dots show you the values of *distance* from your walk.

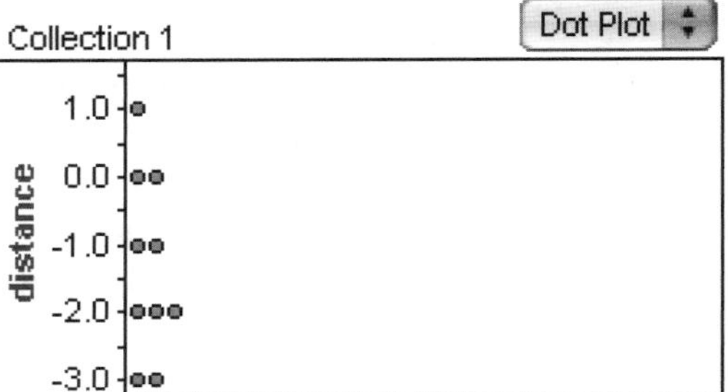

8. Choose **Line Plot** from the pop-up menu in the graph.

9. Choose **Rerandomize** again; you'll see the graph wiggle. (*Note:* The graph may move out of its original bounds. To change the bounds to fit your new values, choose **Line Plot** from the pop-up menu.)

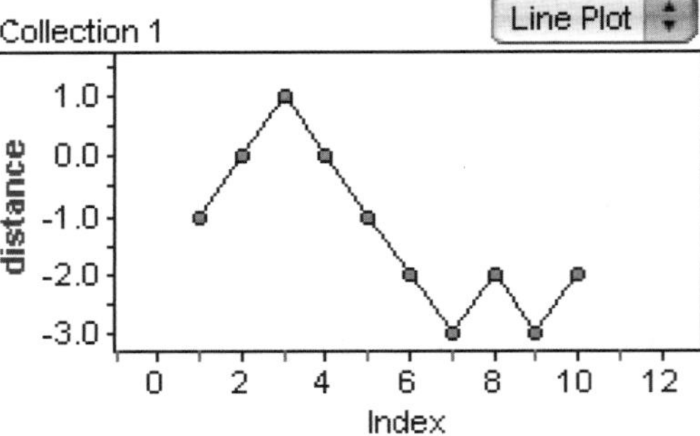

10. Rerandomize again and write down the final distance. Repeat this until you have recorded 20 values.

Each random walk is different. We want to know, on the average, how far you are from the place where you started.

Q4 Calculate (by hand or with a calculator) the average of the positions you recorded. What do you get? What do you expect to get in the long run? Explain your reasoning.

11. This time, calculate the average of the *absolute values* of the positions.

Q5 What did you get for the average of the absolute values? Explain the difference between the meanings of the two averages. When would it be useful to use the first average? The second average?

INVESTIGATE

It is not obvious what to expect in the long run from the average of the absolute values. But if you do more walks, you should get a better idea. Fathom will help you record the final positions and calculate the averages.

To do that, you need to find the last value for *distance* in the simulation. You'll call that *final*. Then you need to collect a set of final distances so that you can average them.

12. Double-click the collection icon (box of balls) to show the inspector. Click the **Measures** tab. Make a new collection attribute (or *measure*) by clicking the <*new*> label, typing `final`, and pressing Enter.

13. Double-click the Formula column to the right of *final* to show the formula editor. Enter this formula: `last(distance)`. The function *last*() returns the last value in the list. Leave the inspector open, and choose **Rerandomize** from the **Collection** menu to see the value of *final* change. Be sure that it works before closing the inspector.

14. Now you'll get Fathom to collect values for *final*. Select the collection. Choose **Collect Measures** from the **Collection** menu. A new collection called Measures from Collection 1 should appear.

15. With the new collection selected (it should already be selected), drag a case table from the shelf. Now you can see the various values for *final*, which represents different ending positions for the random walk. This list should resemble the one you made by hand.

16. Make a new graph and drag *final* to the horizontal axis. Change the graph to a histogram by choosing **Histogram** from the pop-up menu in the graph.

17. With the graph selected, choose **Plot Value** from the **Graph** menu. The formula editor appears. Enter `mean(final)` and click **OK** to close the editor. The value and a line appear on the graph.

Q6 Sketch the graph. Explain what the graph represents in terms of the walk. That is, where did those numbers come from? Be precise and concise. What is the value of the mean of the *final* values?

18. Now add the mean of the absolute values to your graph. Plot another value with the formula $mean(|final|)$. Sketch its position on the graph you drew.

Q7 Which value is larger, the mean of the values of *final* or the mean of the absolute values? Do you think this will always be true? Explain.

19. Now you will repeat your experiment. Do not rerandomize. Double-click the measures collection to show its inspector. Click the **Collect Measures** tab. Click **Collect More Measures** to collect a total of 10 measures. If you position the inspector carefully, you can see both graphs update.

Q8 Increase the number of measures to 40. Collect measures again. (There should now be a set of 50 measures.) What do you think are reasonable values for the "eventual" mean of the values of *final* and of the absolute values of *final*?

EXPLORE MORE

1. How will the mean of the absolute value change if you collect 400 walks, say, instead of 40? Explain.
2. How will the mean change if the walk is 40 steps instead of 10? Explain why and do the experiment. Compare your results to your prediction.
3. If you've studied the binomial theorem and expected values, compute the theoretical mean of the absolute value and compare it to the result of your experiment.

Exploring Sampling

In this activity, you'll learn about sampling with and without replacement. You'll use what you've learned to simulate the probability of drawing a pair.

MAKE A CONJECTURE

Imagine that the teacher has a jar containing pieces of paper with the names of every student in the class. The teacher draws a name, writes it down, and puts the paper back in the jar. She does this 10 times. This is sampling *with replacement,* because the names are put back in the jar.

Q1 How many names will the teacher write down? How many *different* names will the teacher write down? Is it possible that the teacher will draw the same name 10 times in a row?

Now the teacher draws 10 names but does not put the papers back in the jar. This is sampling *without replacement.*

Q2 How many different names will the teacher write down? Is it possible for the same student to be picked twice?

Q3 If there are 30 students in the class, how many names can the teacher draw before running out of names if she is sampling without replacement? Sampling with replacement?

EXPERIMENT

Now you'll simulate this situation in Fathom.

1. Open a new Fathom document.
2. Make a new case table and give it one attribute, *name.* Type in eight different names, including your own. The collection—a box of gold balls—appears.
3. Select the collection and choose **Sample Cases** from the **Collection** menu. A new collection named Sample of Collection 1 appears. Make a case table for that collection.

Q4 How many names are in the case table? Does it appear to be sampling with or without replacement? Explain.

Collection 1

	name
1	Heather
2	Christian
3	Elizabeth
4	Bill
5	Jonas
6	Rommel
7	Marina
8	Aneesa

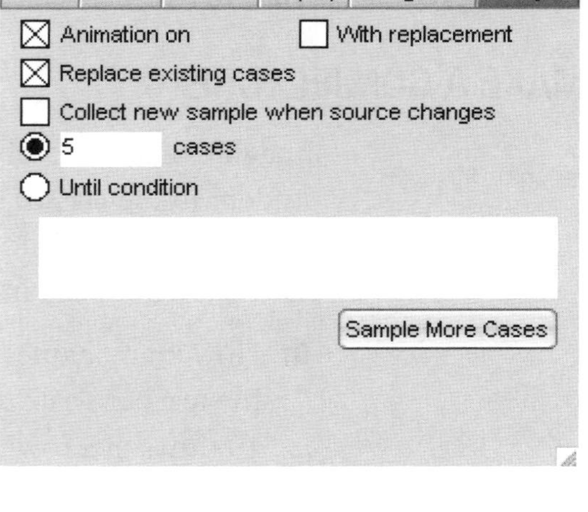

4. Double-click the sample collection (the second box of balls) to show its inspector. Click the **Sample** tab at the far right. Set the number of cases to 5. This means that 5 names will be chosen.

5. Click the **Sample More Cases** button repeatedly.

Q5 Describe what happens.

6. In the inspector, change the number from 5 to 3. Click **Sample More Cases** again. Count the number of times you have to click **Sample More Cases** until you see the same name appear twice in the same sample of 3.

Q6 How many times did you have to sample? Try the experiment again. Was your result about the same?

Now you will sample *without replacement.*

7. In the inspector, uncheck the With Replacement box. Click the **Sample More Cases** button repeatedly.

Q7 Will the same name ever appear twice in the same sample of 3? Explain. What do you think would happen if you changed the sample size to 8?

8. Check your prediction by changing the number from 3 to 8—the number of names in your collection. Click the **Sample More Cases** button repeatedly.

Q8 What happens in the case table?

9. Now increase the number from 8 to 10. Click the **Sample More Cases** button repeatedly.

Q9 Describe what happens. Watch the inspector closely.

Now you'll use what you've learned about sampling to simulate picking cards from a deck of cards.

10. Open the document **DeckOfCards.ftm.** Double-click the collection to show the inspector.

Q10 How many cases are in the collection? What are the attributes?

11. Select the collection and choose **Sample Cases** from the **Collection** menu. A new collection appears, called Sample of Deck. Open the collection by dragging a corner of the icon.

Q11 Click the **Sample More Cases** button several times. Describe what happens.

INVESTIGATE

Now you will make a simulation to help you determine the chance of getting a pair when you draw two cards.

12. Change the number sampled from 10 (the default) to 2. Uncheck the Animation on box. When you click **Sample More Cases** (whether in the inspector or in the collection), you now get two cards.

13. To keep track of the number of pairs, you can record the results in a *measure,* or collection attribute. Click the **Measures** tab in the inspector to go to that panel. (You'll see a measure, *cardSize,* that controls how the cards look.) Click <*new*> to create a new measure. Call it *pair.*

14. Double-click the Formula cell to the right of *pair.* The formula editor appears. Give *pair* a formula that will be true if the two cards in the collection are a pair and false if they are not. A pair occurs when the values for *number* are the same. Three functions that might help are *first*(), *last*(), and *uniqueValues*(). They're all in the Statistical section in the Functions list.

Q12 What is your formula?

Now you'll collect some different samples—different sets of two cards.

15. With the Sample of Deck collection selected, choose **Collect Measures** from the **Collection** menu. A new collection appears, called Measures from Sample of Deck. Show this collection's inspector and go to the **Cases** panel.

Q13 What attributes does this collection have? How many cases does it have?

16. Click the **Collect Measures** tab at the far right. Uncheck the Animation on box. Check the Replace existing cases box so that you get a new set of samples. Increase the number of measures to 200 and click **Collect More Measures.** Be patient. You are collecting 200 samples of pairs of cards.

17. With the Measures from Sample of Deck collection selected, drag a graph from the shelf. Go to the **Cases** panel of the inspector to see the attributes. Drag *pair* to the horizontal axis of your graph.

Q14 How many of your 200 samples were pairs? How do you know? (You can click on the bar for "true" and see the number of "true" cases in the bottom-left corner of your Fathom window.)

Q15 In the entire class, how many pairs were there? Out of how many samples?

18. Show the inspector for the Sample of Deck collection (not the measures collection)—the one where you made the pairs. On its **Sample** panel, uncheck the With replacement box. You will now sample *without replacement.*

19. Show the inspector for the Measures from Sample of Deck collection, and go to the **Collect Measures** panel. Make sure the Replace existing cases box is checked so that you will get 200 new samples. Click **Collect More Measures.** You'll (slowly) get the data on 200 samples.

Q16 How many of those samples were pairs? In the entire class, how many pairs were there? Out of how many samples?

Q17 What is the empirical probability of getting a pair when drawing from a 52-card deck *with replacement*? What is the probability *without replacement*? Explain, in words, why one probability is greater than the other.

EXPLORE MORE

1. Find the theoretical probabilities for drawing a pair from a 52-card deck with replacement and without replacement.
2. Modify the simulation to compute the probability of drawing two cards and have one be an ace and the other a king, queen, jack, or ten (getting a blackjack).
3. Modify the simulation to compute the probability of getting a pair in a *five*-card sample (a pair in poker). The *uniqueValues* function will help.

Rolling Dice

Sometimes when you sample or collect measures, you don't know exactly how many things you want to collect. Instead, you want to sample (or collect) until some condition is met. In this activity, you will explore the answer to a traditional question: On the average, how many times do you have to roll a die to get a six?

MAKE A CONJECTURE

Before doing the simulation, think about what you expect to see.

Q1 On average, how many times do you think you have to roll a six-sided die to get a six?

EXPERIMENT

1. Open the document **RollingDice.ftm.** It should have two collections: Single Die and Sample of Single Die. Make sure you can see a case table for Sample of Single Die.
2. Double-click the Sample of Single Die collection to show the inspector. Click the **Sample** tab. The **Sample** panel should be set to sample two dice, with replacement.
3. You want to set up the simulation to roll the die until it shows a six. Click the **Until condition** button. The formula editor appears.
4. Enter an expression that will tell Fathom when to *stop* collecting samples: `count(face=6)>0`. Click **OK** to close the formula editor. Your inspector should look like the one shown here.

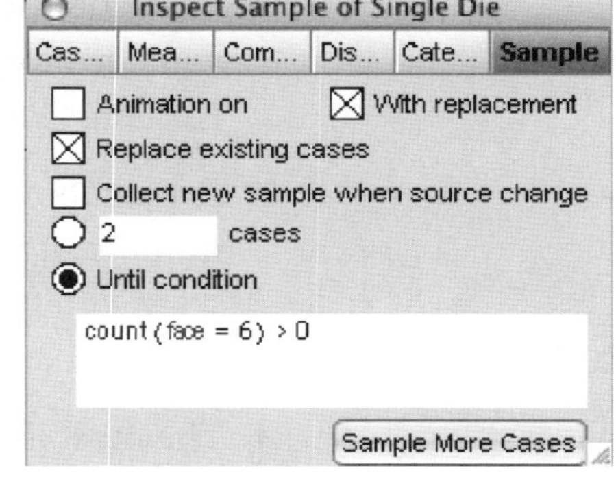

Q2 Click **Sample More Cases** repeatedly. Describe what happens to the case table.

5. Now you will collect the numbers of die rolls that it takes to get a six. Click the **Measures** tab of the inspector.
6. Make a new measure, *numberOfRolls,* and give it the formula *count*(). This will be the number of cases in the Sample of Single Die collection. Close the inspector.
7. Select the Sample of Single Die collection and choose **Collect Measures** from the **Collection** menu. A new measures collection appears, called Measures from Sample of Single Die.

8. Make a case table for the new collection. You will see *numberOfRolls* for five runs of the simulation, because Fathom collects five measures by default. Show the measures collection's inspector and click the **Collect Measures** tab. Change the number of measures from 5 to 10 and check Replace existing cases. Click **Collect More Measures.** The simulation runs 10 times, collecting the numbers of rolls in the Measures from Sample of Single Die collection's case table.

Q3 Make a histogram of *numberOfRolls*. Describe the graph. Which bar is the tallest? What is the shape of the graph overall?

9. Select the graph and choose **Plot Value** from the **Graph** menu. Give it the formula *mean*(*numberOfRolls*). Close the formula editor.

Q4 Sketch your graph. Explain in words what the number being plotted means.

10. Collect measures again, watching the graph. Continue to collect measures to answer the original question: What is the average number of rolls you need in order to get a six? Alter the parameters on the **Collect Measures** panel of the Measures from Sample of Single Die inspector as you see fit. (*Hint:* If you decide to collect a large number of measures, it will speed things up to uncheck the Animation on box.)

Q5 What is your answer for the original question: On the average, how many times do you have to roll a die to get a six?

Q6 Based on the simulation, what do you think is the *most likely* number of rolls you need to get a six (that is, the number that happens most frequently)? Explain. Sketch or refer to a graph if you need to.

Q7 Explain how the most likely number of rolls can be different from the average number of rolls.

EXPLORE MORE

1. The most likely number of rolls is the *mode.* You know the mean. What's the *median* number of rolls you need to get a six?
2. Suppose you changed the "middle" collection—the sample collection—to sample *without* replacement. What would happen to the mean number of rolls it would take to get a six?
3. On the average, how many rolls does it take to get a five *and* a six? A five *or* a six? Make predictions, then simulate both situations. Which is more likely, a statement with *and* in it or the same statement with *or* in it? Explain your answer and give examples.

Pocket Pennies

Look at a sample of five pennies from your pocket or wallet. Are they mostly new pennies? What is the year of the oldest penny? In this activity, you will look at the distribution of the dates for a large collection of pennies. You will look at both the mean of the ages of the collection and a collection of means from a number of samples from the collection. You will explore what happens when you create sampling distributions of a mean.

INVESTIGATE

1. Open the document **PocketPennies.ftm** (or open the file of data that your class prepared). You should see a collection and a case table.

2. Create a new attribute, *Age,* with a formula that calculates the difference between the current year and *Year.*

Q1 If you were to make a histogram of *Age* for all of the pennies from the collection, what would the shape of the distribution look like? Sketch your prediction.

3. Make a histogram of *Age.*

Q2 How accurate was your prediction? Does the shape of the distribution surprise you? Estimate the mean and standard deviation of the distribution.

4. Drag a summary table from the shelf. Drag *Age* from your case table and drop it on the down arrow. Choose **Add Basic Statistics** from the **Summary** menu.

Q3 Write down the mean and standard deviation for *Age.* How do these differ from your prediction in question Q2?

5. Now plot the mean and standard deviation on your graph. Choose **Plot Value** from the **Graph** menu and use the formula editor to graph $mean()$, $mean() + stdDev()$, and $mean() - stdDev()$.

6. Take a random sample of size 5 from the ages of the pennies. Click on the Pocket Pennies collection to select it, then choose **Sample Cases** from the **Collection** menu. Double-click the Sample of Pocket Pennies collection to show its inspector. On the **Sample** panel, change the sample size to 5. Uncheck the With replacement box. Click **Sample More Cases** to re-collect your sample.

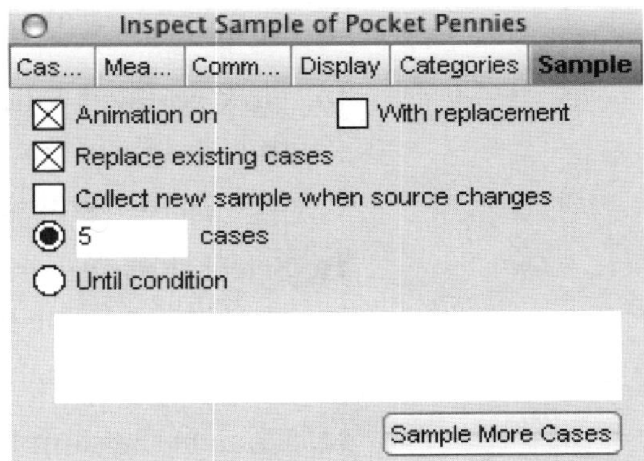

7. Now you will create measures to keep track of the mean age of each sample and the size of each sample. In the inspector for Sample of Pocket Pennies, click the **Measures** tab. Create a measure, *MeanAge,* with the formula *mean*(*Age*). Define a measure called *SampleSize* with the formula *count*().

Q4 What is the mean for your current sample? How does this compare with the mean for the whole collection? If you were to make a histogram of the mean ages from several samples, how do you think the mean of the values would compare to the mean of *Age* in the original population? Remember, your new graph will be a graph of *MeanAge* for different samples, not a graph of *Age.*

8. Now you will collect *MeanAge* from 100 samples. Select the Sample of Pocket Pennies collection and choose **Collect Measures** from the **Collection** menu. A new collection called Measures from Sample of Pocket Pennies will appear. Double-click the new collection to show its inspector. On the **Collect Measures** panel, change the number of measures to 100. To speed up your process, uncheck the Animation on box. Click **Collect More Measures.**

9. Make a case table for Measures from Sample of Pocket Pennies. Make a histogram of the mean ages. Compute the mean and standard deviation of *MeanAge* (you can plot the values on your graph or create a summary table).

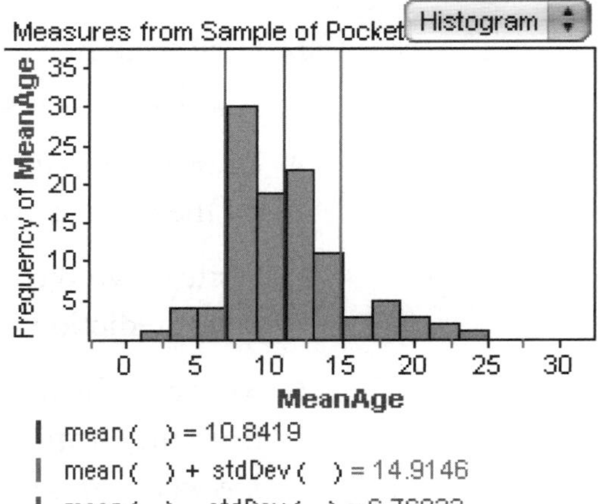

Q5 How do the values for mean and standard deviation of *MeanAge* compare to your prediction from Q4? Do you think that changing the sample size will affect the values?

10. Now you will collect measures for samples of larger sizes. Show the inspector for the Sample of Pocket Pennies collection. On the **Sample** panel of the inspector, change the sample size to 10.

11. Select the measures collection to show its inspector. On the **Collect Measures** panel, make sure that Replace existing cases is not checked. This allows you to keep all of your measures in the same collection. Click **Collect More Measures.**

12. Change the sample size to 25 and collect 100 more measures. (Change the sample size in the inspector for Sample of Pocket Pennies. Then select the

Measures from Sample of Pocket Pennies collection and choose **Collect More Measures** from the **Collection** menu.)

13. Drag the attribute *SampleSize* from the case table for the measures collection to the vertical axis of the histogram for *MeanAge*. Hold down the Shift key as you drop. This will split the histogram into three categories based on the sample size.

14. Create a summary table for the measures. Again, hold down Shift as you drag *SampleSize* to the column of the summary table. Compute the mean and standard deviation for each of the three sampling distributions. To add the standard deviation, select the summary table and choose **Add Formula** from the **Summary** menu. Type `stdDev()` in the formula editor.

Measures from Sample of Pocket Pennies

		MeanAge
SampleSize	5	10.268571 105 4.177396
	10	10.395 100 3.1506092
	25	10.7764 100 1.979312

Q6 You now have a histogram of *Age* for the original collection and histograms of *MeanAge* for three different sample sizes. As your sample size increases, what seems to be true of the shape of the histogram of *MeanAge*? What happens to the mean? The standard deviation? What do you predict will happen if you increase the sample size?

15. Test your prediction by increasing the sample size two more times. Change the sample size to 50 and collect 100 measures. Then increase the sample size to 100 and collect 100 measures. Expand the summary table for measures to see the new sample sizes.

Q7 What are the mean and standard deviation for your new measures? Do they match your prediction?

Q8 Your screen is full of collections, tables, and graphs. Make sure that you understand what kind of data is represented in each. What does one case in the Pocket Pennies collection represent? What does one case in the Sample of Pocket Pennies collection represent? What does one case in the Measures from Sample of Pocket Pennies collection represent?

EXPLORE MORE

1. Graph a normal curve on top of each histogram of *MeanAge*. Use Fathom Help to find out how to graph it. What do you observe about the fit of each histogram with the normal curve?

2. Use a normal quantile plot to investigate the closeness to normality. Which sample size produces a distribution closest to normal?

Orbital Express

You will need

- two kinds of paper
- stack of index cards
- tape measure
- marker for your center
- masking tape
- recording sheet
- pen or pencil

You work in the design and testing department for Orbital Express, a big delivery company. The company has decided to start delivering packages by dropping them from orbit onto the customers' houses. It is testing two competing designs for the new re-entry vehicle. Your job here is to test the two designs and report which is better. The two designs cost the same to build, so your objective is to find out which vehicle gets the package closer to its target.

EXPERIMENT

Your teacher will show you the two designs. They are two different types of paper, wadded up into balls. You'll test the designs by dropping them from "orbit" and measuring how far they land from the target. The target is the marker. You will measure the distance from the marker to where the wad of paper comes to rest, not where it first hits. (People aren't going to *catch* packages falling from orbit; they'll wait until the packages stop, then walk out and pick them up.)

Note: Before you begin collecting data, you may want to practice a few drops. Make sure that you are being consistent.

1. Test each design seven times. Keep track of your results (design type and distance) on your recording sheet.

INVESTIGATE (BY HAND)

2. Record each distance on a piece of index card. Make sure to write the design type on the card as well. (Your teacher may give you two different colored cards to distinguish between the designs.)
3. Stretch your tape measure on the floor and tape it down. Set the cards opposite their recorded measurements—one design on one side of the tape, the other design on the other side.

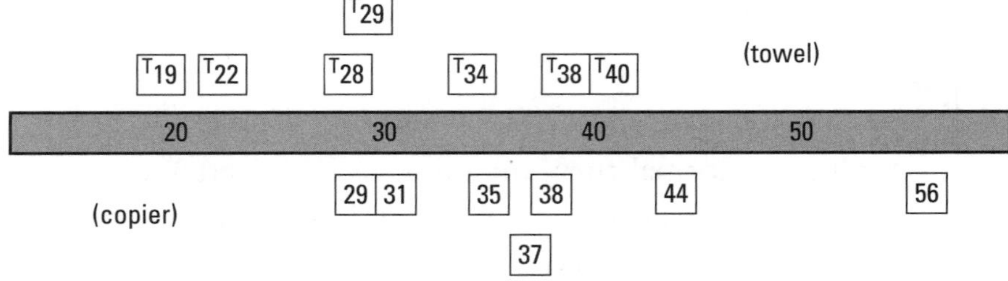

Q1 Which is the better design? Explain why.

4. You will need to justify your choice mathematically. Develop a formula for a *statistic*—a single number that describes how much better one design is than the other. The statistic should be *small* if the two papers are *alike* and *larger* the more *different* they are.

Q2 Use your statistic to analyze your data. What number do you get? (This value is called the *test statistic.*) Does your statistic fit the rule above? You may need to revise your formula.

Q3 Does your statistic show that there really is a difference between the two designs? If it does, how small would it have to be before you were no longer convinced? If it does not show a real difference, how big would it have to be before you were convinced?

Now you will explore whether any difference you found is "real" or due to chance. Even if there were no relation between the design and the distance—if the designs were really the same—there would still be a difference when you did the experiment, because there's some random variation. You will calculate how much difference to expect in your statistic.

5. Take your cards and shuffle them. Deal them out, placing them on their measurement on the tape. The first seven cards will go on one side of the tape, the second seven on the other side. Compute (and record) your "shuffled" statistic.

6. Repeat step 5 three times, recording the "shuffled" statistic each time.

Q4 Revise your answer to question Q3 based on your results. Are all of the values of the *test statistic* from your shuffles greater than the values from the original experiment? How did the shuffling experiment influence your opinion about the difference between the two designs?

Q5 What variables affect how close to the target the vehicle lands? How did you try to control most of them?

Q6 How did your group decide to measure the distance? What did you do about "interference"?

Q7 Did anything surprise you in the shuffled data? What does the shuffling accomplish? Do you think shuffling four times is enough?

Q8 What is the null hypothesis in this situation?

INVESTIGATE (WITH FATHOM)

You shuffled your cards and computed your statistic four times by hand. But to really analyze the situation, you should do it many more times. To be practical, this requires a computer.

7. Open the document **OrbEx.ftm.** It has an empty setup, so you don't have to build everything yourself (though you could). It has several different collections. You'll work with them all. Start with Drop Data. It has a case table already open, with 14 cases in it.

8. Enter the data. You should have 14 cases—7 with each kind of paper. Put the kind of paper (for example, "towel") under *paper* and the distance for each trial under *distance.*

9. Explore the data (for example, make graphs) to see if they look right. Make a graph that compares the two types of paper. It should have *paper* on one axis and *distance* on the other. Sketch your graph.

Q9 What does the graph suggest as to which paper is better?

Now you'll enter the statistic you developed—the formula that describes how different the two designs are. Because this statistic is a property of the entire collection, and not of individual cases, it should be a *measure.*

10. Double-click your original "source" collection—Drop Data—the one with the real data in it. Its inspector appears. Click the **Measures** tab.

11. Make a new measure, called *myMeasure.* Press Enter to finish naming the attribute.

12. Double-click the formula cell for the measure. The formula editor appears. Enter the formula for your statistic and click **OK.**

Q10 What is the formula for your statistic? What is the value of *myMeasure*? You can see the value of the statistic in the inspector.

13. Now you will set up the Scrambled Drop Data collection. Select the collection and drag a case table from the shelf. Double-click the collection to show the inspector. Click the **Scramble** tab. Choose **paper** from the pop-up menu. Click the **Scramble Attribute Values Again** button. Watch the case table to make sure that the paper types are shuffled. Then click the **Measures** tab of the inspector.

Q11 What's the value of *myMeasure* for that collection?

You need a place to collect the values of *myMeasure* for the scrambled data. This will be a *measures collection.*

14. Select the Scrambled Drop Data collection and choose **Collect Measures** from the **Collection** menu. A new collection appears, called Measures from Scrambled Drop Data.

15. Make a case table for this new collection. You'll see five cases, with values for *myMeasure.*

16. Double-click the measures collection to show its inspector and go to the **Collect Measures** panel.

17. There you can tell Fathom how many measures to collect. Change it to collect 100 measures and uncheck the Animation On box. Then click **Collect More Measures.** You'll see 100 new values of *myMeasure* appear—one from each scramble.

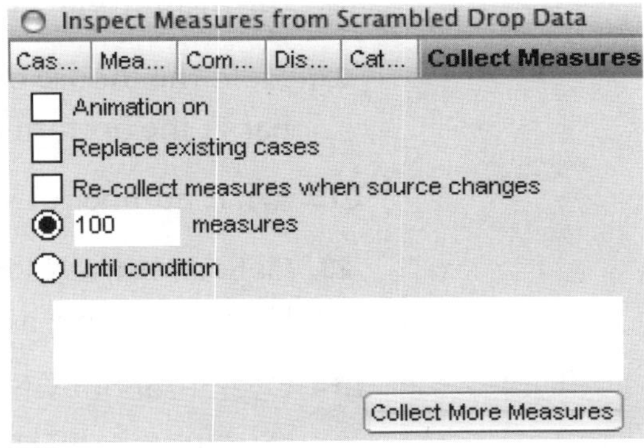

Q12 Your window is getting crowded. Describe what each collection contains. Why do you need three?

18. Drag a new graph from the shelf. Drag the name *myMeasure* from the table to an axis of the graph, then choose **Histogram** from the pop-up menu. Sketch the histogram.

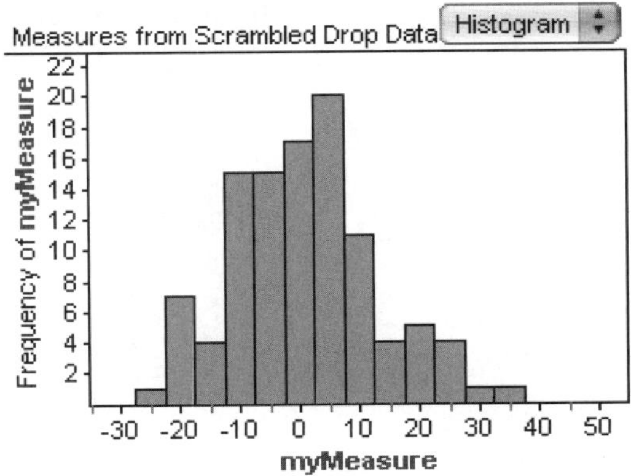

This distribution in your new graph shows how your statistic *myMeasure* is distributed for situations in which the kind of paper has no influence on the distance. It shows what the situation is like when the *null hypothesis* is true. You need to find out where your original test data are in this distribution. Is it unusual (in which case it would not happen often if the null hypothesis were true) or right in the distribution (in which case it's consistent with the null hypothesis)? You wrote down your statistic in Q10. Now you will add it to the graph.

19. Select the measures histogram and choose **Plot Value** from the **Graph** menu. The formula editor appears. Enter the value of the statistic for your test data and click **OK.** The value appears at the bottom of the graph, and a line appears showing where that value is in the distribution. Add that line to your sketch.

Now you want to find out how many of the 105 shuffles are at least as extreme as your source collection.

20. Drag the edge of a histogram bar so that one edge of a bar lines up with your statistic.

21. Select all the bins outside the line, that is, farther than the line from the center of the distibution. Hold down the Shift key as you click on each one.

22. Hold the mouse over the measures collection (*not* Drop Data). Look in the status bar at the bottom of the Fathom window to see how many shuffles are selected.

Q13 What number of shuffles are selected? What percentage?

23. Collect measures five more times and record what percentage of shuffles are at least as extreme as your test statistic.

Q14 Overall, about what percentage of the scrambled collections are at least as extreme as your original data?

Q15 Do you think one design of a re-entry vehicle for Orbital Express is better than the other? Based on your data and analysis, explain why or why not.

Creating Error

In this activity, you will look at how errors affect the way you interpret linear fits to data.

EXPERIMENT

1. Open a new Fathom document. Drag a new case table from the shelf and add 100 new cases.
2. Create two attributes—*cause* and *effect*—with these formulas: For *cause,* use *randomNormal*(100, 10). For *effect,* use *cause.*
3. Make a scatter plot of *effect* as a function of *cause,* and show the least-squares linear regression line.

Q1 What is the slope of the least-squares line? What is the value of r^2? Is this what you would expect?

You have set up a very simple situation. Now let's make it more complicated. So far, *effect* has been perfectly related to *cause.* Now you'll add error to *effect* and see what happens.

4. Make a slider and name it *SD* (for standard deviation).
5. Make a new attribute, *error,* and give it the formula *randomNormal*(0, *SD*).
6. Now change the formula for *effect* to *cause* + *error.* This adds a random, normally distributed amount to *cause.* That random amount has a mean of 0 and a standard deviation of *SD,* in this case, 5.

Q2 Adjust the slider. What happens when *SD* is near 0?

Q3 As *SD* gets larger, what happens to r^2, the square of the correlation coefficient? As *SD* gets larger, what happens to the slope of the least-squares line? (You can increase the scale of *SD* by dragging on the axis.) Explain why this happens.

7. Sometimes we get cause and effect mixed up. Make a second scatter plot. Put *effect* on the horizontal axis and *cause* on the vertical axis. Add a least-squares line.

Q4 Move the slider some more. What happens to the slope and the correlation coefficient in the new graph? Explain why the slope and the correlation coefficient behave differently in the other scatter plot.

INVESTIGATE

So far you've been looking at basically linear data. Now you'll explore how measurement error can obscure the true shapes of functions. You will also see why residual plots are useful.

8. Make two new attributes, *time* and *value*. Give *time* the formula $\frac{caseIndex}{100}$. Give *value* the formula $time^2$. (Type `time^2`. The ^ will not appear—it just lets you type the exponent.)

9. Make a graph of *value* as a function of *time*. The graph you see should be familiar: It's the $y = x^2$ parabola between 0 and 1. It looks curved, obviously curved—for the moment. Now you will try to fit a line to it.

10. With the graph selected, choose **Least-Squares Line** from the **Graph** menu. A line appears.

11. Choose **Make Residual Plot** from the **Graph** menu. This shows how far each of the points in the first graph is, vertically, from the line. You may want to stretch the graph vertically to make more room for the residual plot.

Q5 Describe what is happening in the function and in the residual plot between $time = 0$ and $time = 0.5$. Explain why this happens.

Right now, everything is nice and smooth. To shake things up, you'll add randomness as you did with the line.

12. Double-click the *SD* slider near the axis and change its axis to go from 0 to 1.2. Set the slider to about 1.00.

13. Now edit the formula for *value*. Change it to $time^2 + randomNormal(0, SD)$.

14. The graph will change, and many points will be out of range. Choose **Scatter Plot** again from the pop-up menu to rescale the graph.

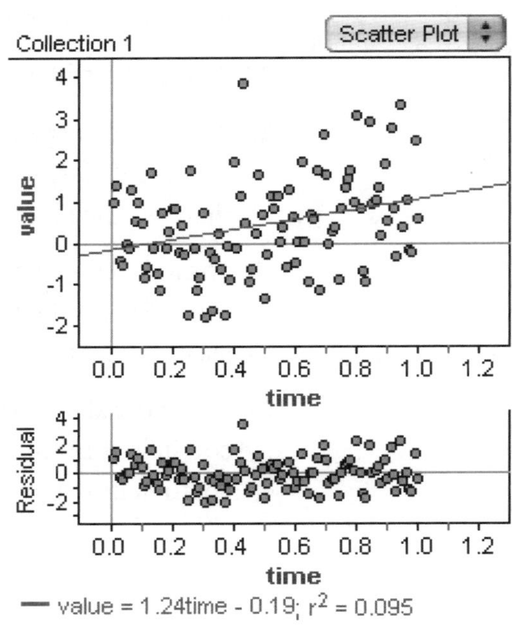

If everything has gone according to plan, you probably see that the graph seems to increase somewhat, but that *you can no longer tell that it's curved.* The randomness is so great that the curve is overwhelmed. You can confirm this by looking at the residual plot. It looks flat and random. That is the sign that the model—the straight line—is a good model for your data.

Yet you know that the "real" data are curved. The question you will explore is: How much randomness can that curved model take before it no longer looks curved?

15. Adjust the *SD* slider to near 0 and rescale the graph.

Q6 What do you notice about the original graph? What about the residual plot?

16. Gradually increase the slider, rescaling the graph as necessary.

Q7 What is the smallest value of *SD* that makes the residual plot look flat and random?

17. Now repeatedly choose **Rerandomize** from the **Collection** menu. (This makes Fathom reassign all the error values.)

Q8 What changes in the graph when you rerandomize? Does the graph generally appear curved—or flat and random?

18. Readjust the slider, repeatedly rerandomizing, to find the largest value for *SD* you can use and *still see the curvature in the residual plot most of the time.*

Q9 What value did you find for *SD* in step 18?

EXPLORE MORE

1. Leave *SD* at the critical value you found in step 18. Add 10 to the formula for *time*, so it is $10 + \left(\frac{caseIndex}{100}\right)$. Sketch the new graph (including the residual plot) and explain why it looks so different.
2. Change the formula for *time* so that the positions of the points are random within the interval [0, 1] instead of evenly spaced. What formula did you use? Does that make any difference in the amount of error you can put in and still detect the curvature?
3. Change the number of cases (by adding and deleting them) without changing the range of *time* values. Does that make any difference in the amount of error you can put in and still detect the curvature?
4. If you're trying to detect an effect (for example, curvature), you have a better chance if your measurements have less error. This activity helped quantify the amount of error you can have and still detect the effect. Give some suggestions as to how you can improve your chance of detecting an effect if you're looking for one that's right on the edge of detectability.

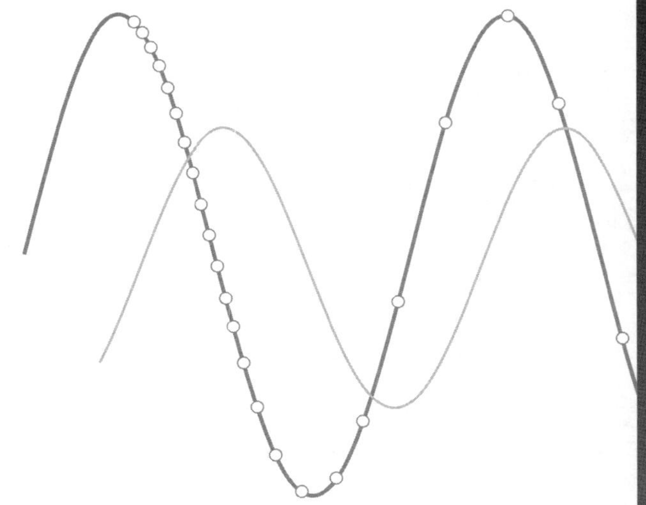

Activity Notes

MAMMALS' BRAINS (PAGE 3)

Activity Time: 30–50 minutes

Required Document: Mammals.ftm

Fathom Prerequisites: Students should be able to

- Start Fathom
- Open a document

Fathom Skills: Students will learn how to

- Work with case tables
- Define an attribute with a formula
- Create graphs (dot plots, histograms, box plots)
- Select cases in a case table or graph
- Create a summary table of basic statistics

Mathematics Prerequisites: Students should be able to calculate the ratio of two quantities and find the median of a data set.

Mathematics Skills: Students will learn how to use one-variable graphs (dot plots, histograms, and box plots) to find particular values (such as greatest, least, and median) and use ratios to compare quantities. *Optional:* Students will explore bivariate data (see Extensions 3 and 5).

General Notes: At first, the mathematics in this activity may seem relatively simple—to identify particular values in a data set and to calculate ratios. However, you may be surprised that many students don't fully understand the need for ratios when comparing quantities of unequal size. For example, when a student looks only at the brain weights, she might say, "The African elephant has the largest brain." However, it's unfair to judge a mammal's brain size without considering the overall size of the mammal. When the same student looks at the ratios of brain weights to body weights, she may revise the conclusion to "The African elephant has the smallest brain."

The idea that the same data set can give two entirely different results is a subtle, yet important, aspect of this activity. The catch is to fully understand the definitions of "largest" and "smallest." Absolute brain weight and the ratio of brain weight to body weight are both acceptable ways to define brain size, albeit the latter is arguably more meaningful. Seeing firsthand that the same data can be "manipulated" to give different conclusions will help students be careful and critical when they run across data in the media.

While comparing attributes and calculating ratios, Algebra 1 students will also get valuable practice in dimensional analysis. In the activity proper, students need to convert between grams and kilograms and understand what it means for a ratio to have no units. If you use Extension 2, students can also get exposure to derived units.

This activity is designed to be an easy first-time introduction to Fathom. The step-by-step worksheet leads students through many Fathom fundamentals, such as what an attribute is, how to create a case table, and how to make a graph. In order to save room, the activity does not give specific instructions for starting Fathom or opening a document; most students will have enough computer experience to accomplish these tasks without explicit instructions.

Although written primarily for Algebra 1, this activity can be successfully used for Algebra 2, Precalculus, or Statistics. First, if you have never used Fathom in these upper-level classes, you may want to use this activity as a gentle introduction to the software. Second, the concept of "largest" brain naturally leads to the question of intelligence, and the scientific study of animal intelligence provides an excellent opportunity for curve fitting and data transformation (see Extension 5).

MAKE A CONJECTURE

Q1 Possible answer: elephant, human, beaver, rat. Students might pick this order based on relative size of the mammals.

Q2 Possible answer: yes

Q3 Possible answer: human, elephant, rat, beaver. Students might pick this order by assuming that more intelligent mammals have larger brains compared to their overall body size.

INVESTIGATE

Q4 1320 g

Q5 0.28 kg. *Note:* Students will notice that the collection inspector and/or case table has some blank cells. This means that data were not available. Encourage students to leave these cells blank and to avoid the temptation to fill in meaningless data, such as zeros.

Q6 Most: African elephant, 5712 g; least: lesser short-tailed shrew, 0.14 g

Q7 African elephant, human, mountain beaver, rat

Q8 African elephant, human, mountain beaver, rat. Yes, this is the same order as for brain weights.

Q9 Students should use the dot farthest right in the graph of *BrainWeight:* African elephant, 5172 g.

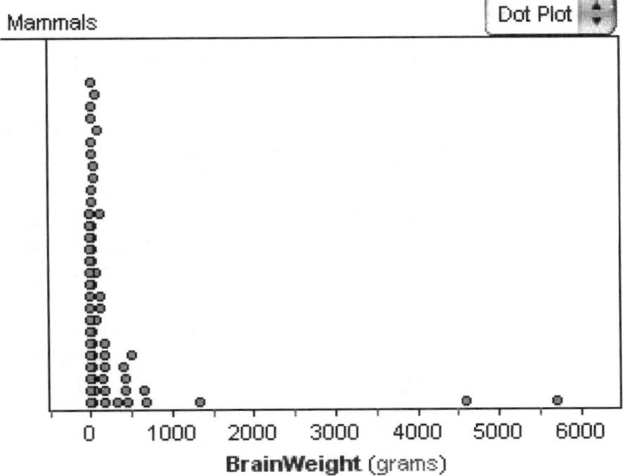

Q10 Because the dots are so densely clustered at 0 g, some students may have trouble picking out the least value. Other students may discover ways to adjust the axes and be able to zoom in enough to find the least value. The least value is still 0.14 g, the lesser short-tailed shrew.

Note: Even with the densely clustered dots, some students may be lucky enough to click at the bottom of the first stack of dots and find the lesser short-tailed shrew. This may lead them to erroneously believe that the stacks of dots always go least to greatest from bottom to top. This is not always the case. Actually, the dots are stacked relative to the cases' order in the case table. Students who find the lesser short-tailed shrew at the bottom of the stack probably used **Sort Ascending** when answering Q6. As a counterexample, if students had last used **Sort Descending,** the lesser short-tailed shrew would have been at the top of the first stack of dots.

Q11 No, not all of the brain weights go in the same order as the body weights. For example, the third largest body weight belongs to the giraffe, which has the fourth largest brain weight, while the third largest brain weight belongs to the human, which has the thirteenth largest body weight.

Students could answer this by clicking dots in reverse order in the dot plot of *BodyWeight* and noticing that the dots in the dot plot of *BrainWeight* are not in the same order. Students could also sort the case table by *BrainWeight,* and then by *BodyWeight,* and notice that the species do not stay in the same order.

This means that some mammals have proportionately larger or smaller brains for their overall size. The brain-to-body ratios (coming up in steps 8–11) will account for brain size relative to the overall size of the mammal.

Q12 Giraffe (680 g) and horse (655 g). Students will probably click the bar between 500 and 1000, and see which cases are highlighted in the case table.

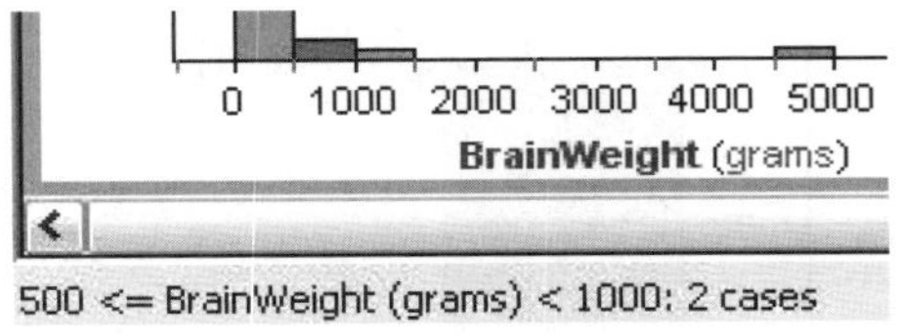

Note: If your students have formally learned about histograms, you should point out that the bin is officially $500 \leq x < 1000$, which does not include the upper bound.

Q13 Possible answers: 6 g/kg, 0.006 g/g, 0.006 kg/kg, or 0.006 (no units). All four of these ratios are equivalent. Because both measurements are weights, it is best to convert to the same units (either grams or kilograms) before finding the ratio, and then write the ratio 0.006 without units.

Q14 0.006; technically there are no units. *Note:* For students who could find only the ratio 6 g/kg for Q13, you should explain how Fathom performs unit conversions on compatible units, resulting in a value that has no units.

Q15 Largest: ground squirrel, 0.0396; smallest: African elephant, 0.00086. No, these are not the mammals that had the brains that weigh the most and least; in fact, the African elephant is now on the opposite end of the spectrum.

Q16 Human, rat, mountain beaver, African elephant. This may not be the same order predicted in Q3.

Q17 It means, for example, that the human's brain is proportionately larger than the brains of the other mammals.

Q18 More mammals have brain-to-body ratios below 0.01. In the box plot, the median value falls below 0.01, so more than 50% of the mammals have brain-to-body ratios below 0.01.

Students could also create a histogram and adjust the bin widths to show that 41 cases have brain-to-body ratios below 0.01.

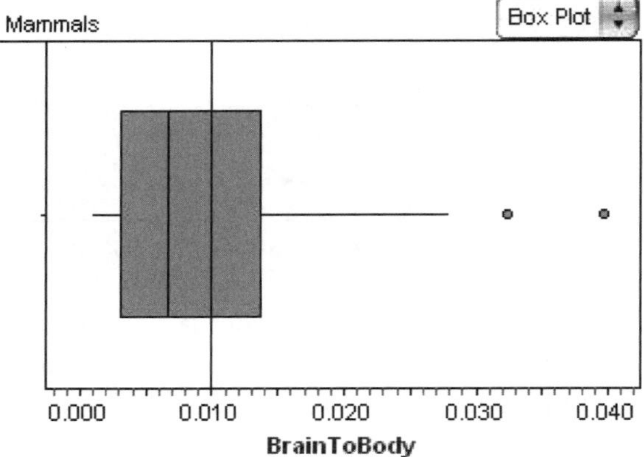

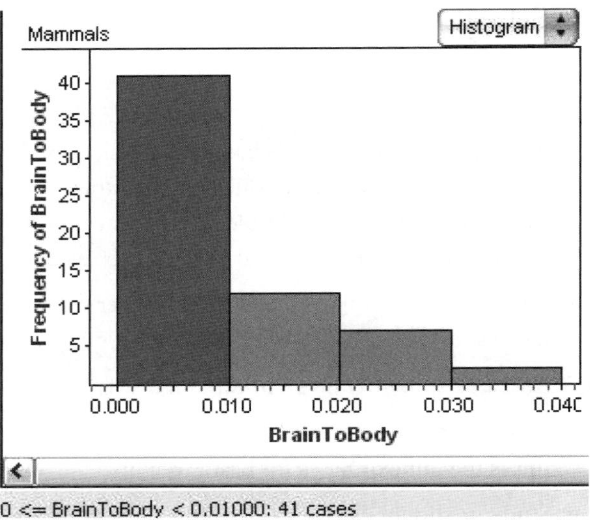

Q19 Possible answers: median: 0.0065; interquartile range: 0.0105

Q20 Median: 0.0066; interquartile range: 0.0108

Mammals

BrainToBody	0.0096242136 0.00085843102 0.0030857143 0.0066108564 0.013842482 0.03960396 0.010756768

S1 = mean( )
S2 = min( )
S3 = Q1( )
S4 = median( )
S5 = Q3( )
S6 = max( )
S7 = iqr( )

Q21 Any answer with a reasonable explanation is acceptable. Some students might use the median or mean exactly as calculated in the summary table; they might try combining a measure of center with a measure of spread to give a range of values; they might use the distribution in a dot plot to make a subjective answer based on where the dots cluster; or they might use a histogram and pick out bins that have more values than others (essentially the mode). Some students may not give a value at all, preferring to argue that the data have so much spread that it is meaningless to state a "typical" value.

EXPLORE MORE

1. The formula for brain-to-body percentage is 100(*BrainWeight*/*BodyWeight*). Students should notice that the only difference between these values and the brain-to-body ratios is that the decimal point is moved two places to the right. Even the graphs will look the same except the axes will differ by a factor of 100. Students should realize that this makes mathematical sense because they've only multiplied the brain-to-body ratios by 100.
2. Students might say that neither brain weight nor brain-to-body ratio is a good way to judge intelligence. To support their answers, students might point to the position of "intelligent mammals" (such as human and chimpanzee) relative to less intelligent mammals. For example, if we use brain weight as a judge of intelligence, both species of elephants are more intelligent than humans, and the chimpanzee is on about the same level as a donkey. Using brain-to-body ratio as a judge of intelligence makes the ground squirrel the most intelligent mammal and there are seven other mammals more intelligent than humans.

EXTENSIONS

1. When making the box plot of *BrainToBody*, students will notice that two points appear at the end of the right whisker. Discuss why these two points may be excluded from the rest of the whisker. You may want to introduce the term *outlier.*

   For students who have already learned about outliers and different methods of calculating outliers, ask them to verify that these two points surpass the criterion *median* ± 1.5 *IQR.*
2. The data used in this activity come from a classic study of the sleep habits of 62 mammals (originally published in the article "Sleep in Mammals: Ecological and Constitutional Correlates" by Allison Truett and Domenic V. Cicchetti (1976), *Science,* November 12, vol. 194, pp. 732–734). Although the activity proper examines only brain weight and body weight, there are rich connections between the other attributes as well.

   Have students explore ratios of other attributes for these mammals, such as dreaming sleep to total sleep, length of gestation to life span, or brain weight to length of gestation. Use the ratios to phrase and answer questions such as "Which mammal dreams the most?" or "Which mammal spends relatively the most time developing in the womb?"

   Note: Depending on the attributes chosen, students may encounter situations when Fathom will create a "derived unit." For example, when comparing brain weight to length of gestation, the units (grams and days) cannot be converted into compatible units. Instead, the attribute *BrainToGestation* has the unit grams per day.
3. To extend this activity beyond one-variable statistics, have students make scatter plots for pairs of attributes, such as *BrainWeight* versus *BodyWeight.*

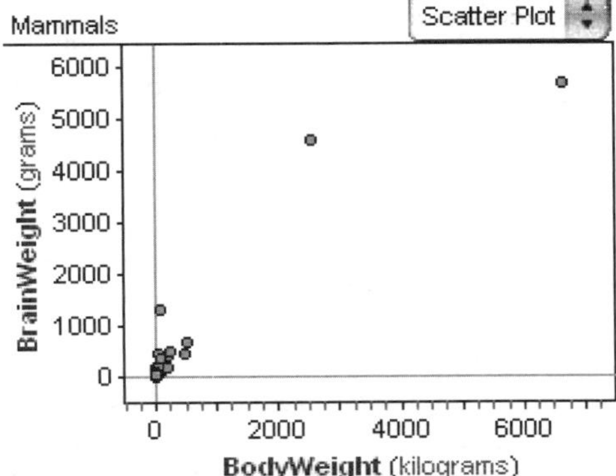

Some bivariate graphs show clear relationships; this one, in particular, implies that as body weight increases, brain weight also tends to increase. Students can try fitting a line or any other function to the graph. (See Extension 5 for an exponential function that models this relationship.) *LifeSpan* versus *Gestation, TotalSleep* versus *Gestation,* and any combination of the three sleep attributes also provide graphs that have recognizable patterns.

As a further extension, students could try comparing some of the categorical attributes (*Predation, Exposure,* and *Danger*) with the numerical attributes or with each other. They can find an explanation of these attributes by double-clicking the collection to show the inspector and then clicking the **Comments** tab.

4. Some students may be interested in researching the study of intelligence in different species and writing a short paper on the mathematics used in this field of science. Two key words that students should research are *allometry* (the study of the growth of one part of an organism in relation to the growth of the whole organism) and *encephalization* (the amount of brain mass relative to body size).

   Students will learn that some scientists use exponential functions to estimate brain weight as a function of body weight. Then the *encephalization quotient*—the ratio of actual brain weight to estimated brain weight for an animal of that size—is used to judge relative intelligence. Animals that have an actual brain weight greater than the estimated brain weight (an encephalization quotient greater than 1) are considered more intelligent.

   Students may also run across competing theories on intelligence, such as judging intelligence based on the number of neurons in the brain rather than on brain size.

5. Students in Algebra 2, Precalculus, or Statistics can perform log-log transformations to find an exponential model for predicting brain weight as a function of body weight. As mentioned in Extension 4, some scientists use exponential functions to calculate the ratio of actual brain weight to expected brain weight (the encephalization quotient), which is an indicator of relative intelligence.

   First, create the attributes *logBody* and *logBrain* and create a scatter plot. (*Note:* Before taking logarithms, change the units for both *BodyWeight* and *BrainWeight* to grams or kilograms.) Use a least-squares line on the transformed data and work backward to derive an exponential function that fits the original data. Below, *logBrain* versus *logBody* is modeled by the least-squares line *logBrain* = 0.752 *logBody* − 1.3. This converts to the exponential function *BrainWeight* = 0.05 *BodyWeight*$^{0.752}$. (*Note:* In order to get appropriate units, enter the function as

```
BrainWeight = 0.05 scalar(BodyWeight)^0.752 g
```

Mammals' Brains, Extension 5

Mammals

Mammals

	Species	BodyWe...	logBody	BrainWe...	logBrain	EstBrain	EQ
units		grams		grams		grams	
1	Human	62000 g	4.79239	1320 g	3.12057	200.839 g	6.57242
2	Rhesus monkey	6800 g	3.83251	179 g	2.25285	38.108 g	4.69717
3	Baboon	10550 g	4.02325	179.5 g	2.25406	53.022 g	3.38539
4	Owl monkey	480 g	2.68124	15.5 g	1.19033	5.19115 g	2.98585
5	Chimpanzee	52160 g	4.71734	440 g	2.64345	176.363 g	2.49485
6	Ground squirrel	101 g	2.00432	4 g	0.60206	1.60775 g	2.48794
7	Patas monkey	10000 g	4	115 g	2.0607	50.9296 g	2.25802

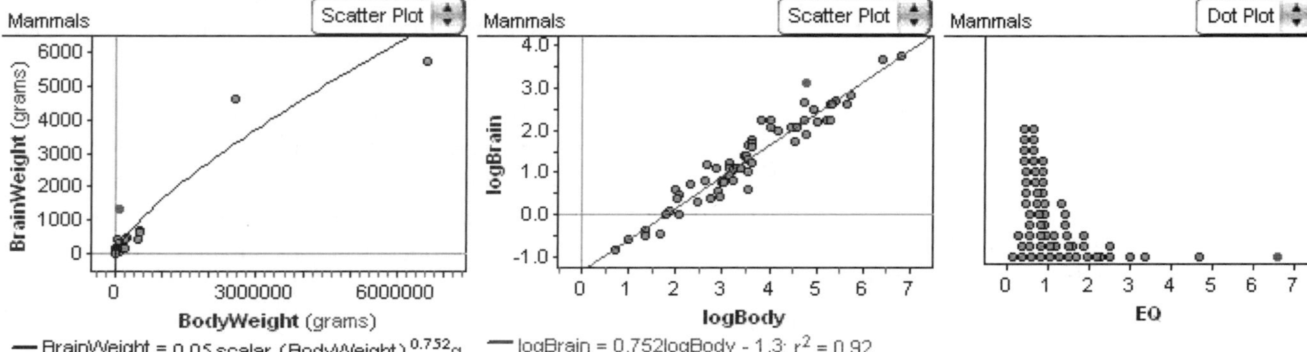

The function *scalar* removes the units from *BodyWeight* during the calculation, and then "g" reapplies grams. Otherwise, the units would be $g^{0.752}$.)

The same exponential function is used to define an attribute (*EstBrain*) that calculates the estimated brain weights, and then another attribute (*EQ*) calculates the encephalization quotient. Notice that *EQ* puts the mammals in an order that most people (and many scientists) find reasonable, with humans as the most intelligent, followed by many of the primates. *(See bottom of previous page.)*

READING THE NEWS (PAGE 7)

Activity Time: 50–80 minutes

Materials:

- One copy of the front section of a newspaper for each pair of students
- Centimeter rulers
- Clocks with a second hand or stopwatches

Fathom Prerequisites: None

Fathom Skills: Students will learn how to

- Create a collection by entering data into a case table
- Create attributes
- Create graphs (scatter plots)
- Graph lines of fit (movable lines)
- Plot a function
- Trace a function
- Add multiple attributes to an axis

Mathematics Prerequisites: Students should be able to make and understand a scatter plot of points and find the slope of a line by counting rise over run or using two points in the slope formula.

Mathematics Skills: Students will learn how to interpret slope as a rate or speed and compare slopes based on their graphical and numerical representations. Students will also find a direct-variation linear equation to model data that are roughly linear; identify the slope of a direct-variation linear equation as the coefficient of the independent variable; and use a slope or a linear equation to extrapolate data. *Optional:* Students will analyze one-variable statistics (see Extension 1).

General Notes: This activity is about slope and direct variation. Students consider the question "How long would it take to read the front section of the newspaper aloud?" First, students collect data and do an analysis offline, primarily using slope to extrapolate. Then students use Fathom to do further analysis, extrapolating with linear equations. Because the data will be very close to a direct variation, this is an excellent opportunity for Algebra 1 students to practice slope and linear equations while learning the basics of statistical linear modeling.

Because the activity requires collecting data, by-hand analysis, and then Fathom, you might plan to use the activity over two or more days. For example, you could do data collection and by-hand analysis on the first day, and then go to the computer lab and use Fathom on the second day.

While collecting data, students might encounter many interesting sources of variability. Here are some issues for you and your students to consider:

- This is not a race. Students should read as if they are radio announcers.
- Every reader should read new material each time, because rereading is faster.
- Every reader should read from columns of the same width. Pictures don't count, but students will have to decide how to incorporate headlines, changes in font size, and other irregularities.
- Students vary in their ability to measure time accurately. You may want to measure it for them or let them practice beforehand.

When students make a by-hand scatter plot of their data, it is assumed that they can plot coordinate pairs, recognize a relationship in the bivariate data, draw a line to fit the data, and calculate the slope of the line. Depending on your students' experience with these concepts, you may need to offer guidance through steps 4–5 and questions Q5–Q9.

The slope in this activity represents a rate or speed—centimeters per second—and students are expected to use this rate to extend the relationship and extrapolate data. Because the slope is a ratio, you may want to compare this activity to the previous activity, Mammals' Brains, in which the brain-to-body ratios did not represent a constant rate that could be applied to all species. Additionally, those ratios had no units (grams over grams cancelled), whereas the ratio in this activity does have a derived unit (centimeters per second).

For brevity, the by-hand portion of the activity has students extrapolate only twice: once with the raw data (Q4) and once with the slope (Q9). You may prefer to stop at these two questions, discuss their solutions with the entire class, and ask additional extrapolation questions. If you do, be sure to use an equal number of questions that require extrapolating given the independent value and given the dependent value.

The online part of the activity hopes to show students how technology can help make calculations easier. However, be careful not to undermine the importance of the by-hand methods. Students, especially those in Algebra 1, should have ample experience approximating lines of fit and finding the equation of a line both by hand and with technology.

After students finish the activity, and have had a lot of experience with their own and their partner's slope/reading speed, you may challenge them to extend their conceptual understanding. For example, ask, "What do you think is the steepest slope anyone could possibly have in this situation?," "Is it possible to have a slope of 0?," and "Is it possible to have a negative slope?"

Another good topic of discussion is whether or not students read at a constant rate. Ask, "Did you read at a constant rate?," "How do you know?," "How can you use the graph to identify when you read a little bit faster or a little bit slower?," and "Comparing your graph to your partner's graph, who read more closely to a constant rate?" Obviously, a constant rate would make the points perfectly linear, while a little faster or slower would make the points fall above or below the line of fit, respectively. Determining who read more closely to a constant rate can be done qualitatively or quantitatively; you could even extend the quantitative analysis into an introduction of residuals, residual plots, and residual squares.

Although written primarily for Algebra 1, this activity can be successfully used for Algebra 2, Precalculus, or Statistics. In addition to using a movable line, have students compare the results using median-median lines and/or least-squares lines. You can use these alternative models to discuss the danger of extrapolating too far beyond the domain and range of the known data. For example, have students answer Q13 for each of the different models and record how much the results vary. This will illustrate how small changes in the slope are magnified into big differences as you extrapolate farther away from the data. Extension 2 offers another idea that can help Algebra 2, Precalculus, and Statistics students better understand the sensitivity of the least-squares line.

MAKE A CONJECTURE

Q1 Answers will vary.

Q2 Answers will vary.

INVESTIGATE (BY HAND)

Almost every answer for this activity will vary depending on your newspaper and the speed at which a student reads. The following answers give sample answers as a point of reference only.

Q3 A typical page might have 150 vertical centimeters of text. Students should pick a representative page and measure the total vertical distance of all columns.

Q4 A typical reading rate is 0.2 centimeter per second, so the table of data might show 2 centimeters in 10 seconds. If a typical page has 150 centimeters, students would need 150 ÷ 2, or 75 ten-second periods—750 seconds total—to read one page. A similar result could be calculated using any time-distance pair from the table of raw data.

Q5 Yes, the lines should go through (0, 0). If you have no time to read (0 seconds), you won't be able to read anything (0 centimeters).

Q6 A typical slope is 0.2 centimeter per second.

Q7 The slope is the average reading speed in centimeters per second.

Q8 Because the slope represents speed, the faster reader should have the steeper line, that is, the line with the greater slope.

Q9 Students need to multiply the slope by the time. For example, 0.2 cm/s • 100 s = 20 cm.

INVESTIGATE (WITH FATHOM)

Q10 Here's a typical graph with the linear equation *VertDist1* = 0.206 cm/s *Time.*

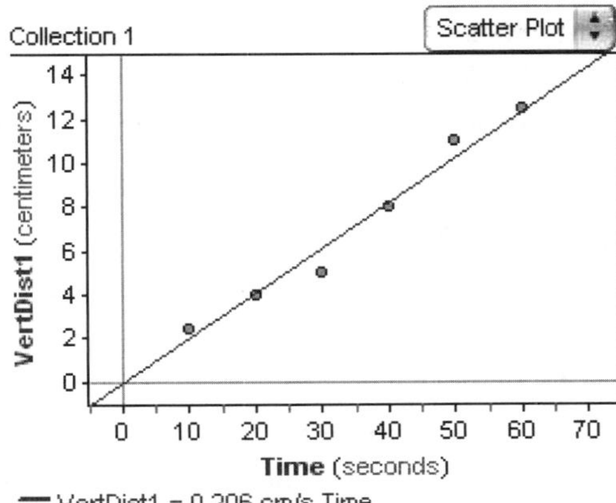

Q11 The coefficient of *Time* represents the slope of the line and should be close to the slope calculated in Q6. (*Note:* You may need to define *coefficient.*)

Q12 Here's a sample dot plot for a student who reads about 0.2 cm/s and another who reads about 0.1 cm/s. The equations of the two lines are both in the form *VertDist1* = *slope* • *Time,* so you can identify the faster reader by looking at the coefficient of *Time.*

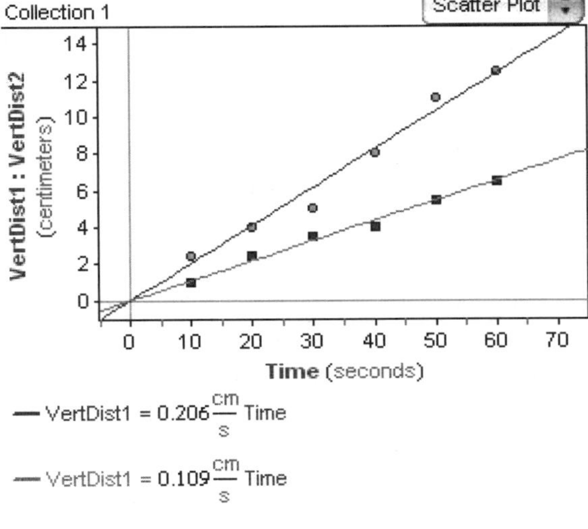

Q13 The sample answers use the function and graph from Q10. Note that parts a and d require students to match a particular value of *Time* (the independent value) and read the coordinate for *VertDist* (the dependent value). Part b requires students to match *VertDist* and read *Time.* Students may need to reduce the size of the graph or adjust the axes in order to trace far enough.

a. (99.943 s, 20.588 cm), approximately 20.6 centimeters

b. (728.20 s, 150.01 cm), approximately 728 seconds, or 12 minutes. *Note:* This answer uses the 150 cm approximated in Q3.

c. If a typical front section is 8 pages, multiply answer b by 8; approximately 5826 seconds, or 97 minutes. *Note:* Students will probably have trouble tracing until *VertDist* is 1200 cm. That's why this solution uses multiplication.

d. (1802.0 s, 371.21 cm), approximately 371 centimeters, or 2.5 pages

Q14 Based on the answer to Q13c or d, students are likely to say, "No, listening to a half-hour news broadcast is not the same as reading the front section of a newspaper."

Q15 Some students might recognize that a written report in the newspaper contains much more detail than a typical spoken report on the radio. So, one way to make the timing about the same would be to edit each newspaper story down to the essential content. Other students might realize that a typical news broadcast reports on only a few "big" stories, whereas a newspaper tends to include major and minor stories. So, another option would be to read only, say, every other story in the newspaper. Lastly, some students might suggest getting a different newspaper that focuses only on major national stories and includes a lot of pictures, graphics, and/or advertising. For example, reading *USA Today* might be more equivalent to listening to a news broadcast than, say, reading the *New York Times.*

EXPLORE MORE

1. When the attributes are swapped, the slope represents the number of seconds per centimeter, or how long it takes to read a given amount of text. This is the reciprocal of the slopes used previously in this activity.

2. These questions give students mental exercise thinking about function scaling. Some students might be interested in actually collecting raw data, but encourage them to think through the situation first.

   If the columns were twice as wide, it would take you twice as long to read each line and you'd cover half the vertical distance. So, in general, this would halve the slope.

   If the columns were half as wide, it would take you half as long to read each line and you'd cover twice the vertical distance. So, in general, this would double the slope.

EXTENSIONS

1. Have students make two separate scatter plots for *VertDist1* versus *Time* and *VertDist2* versus *Time.* Without changing the data points, find ways to make the graphs look like you read faster than your partner. Find ways to make it look like your partner reads faster. Can you make it look like you both read at the same speed? Explain how to tell which person actually reads faster, no matter what the graphs look like.

   In step 14 of the activity, putting both *VertDist* attributes on the same graph means that one set of points always looks steeper than the other (unless the students read at the same speed). However, creating separate graphs allows you to rescale one graph's axes to give the appearance of steepness. The graphs that follow use different vertical scales to give the impression that the second graph is steeper. But, when you calculate the slopes (see the equations), the first graph is really steeper. This is a good opportunity to discuss ways that data can be distorted, as is occasionally done in the media.

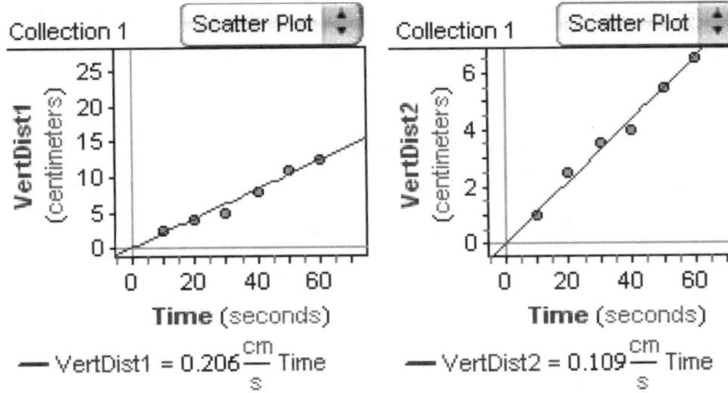

2. For students who are studying the least-squares line, have them make a graph of *VertDist* (1 or 2) versus *Time*. Add a least-squares line and lock the intercept at zero. Now drag any one point. Watch how coordinates of the data point change in the case table and how the value of the slope changes in the linear equation. Also, watch how the value of r^2 changes. Experiment to find the largest and smallest slopes you can get by dragging one point to different locations.

   Points can be dragged outside of the window into areas that are meaningless for this situation, such as the second, third, or fourth quadrants. If you restrict points to the first quadrant, the smallest slope will be close to 0. The largest slope depends on the data, but it will probably be smaller than 3.5. If you allow the points to be dragged anywhere, you can get just about any slope.

   Note: Dragging points is dangerous because you usually want to avoid inadvertently changing your data. Fortunately, you can always use **Undo** to make things right again.

SLOPE-INTERCEPT FORM (PAGE 11)

Activity Time: 30–50 minutes

Required Document: SlopeIntercept.ftm

Optional Document: SlopeInterceptPREMADE.ftm

Fathom Prerequisites: Students should be able to

- Create attributes defined by formulas
- Make a scatter plot of two attributes

Fathom Skills: Students will learn to how to

- Create sliders
- Graph lines of fit (median-median lines)
- Duplicate graphs
- Link graphs' axes
- *Optional:* Add multiple attributes to an axis (see Explore More 1)
- *Optional:* Plot functions (see Extension 2)

Mathematics Prerequisites: Students should be able to find the slope of a line by counting rise over run or using two points in the slope formula.

Mathematics Skills: Students will learn how to transform bivariate data by manipulating a table of coordinates; predict the graphical and functional transformations that result from transforming data; and determine the effects of the parameters m (slope) and b (y-intercept) on the linear equation $y = mx + b$.

General Notes: You and your students will immediately notice that this activity is different from most Fathom activities. Instead of analyzing real-world data with variability, this activity uses data generated by a linear function. This allows you to use Fathom as a tool for algebraic manipulation.

In this activity, students will transform a set of linear data and see how the equation of the line of fit changes. In turn, students will learn how the parameters m (slope) and b (y-intercept) affect the graph of the linear equation $y = mx + b$. This gives students in-depth experience with the multiple representations of function: table, graph, and algebraic equation.

If you make extensive use of graphing calculators in your algebra class, the structure of this activity may seem familiar. Transforming the data by creating new attributes is very similar to creating lists on a graphing calculator. And using sliders to explore the effects of parameters is similar to widely used programs that explore function parameters. Fathom, however, adds a level of sophistication by allowing students to see either several graphs that each show one line or, by adding multiple attributes to an axis, one graph that shows several lines. For these reasons, you may find this Fathom activity to be a good supplement to your use of graphing calculators.

Be aware that there is a subtle distinction between transforming data and transforming a function that might confuse some students. For example, consider that you have data in the form (x, y) from the line $y = x$. When you transform the data into the form $(x, y + 5)$ by translating each point up 5 units, the line that fits is now $y = x + 5$. Some students may be puzzled because you add to the y-coordinate, yet the equation compensates by adding to the x-value. One explanation is that the equation must maintain the same equality as before the data were transformed, or $y = x$. So, if you add to the y-coordinate, the equation must add the same amount to the x-coordinate—substituting $(x, y + 5)$ into $y = x + 5$ gives $y + 5 = x + 5$, or $y = x$. Another explanation is that the equation must undo the transformation in order to be consistent with the original data. For this explanation, rewrite the transformed equation as $y - 5 = x$; when you substitute $(x, y + 5)$, you get $y + 5 - 5 = x$, or $y = x$. The latter explanation is more useful because it helps explain a wider array of function transformations. For example, in this linear scenario, it explains why data transformed to the form $(x + 3, y)$ are modeled by $y = x - 3$. In general, it explains why data in the form (x, y) from the function $y = f(x)$ can be transformed into $(x + h, y + k)$ and the function $y - k = f(x - h)$.

Please note that this activity as written is designed to teach linear equations in slope-intercept form *and* to teach students how to use several of Fathom's features, such as sliders and duplicate graphs. If your students are already familiar with Fathom, or you want to avoid the time required to teach the software to novice students, you may prefer to use the document **SlopeInterceptPREMADE.ftm,** which has the sliders and graphs prepared for you. That way, students can complete the worksheet by answering only the questions beginning with Q2.

For students in Algebra 2 or Precalculus, you can use this activity as an introduction to function transformations. You can also change the formula for y in the case table and explore transformations of nonlinear functions (see Extension 2). However, if you want to do an entire activity on transformations of a variety of functions, see the activity Function Transformations in the Algebra 2 chapter of this book, page 38.

INVESTIGATE

Q1 The equation is $y = x$. *Note:* This step uses the median-median line for convenience. If your students are familiar with this line, you may want to discuss why it fits the points perfectly.

Q2 Each coordinate *yPLUSb* is 4 more than the corresponding coordinate y. Students will probably guess that this will make each point in the scatter plot move up 4 units.

Q3 Each point in the scatter plot of $(x, yPLUSb)$ is 4 units up from the corresponding point in the scatter plot of (x, y).

Q4 The equation changes to $y = x + 4$, which students might explain as "4 was added to x in the equation."

Q5 The y-intercept is 4.

Q6 Students should highlight that the points move up (or down, for negative) the same amount as b, the equation is always in the form $y = x + b$, and the y-intercept is always the same as b.

Q7 a. $y = x + 2$

b. $y = x - 3$ or $y = x + (-3)$

c. $y = x + 20$

For the graphs in parts a and b, you may want to have students verify their answers by adjusting slider b. For the graph in part b, students will also need to adjust the domain and range of the graph's axes. The value of b for part c is purposefully beyond the range of the slider; this will force students to extend the concept of y-intercepts beyond what they can readily graph.

Q8 Students should highlight that the points are m times as far away from the x-axis and the equation is always in the form $y = m \cdot x$.

Some students may explain the effects of m on the scatter plot by describing special ranges of values, such as values greater than 1, values between 0 and 1, and negative values. Other students might describe how the slope of the line changes as m changes from $+10$ to -10 (from steep going up, to not-so-steep going up, to horizontal, to not-so-steep going down, to steep going down) or notice that m rotates the line.

Because students just finished examining the y-intercept, some might notice that the y-intercept is always 0 in these cases.

Q9 Answers will vary depending on how much experience students have with slope. If you encourage students to think about the formula for slope (or the rise-over-run definition), then they should be able to recognize that the slope is always the same as m.

Q10 a. $y = 0.25x$

b. $y = -3x$

c. $y = 15x$

Note: Similar to the graph in Q7c, the graph in Q10c intentionally uses a value that is beyond the range of the slider.

Q11 a. $y = 2x + 4$

b. $y = -1x - 5$

c. $y = 0.75x - 9$

d. $y = 12x$

e. $y = 3.5x + 2$

Q12 The linear equation $y = mx + b$ is called slope-intercept form because the value of m tells you the slope of the line and the value of b tells you the y-intercept.

EXPLORE MORE

1. The lines are *parallel* because they have the same slope.

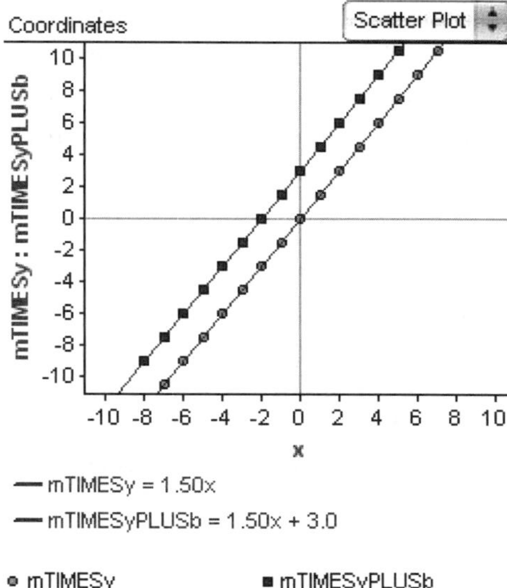

2. When using m and b with the x-coordinates, b relates to the x-intercept and m relates to the reciprocal of the slope. Hence, the equation for (*mTIMESxPLUSb*, y) is $y = \frac{x}{m} - b$.

EXTENSIONS

1. If your students have already learned about transformations, review the four fundamental types of transformations: translations, reflections, rotations, and dilations (sometimes called stretches or shrinks). Ask, "What type of transformation happens to the graph of the points (x, y) when you add b to y?," "What type of transformation happens when you multiply m times y?," and "Can you find a way to change the y-coordinates to create the remaining types of transformations?"

   Changing the coordinates from (x, y) to $(x, y + b)$ generally creates a vertical translation, although in the linear case it may also look like a horizontal translation. Changing the coordinates from (x, y) to $(x, m \cdot y)$ generally creates a vertical dilation, although in the linear case it may look like a rotation to some students and when $m = -1$ it is also a reflection across the x-axis. Here are some other transformations that students can easily discover within the confines of this activity: $(x + b, y)$ creates a horizontal translation; $(m \cdot x, y)$ creates a horizontal dilation; $(x, -y)$ creates a reflection across the x-axis; $(-x, y)$ creates a reflection across the y-axis; (y, x) creates a reflection across the line $y = x$; $(-x, -y)$ creates a 180° rotation about the origin; $(-y, x)$ creates a 90° counterclockwise rotation about the origin; and $(y, -x)$ creates a 90° clockwise rotation about the origin.

2. You or your students may notice that the values for y in the case table are gray. That's because the y-coordinates are defined by the formula $y = x$. Students in Algebra 2 or Precalculus, in particular, can edit the formula to $y = x^2$ or $y = |x|$, for example, and explore the effects of changing the coordinates. In what ways are the results the same? In what ways are they different?

   Students should find that adding to the x- or y-coordinates creates a horizontal or vertical translation; multiplying the x- or y-coordinates creates a horizontal or vertical dilation; and negating the x- or y-coordinates creates a reflection across the y- or x-axis.

   If students want to explore the effects on the functions that fit the points, they should turn off the median-median line and choose **Plot Function** from the **Graph** menu. This will be more challenging, because students need to have an idea of what function to graph.

   By using nonlinear functions, students should begin to see that the equations that fit the points need to undo the transformations. Hence, the points $(ax + h, by + k)$ are fitted by the function $\frac{y-k}{b} = f\left(\frac{x-h}{a}\right)$, or $y = b \cdot f\left(\frac{x-h}{a}\right) + k$.

   If you want to pursue this extended extension with Algebra 2 or Precalculus students, see the activity Function Transformations in the Algebra 2 chapter of this book, page 38.

THE OCEAN TRAIN (PAGE 15)

Activity Time: 40–55 minutes

Materials:

- One copy of the train schedule (page 18) per group. Note that page 18 has two copies of the schedule.

Optional Document: OceanTrain.ftm

Fathom Prerequisites: Students should be able to

- Create a collection by entering data into a case table
- Create attributes and define them with formulas
- Make a scatter plot

Fathom Skills: Students will learn how to

- Work with units
- Manipulate data by creating and combining attributes
- Graph lines of fit (movable lines)

Mathematics Prerequisites: Students should be able to make a scatter plot of points; find the slope of a line by counting rise over run or using two points in the slope formula; and interpret slope-intercept form of a linear equation.

Mathematics Skills: Students will learn how to accurately read a nonstandard table of data; find a slope-intercept linear equation to model data that are roughly linear; interpret slope as a rate or speed; compare slopes based on their graphical and numerical representations; and manipulate and transform data so that they can be best modeled by a linear function.

General Notes: Like Reading the News, this activity is about slope and equations of lines. Students graph data that are roughly linear and model them with linear equations. They must be able to interpret the slope as a rate or speed, as is appropriate for the context of the data. However, there are two key differences. First, the data in this activity do not logically start at the origin. So, students must work with an equation in slope-intercept form and interpret the meaning of the intercept. Second, the data require some manipulation and transformation before they have a good linear pattern.

Here's a synopsis of the activity: Students begin by reading and interpreting a schedule for the Ocean, a Canadian passenger train. The schedule is not a standard "textbook" table, so students have to use a lot of problem solving to fully understand all of the data. Then they enter the data into Fathom and make scatter plots of distance versus time. However, because the data have many layers (time zones, days, hours, and minutes), students need to define new attributes and combine attributes to get an acceptable representation of time. After making the data look linear, students use movable lines to answer questions about the train's speed.

For all of the graphs in this activity, slope is the same as speed, as long as the right attributes are on the right axes. You might get in the habit of pointing to the vertical axis, saying "per," and pointing to the horizontal. You could also explain that slope is rise (vertical) over run (horizontal), and speed is distance over time, so kilometers goes on the vertical axis and time on the horizontal axis.

If your students have done the activity Slope-Intercept Form, they already know how to define attributes with formulas. In this activity, however, students will gain a deeper appreciation of formulas. Here, they combine attributes to accomplish something useful—to convert days, hours, and minutes into a useful measure of time. The idea that transforming data creates changes in the graph of the data is still visible, as the points gradually become more and more linear.

The portions of the activity that require students to manipulate the data are purposefully left open-ended, as opportunities for discovery learning. For example, question Q8 and step 4 ask students to find a way to make the data look like one line without suggesting what attributes and formulas to use. This allows students to find alternative, even unique, solutions that they may not have found if the worksheet had told them to simply add 1 day (24 hours) to each *Hour* after midnight. The discovery approach may be challenging for many students, and some may not "fix" the problem on the first try, yet Fathom allows students to easily change, correct, or undo their wrong steps.

The open-ended approach may be frustrating to some teachers, too. If you prefer to have a more guided activity, you can periodically stop and have a class discussion to help students realize the optimal solutions. For Q8, one solution is to first create an attribute that measures days elapsed and add that to *Hour.* For step 5, one solution is to add *Minutes* to the sum of days elapsed and *Hour.* For Explore More 1, one solution is to create an attribute that adjusts for time zones and add that to the sum of days elapsed, *Hour,* and *Minutes.*

This activity will also help students see how Fathom works with units, performing the necessary unit conversions when operating with different units. For example, if you define a new attribute as the sum of an attribute with hours as the unit and another with minutes as the unit, the new attribute will have minutes as the fundamental unit (although, if the units are not specified, some of the cases may be displayed in hours). If students haven't had a lot of experience with units in Fathom, you might want to have them play around with unit conversions. For example, have students change the unit for the attribute *Hour* from h to min and watch how Fathom recalculates the values accordingly. Try changing the unit to days (d) or years (y), and then back to h again.

Some teachers may want to divide this activity over two classes. On the first day, students can read the schedule and enter data into Fathom. On the second day, they can begin analyzing the data with scatter plots and lines. Alternatively, if you can spare only one day, you can omit data entry and give students the pre-made document **OceanTrain.ftm.** This document has the schedule already entered, so you could skip steps 1–2 on the student worksheet.

UNDERSTAND THE DATA

Q1 Tuesday. Students should decode the "x2" below the Ocean train's name.

Q2 1:05 P.M. Students should look at the first column, which is for November to April.

Q3 304 km. Look in the KM column, which measures distance from Halifax.

Q4 Rimouski, at 12:23 A.M. (Eastern Time).

Note: Some students might notice that the schedule includes two time zones. So, it is also possible to say the answer is Amqui, at 12:01 A.M. Atlantic Time.

Q5 Causapscal. Students should follow the arrow and skip over all the cities from Gaspé through Nouvelle, which are cities for the Chaleur train.

Q6 461 km. Subtract their distances from Halifax.

INVESTIGATE

Note: As mentioned in the answer to Q4, some students may notice that the schedule gives times in two time zones. These same students may adjust each value of *Hour* to be consistent with one time zone or another when entering data into their case tables. This will create a few changes to the following answers.

Q7 There are two lines because the attribute *Hour* doesn't account for the fact that the train trip takes place on two days. The bottom-right points are the first day of travel; the upper-left points are the second day.

Q8 One solution is to create a new attribute called *Day* that gives the number of the day. Hence, Halifax to Mont-Joli would be 0 d and Rimouski to Montréal would be 1 d. Then create another new attribute, *DayHour,* that calculates the sum of *Day* and *Hour,* which effectively adds 24 hours to each time on the second day.

Note: Some students might want to use 1 d and 2 d to indicate the first day and second day, respectively. This is all right, though not optimal. In the long run, these students will still get a line with the same slope (speed), which is the fundamental question in this activity.

Note: Students who have adjusted *Hour* for the Atlantic Time zone should consider Amqui, Sayabec, and Mont-Joli as being part of the second day of travel.

Q9 Sample graph and equation:

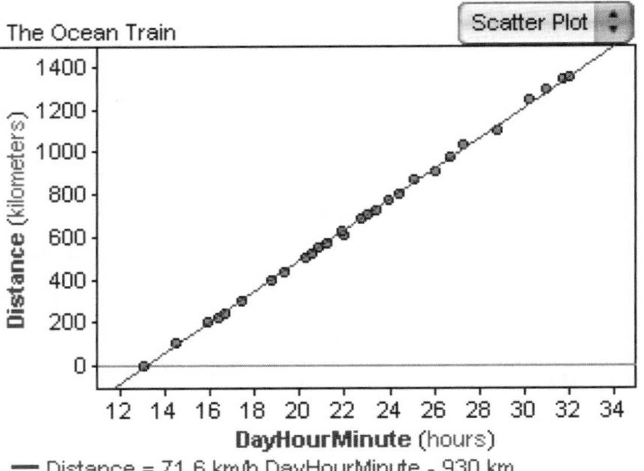

Q10 The slope of the line represents the train's average speed. Reasonable answers are between 70 and 75 kilometers per hour. Compared to automobile speeds, the speed may seem a little too slow, but then it does include stops at stations.

Note: Some students may not have a good conceptual understanding of speeds in kilometers per hour. If they comprehend miles per hour better, encourage them to convert units. For example, 70 km/h is about 43 mi/h.

Note: Students who have adjusted *Hour* for time zones may get a slope/speed as low as 65 km/h.

Q11 Reasonable answers are between −800 and −1000 km. In terms of the train schedule, the intercept shown above, (0, −930), means that if the train were to travel "backward" from its starting time of 1305 to 0000 (midnight) of that day, it would have gone backward about 930 km. Another way to think about this is that by not traveling between 0000 and 1305, the train lost 930 km that it could have traveled.

EXPLORE MORE

1. Students can either consider all times to be Atlantic Time, in which case 1 hour needs to be added to every time in Eastern Time, or consider all times to be Eastern Time, in which case 1 hour needs to be subtracted from every time in Atlantic Time. One way to do this is to manually change the values for *Hour.* If you prefer not to change the original data, then you

could create an attribute *Zone* that is 0 h (or −1 h) for all Atlantic Time stations and 1 h (or 0 h) for all Eastern Time stations. Then define an attribute *ZoneDayHourMin* that sums *Zone, Day, Hour,* and *Minute.* If students readjust the line of fit, they'll probably notice that the missing hour makes the slope decrease quite a lot.

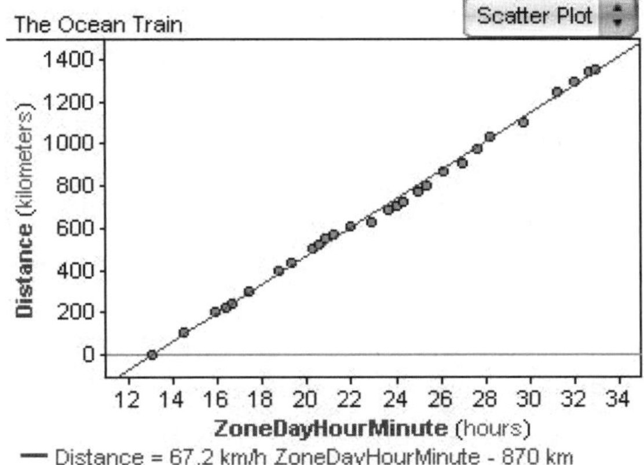

Note: If students seem interested in the results of progressively adjusting the attribute for time, you may want them to further consider this: How do you deal with the stations at which there is a layover (20 minutes at Moncton and 2 minutes at Matapédia)?

Note: Students who have adjusted *Hour* for time zones should not do Explore More 1 because they already have.

2. Answers will vary depending on the groups of points that students zoom in on. In general, steeper slopes represent times when the train traveled at a faster average speed, and shallower slopes represent slower times.

   If students have not had a lot of experience zooming in, either by dragging the axes or with the graph inspector, you may need to provide extra guidance with this item.

EXTENSIONS

1. Teach students about the *prev* function, or have students use Fathom Help to learn about it themselves. Use this function to define attributes that calculate the change in *Distances* and the change in *Time* (*ZoneDayHourMin*) between each station. Then define another attribute that calculates the speed between each pair of stations. Ask "Between which two stations does the Ocean go the fastest? The slowest?"

   This excerpt from the case table shows appropriate formulas and the results for the first five stations. The fastest speed is about 106 km/h between La Pocatière and Montmagny; the slowest speed is about 20 km/h between Campbellton and Matapédia. You might want to discuss possible reasons why the train can go so fast between some stations and so slowly between others.

ChangeKilo	ChangeTime	Speed
kilometers	hours	km/h
Distance – prev (Distance, 0km)	ZoneDayHourMinute – prev (ZoneDayHourMinute, 0hr)	ChangeKilo / ChangeTime
0 km	13.0833 h	0 km/h
103 km	1.41667 h	72.7059 km/h
97 km	1.41667 h	68.4706 km/h
27 km	0.416667 h	64.8 km/h
16 km	0.283333 h	56.4706 km/h

2. Have sudents redo the activity using the data in either **Trans-Siberian Railroad.ftm** or **CoastStarlight.ftm.** Both of these documents are located in the **Sample | Documents | Social Science** folder. Students could compare the trains using the questions in the activity.

OLYMPICS (PAGE 19)

Activity Time: 40–55 minutes

Required Document: Olympics.ftm

Fathom Prerequisites: Students should be able to

- Look at data with the collection inspector or a case table
- Make a scatter plot
- Graph multiple attributes on one axis
- Make a line of fit for a scatter plot
- *Optional:* Create new attributes (see Extension 3)
- *Optional:* Make a one-variable graph (dot plot, box plot, histogram; see Extension 3)
- *Optional:* Create a summary table (see Extension 3)

Fathom Skills: Students will learn how to

- *Optional:* Make a residual plot (see Explore More 1)
- *Optional:* Show and interpret residual squares (see Extension 1)

Mathematics Prerequisites: Students should be able to make a scatter plot of points; find a linear equation to model data that are roughly linear; and interpret slope-intercept form of a linear equation.

Mathematics Skills: Students will learn how to use scatter plots to compare the linear patterns of different data sets and approximate the intersection of two lines from a graph (i.e., solve a system of two linear equations graphically).

General Notes: This activity is intended to reinforce and extend the mathematics skills that students have learned in the previous three Algebra 1 activities. First, students use scatter plots and lines of fit to describe the pattern of Olympic results for the 100-meter dash over time, similar to the use of scatter plots and lines of fit in Reading the News and The Ocean Train. Students are instructed to identify the slope and intercept of the line from the equation, as practiced in Slope-Intercept Form, but students are also required to interpret the slope and intercept in terms of the real-world situation. Then they extend their learning by comparing systems of lines for the 100-meter dash and the 200-meter dash, and for the men's and women's 100-meter dash. The former system is inconsistent (parallel), but the latter system allows students to determine when women Olympians might run as fast as men. (See Extension 3 for ways to work with one-variable statistics, as was done in Mammals' Brains.)

The structure of this activity is designed to model the scientific method. Mathematicians, scientists, and statisticians rarely have a step-by-step process to lead them to conclusions. Instead, they begin with a question or an observation about the way things seem to work and make conjectures about what they think is true; then they gather data that might support (or refute) the conjectures, analyze the data, and revisit their conjectures. This activity encourages students to make conjectures about the data before they look at it. Students are encouraged to use everything they know (including their understanding of athletics, genetics, and physiological differences between men and women) to make conjectures about how the Olympic data will look, change, and compare. Then, as they do their step-by-step analysis in Fathom, they are encouraged to reflect on their conjectures and see whether they were right or wrong. For a more open-ended activity, you might give students only the first page of the worksheet (the Make a Conjecture questions Q1–Q5) and then challenge them to use Fathom to support their conjectures without step-by-step instructions.

Before beginning to analyze the Olympic results in Fathom, you may want to discuss with students what it means for one gold-medal time or distance to be better than another. In the case of timed events (e.g., 100-meter dash), improvement is shown by shorter times; on the contrary, for distance-measured events (e.g., discus throw), improvement is shown by longer distances. So, although "improvement" is frequently equated with something increasing, students will need to look for data that either increase or decrease, depending on the event.

A technical note about the Olympic Games: The worksheet mentions that the Olympic Games have been held every four years since 1896. This is not entirely true for the Winter Olympics. From 1896 to 1992, the Winter and Summer Olympic Games were held in the same calendar year. However, beginning in 1994, Winter and Summer were staggered every two years. So now, although a complete cycle of Olympic Games occurs every four years, there is a set of games every two calendar years.

If you would like to use this activity with Algebra 2 or Precalculus students, be sure to have them try nonlinear functions that could better model the Olympic data. That is, winning times cannot continue to decrease to zero and winning distances cannot continue to increase to infinity. Hence, curved functions with long-run limits would be more appropriate models. (See Extension 2.)

MAKE A CONJECTURE

Q1 Answers will vary depending on estimation skills and experience with track-and-field events. As a guide, the actual Olympic data range from 9.84 to 12 seconds.

Q2 Students will likely guess that the time has gotten shorter. Explanations may include improvements in training techniques, improvements in equipment (such as better shoes), athletes' desires to continually outperform records, or more rigorous selection of competitors.

Q3 Students will likely guess that the 200-meter results will be twice the 100-meter results.

Q4 Students will likely guess that the men's results are better than the women's results. Explanations may include that men are (stereotypically) stronger and can run faster than women, or that men generally have longer legs and can take fewer, bigger strides. They may also cite experience from physical education classes, where boys are likely to have run faster than girls. Students' answers to "How much better?" will rely on their estimation skills and frames of reference. If students have done track-and-field events in physical education class or after-school sports, they might cite differences anywhere from 1 to 5 seconds based on actual experience. The differences in the Olympic data actually range from 0.62 to 1.6 seconds.

Q5 Some students might guess that the differences are getting smaller because female athletes are continually becoming stronger and faster; they might even guess that the gold-medal times will eventually be the same for both genders. Other students might argue that the differences are staying the same because physiological differences between men and women (bone structure, musculature, etc.) mean that men will always be a little faster.

INVESTIGATE

3. You may need to remind some students that *M_100Meter* versus *Year* means that *Year* goes on the horizontal axis and *M_100Meter* goes on the vertical axis.

Q6 The times have clearly gotten shorter (or improved) over time. Here's a sample graph with a median-median line added:

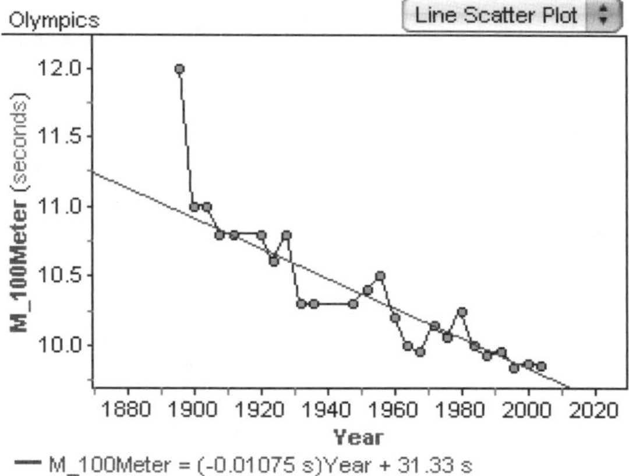

Q7 The greatest improvement was between 1896 and 1900, which is the longest downward segment. In general, downward segments (those with negative slope) represent improvements and upward segments (positive slope) represent setbacks.

Q8 The results for 1896, 1928, 1932, 1936, 1956, 1964, 1968, and 1980 are likely candidates. One method that students might use is to pick out the points that are farthest from the general linear trend.

Q9 For the median-median line, the slope means that the men's gold-medal times are decreasing by about 0.01 second per year. (*Note:* It's important that students realize the slope is defined per year even though the data are for every four years.) The y-intercept has no worthwhile meaning, although some students might try explaining it as the gold-medal time had the Olympics started in year 0.

Q10 2008 gives 9.75 seconds; 2012 gives 9.70 seconds. Students can answer this question either by substituting values into the linear equation and evaluating by hand or calculator, or by tracing the line of fit in Fathom.

Q11 The scatter plot shows that, for either men or women, every 200-meter point is about twice as high as the corresponding 100-meter point. Hence, the 200-meter results are about twice the 100-meter results. To see this clearly, students *must* adjust the vertical axis to begin at zero.

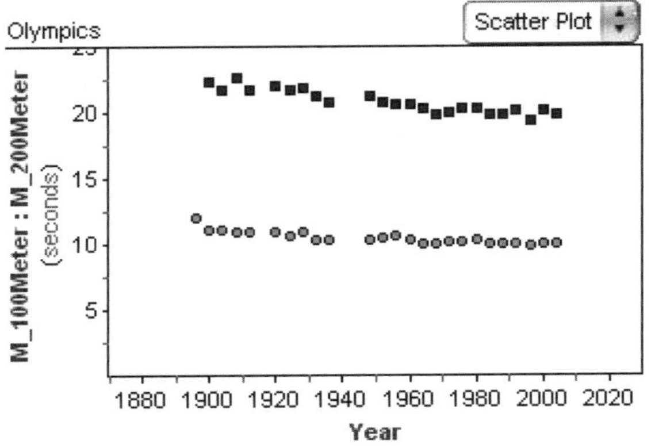

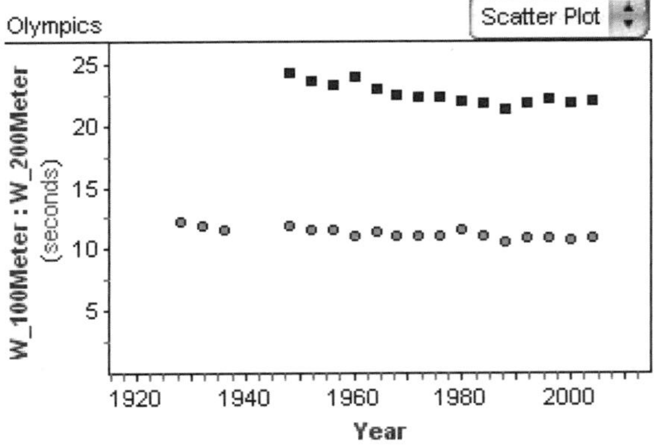

Q12 The graph supports the prediction that the men's results are better (smaller) than the women's results. For the answer to "How much better?" students might cite actual differences (0.62 to 1.6 seconds). Some students might try subtracting the two linear equations and state the difference as a function of time: *Difference* = −0.00512 s *Year* + 11.12 s.

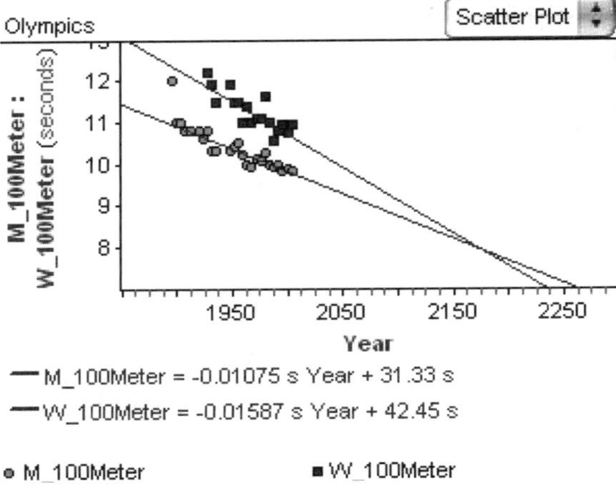

Q13 Yes, the difference is changing over time. You can tell because the lines are getting closer together.

Q14 Students find the intersection of their two lines of fit. For the median-median lines, the intersection is about (2175, 7.9), which means that in 2175 both men's and women's results for the 100-meter dash will be about 7.9 seconds. Because the lines do not fit the data very well and because the prediction is so far into the future, students should not feel confident about this answer. Furthermore, each line continues to decrease toward a winning time of 0 seconds—which is impossible—so the lines are an approximation at best.

EXPLORE MORE

1. You identify outliers from the residual plot by identifying points that are farthest away from the horizontal zero line. Deleting outliers can have a dramatic affect on the line of fit, especially for a least-squares line. Because 1896 is the most obvious outlier, removing this one point significantly improves the lines of fit.

Here's the residual plot for the least-squares line:

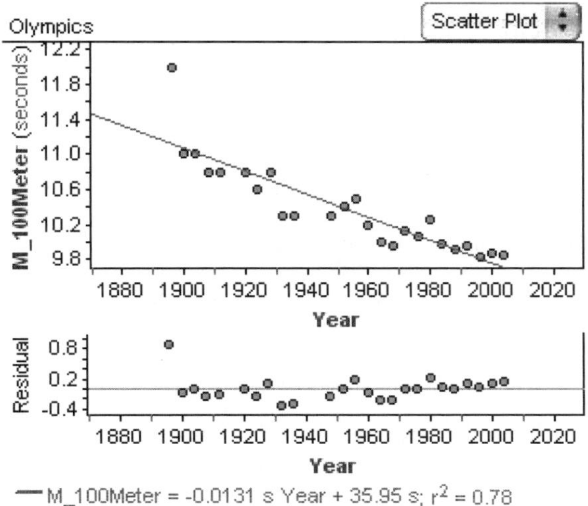

Here's the plot with the case for 1896 deleted:

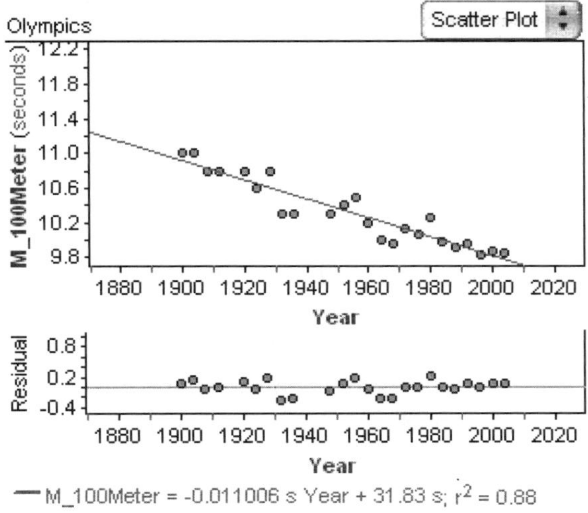

2. The discus results are the closest to showing no difference between genders. Depending on the lines of fit used, someone could argue that a few events (e.g., marathon, high jump, long jump, and javelin) show a constant difference between the genders; that is, the lines of fit are roughly parallel.

EXTENSIONS

1. If you use Explore More 1 to investigate residual plots, a natural extension is to view the residual squares. To show the squares, choose **Show Squares** from the **Graph** menu. Ask students, "How are the squares created?," "How do the squares relate to the residual plot?," and "How do the squares help you identify unusual points?"

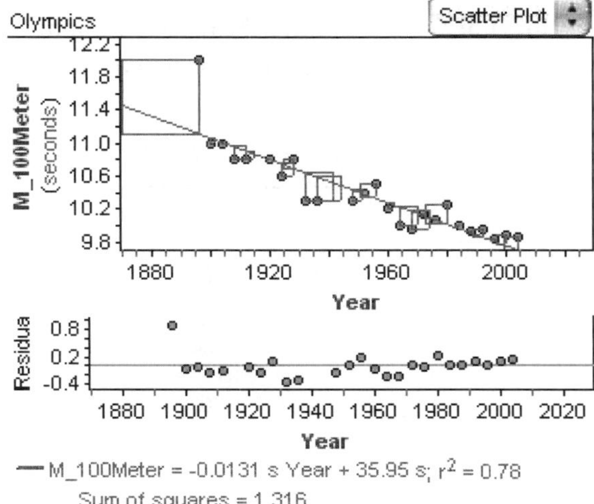

Note: If students have previously used least-squares regression in Fathom or on a graphing calculator, you can explain that the least-squares line minimizes the area of the residual squares.

2. Lines of fit are convenient but they are not always the best way to model data. Within the context of the Olympic data, discuss ways in which lines are of limited use. Ask, "What other mathematical models might be appropriate for describing the Olympic data?"

   Students should realize that linear models do not make long-term sense for most of the Olympic data. Namely, if you extrapolate far enough on a line with a negative slope, the line crosses the horizontal axis and has a value of 0; or, if you extrapolate on a line with positive slope, it goes to infinity. For the Olympics, it doesn't make sense, say, for someone to be able to run the 100-meter dash in 0 seconds or for someone to be able to throw a discus infinitely far. Students might argue that mathematical curves, such as exponential functions, are more appropriate models. Students in Algebra 2 or Precalculus can be challenged to find and plot better models.

3. Step 5 and Q11 can be further analyzed by performing one-variable statistics, similar to those done in Mammals' Brains. Have students create a new

attribute that calculates the ratio *200Meter/100Meter* for each year. Then use dot plots, box plots, histograms, and summary tables to analyze the central tendency and spread of the ratios. This will show that for either men or women the ratio of winning times has remained closely proportional to the ratio of distances, or 2 to 1.

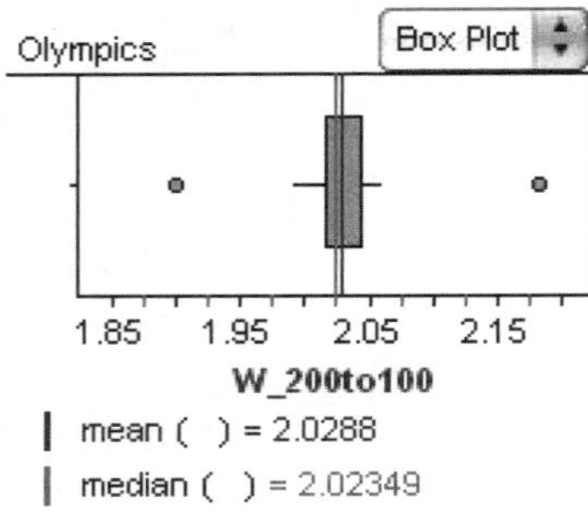

Olympics

W_200to100	2.0287963 2.0234869

S1 = mean ( )
S2 = median ( )

Then have students compare a "speed" event to an "endurance" event, such as the 100-meter dash to the 10,000-meter run (also called the 10K). Endurance races require that a runner maintain his or her stamina, so these athletes tend to run more slowly than sprinters. It is reasonable to assume that the ratio of 10K results to 100-meter results will be greater than the ratio of distance, or greater than 100 to 1. Using Fathom to analyze *M_10K/M_100Meter* gives a mean ratio of 169.

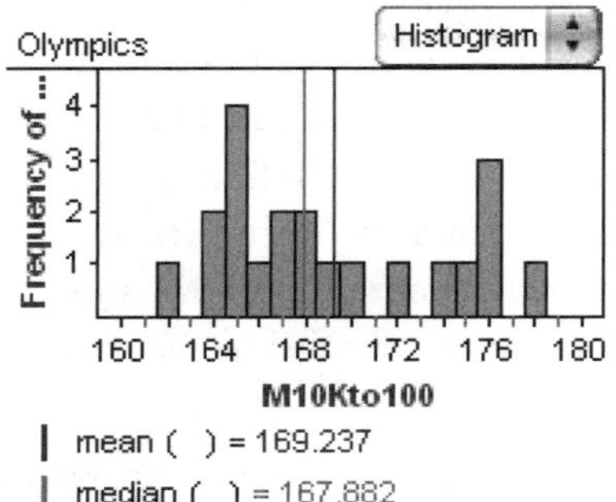

SEQUENCE OF SQUARES (PAGE 22)

Activity Time: 30–55 minutes

Fathom Prerequisites: Students should be able to

- Create a case table and collection
- Create attributes and define them with formulas

Fathom Skills: Students will learn how to

- Use special functions (*prev, next, caseIndex*) in formulas
- Add cases to a case table

Mathematics Prerequisites: Students should be able to recognize patterns in a sequence.

Mathematics Skills: Students will learn how to apply inductive reasoning; use technology to analyze a numeric pattern; and describe relationships *between* the square numbers. *Optional:* Students will recognize quadratic and other polynomial functions by analyzing finite differences (see Extension 1).

General Notes: This is perhaps the simplest, yet most open-ended, activity in this book. Students first use mental math to make a conjecture about a pattern in the sequence of square numbers. Then they use Fathom to analyze the pattern and confirm or refute their conjectures. The real task is being able to use Fathom to do *enough* calculations to support the conjecture. Along the way, students will gain a deeper understanding of square numbers and possibly get an introduction to quadratic functions.

Although this activity is highly appropriate for Algebra 1 students, it also has great extensions for students in Geometry, Algebra 2, or Precalculus. The activity itself is based on inductive reasoning—recognizing a pattern and extending it—but Explore More 1 has students generalize the pattern into proof. This is a great mental exercise for students at any level. In addition, Extension 1 uses the sequence to explore quadratic functions, other polynomial functions, and finite differences.

MAKE A CONJECTURE

Q1 It's expected that students will be able to use mental math to see that the difference between consecutive square numbers is a sequential odd number. Some students may further notice that the difference is twice the square root of the lower square, plus 1. That is, for example, the difference between 4^2 and 5^2 is $2(4) + 1$, or 9. If students don't make this observation in Q1, it's all right; hopefully they will notice it by the time they finish Q2.

INVESTIGATE

Q2 Students could simply type in square numbers for the cases, but this is time-consuming and fraught with human errors. Instead, students could define an attribute *Square* with the formula $caseIndex^2$. The function *caseIndex* refers to the case's row number. Students can then choose **New Cases** from the **Collection** menu to add as many square numbers as they desire.

There are many ways to calculate the differences between consecutive squares: *Square* − *prev*(*Square*) puts the difference beside the second square in each pair, so the sequence of odd numbers starts at 1; *next*(*Square*) − *Square* puts the difference beside the first square in the pair, so the sequence of odds starts at 3; and $caseIndex^2 - (caseIndex - 1)^2$ and $(caseIndex + 1)^2 - caseIndex^2$ give the same results as the *prev* and *next* formulas, respectively.

	Square	Difference
=	caseIndex²	Square − prev (Square)
1	1	1
2	4	3
3	9	5
4	16	7
5	25	9
6	36	11

Q3 Hopefully, students made good conjectures in Q1 and the Fathom calculations support the conjecture. If not, they should now write a new, correct conjecture.

Q4 If students did not originally notice the "square root of the lower square plus 1" pattern, maybe they'll notice it here.

EXPLORE MORE

Here's a brief algebraic explanation:

$$(n + 1)^2 - n^2 = (n^2 + 2n + 1) - n^2 = 2n + 1$$

Although this clearly illustrates the "square root of the lower square plus 1" pattern, some students may not recognize that it also illustrates the "odd number" pattern. You may need to explain that 2 times any number makes an even number, and then plus 1 makes an odd number.

Here's a geometric explanation:

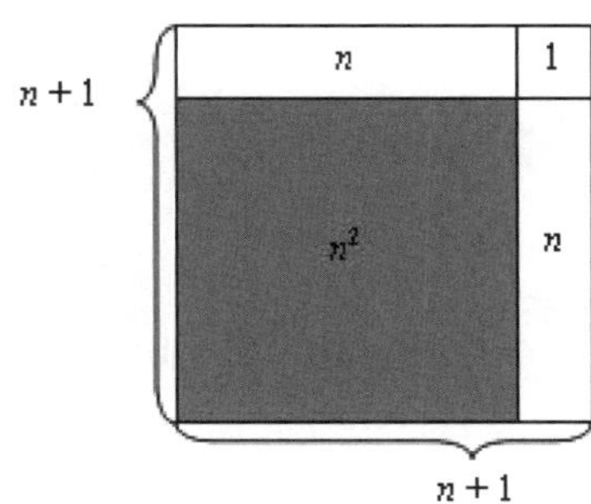

The gray square represents n^2 and the outer square represents $(n + 1)^2$. The difference between the two, the white region, is $2n + 1$.

EXTENSION

1. Have students add an attribute that calculates the differences of the differences. Ask, "What happens?" The second differences are constant.

   Create another collection for cubes. Ask, "How many differences do you need to calculate before the differences are constant?" The answer is three sets of differences.

   Challenge students to conjecture what will happen for $caseIndex^4$, $caseIndex^5$, and so on, and then test their conjectures. Also have them try any quadratic, cubic, quartic, or quintic function (for example, $3caseIndex^2 + caseIndex - 5$). Students should find that the number of differences necessary to get constant values is always the same as the degree.

Now ask, "Assume you are given any sequence of numbers. How could you use what you've learned to determine whether the sequence is modeled by a polynomial function? How would you determine the degree of the function?"

THE CIRCUMFERENCE FUNCTION (PAGE 25)

Activity Time: 30–45 minutes

Materials:

- Many circular objects of different sizes
- Centimeter rulers or measuring tapes
- String

Fathom Prerequisites: none

Fathom Skills: Students will learn how to

- Create a collection by entering data into a case table
- Create attributes with formulas
- Create graphs (scatter plots)
- Graph lines of fit (movable lines)
- Use summary tables to calculate measures of center (mean)

Mathematics Prerequisites: Students should be able to make a scatter plot of points; find the slope of a line; and write the equation of a line in slope-intercept form.

Mathematics Skills: Students will learn how to approximate the value of π by analyzing the relationship between diameter and circumference; think about π as a functional relationship between diameter and circumference and as a ratio of circumference to diameter; find a direct-variation linear equation to model data that are roughly linear; and interpret the slope of a direct-variation linear equation as a constant ratio between the dependent and independent variables.

General Notes: Many geometry teachers already use an activity in which students measure the circumferences and diameters of circular objects and "discover" that the ratio is π. This is the same activity enhanced by an analysis in Fathom. By using Fathom to look at the data with tables, graphs, proportions, and summary statistics, students can get multiple representations of the same concept and gain a deeper understanding of π.

The activity opens by modeling the scientific method—challenging students to make a conjecture before they collect data. Because π is frequently taught in mathematics long before high school, many students will already know that the relationship is $C = \pi d$. Have those students answer questions Q1 and Q2 based on the relationship that they know to be true, but also ask them to conjecture how their experimental measurements might compare to the theoretical formula.

Students then collect data by physically measuring circular objects. You may want to plan ahead and ask every student to bring in two or three circular objects that the entire class can work with. If students don't bring in objects and you don't have access to enough circular objects, use geometry software or a compass to make and cut out a variety of circles. While students are making measurements, make sure that they are using measuring tapes or string to directly measure the circumferences. If they measure the diameter and then calculate the circumference, they will see a proportional relationship, but they will have missed the point! To save class time, you might want to have students collect measurements at home, rather than actually bringing objects to class.

The analysis of the data begins with a scatter plot and a line of fit. You could jump directly to calculating the ratio of circumference to diameter and finding a measure of center. However, jumping immediately to ratios makes the assumption that the relationship is a direct variation, and it doesn't tell you whether the same ratio applies to circles of all sizes. Furthermore, a ratio of two variables is, by its nature, merely a summary. A scatter plot helps you see not only the relationship between the variables, but also whether the relationship continues. And because the scatter plot shows a separate point for each case, it shows all of the information and allows you to make predictions by interpolating and extrapolating. Using a scatter plot is a particularly important first step if you do Explore More 2, in which calculating a ratio alone obscures the importance of the intercept.

While students are fitting lines to the data, you may want to emphasize the functional relationship between *Diameter* and *Circumference*. Review that a function is a relationship in which each input value results in one output value. The students' scatter plots of *Circumference* versus *Diameter* probably pass the vertical line test, and the lines of fit definitely pass the vertical line test. You could also point out that the relationship is actually one-to-one: each input value results in one and only one output value. That is, *Circumference* is a function of *Diameter*, and *Diameter* is a function of *Circumference*. You could illustrate this relationship by swapping the axes in the scatter plot and showing that the resulting graph still passes the vertical line test.

After students have fit direct-variation lines to their scatter plots and seen that the relationship between *Circumference* and *Diameter* is represented by the slope, they go on to the "traditional" method of calculating the ratio of *Circumference* to *Diameter*. The activity uses a summary table to calculate the mean. If your students have enough cases, you might also have them create one-variable graphs (dot plot, histogram, or box plot) to see how the "average" is graphically represented by clusters or mounding. Students could also add other measures of center, such as the median, to the summary table and discuss pros and cons of each summary.

For the sake of geometry students who have never used Fathom before, the worksheet provides ample Fathom instructions. If you are using this activity with novice students, please allow sufficient time for students to learn both the software and the mathematics. On the other hand, if your students are very familiar with Fathom, you can expect the activity to move at a fairly rapid pace. You might even prefer to set up the scenario but omit the worksheet, letting students make their own conjectures, design their own data-collection methods, and do their own Fathom analysis.

MAKE A CONJECTURE

Q1 Students who are familiar with the relationship might say, "The circumference is about 3.14 times the diameter," or state the formula $C = \pi d$.

Q2 Although many students may be familiar with the formula $C = \pi d$, they may never have thought of it as a linear equation with slope π and intercept 0.

EXPERIMENT

Q3 Students will probably use mental math to divide each circumference by the corresponding diameter. They might estimate each ratio to be about 3, which probably supports the conjecture in Q1.

INVESTIGATE

Q4 The points should be roughly linear with intercept 0. The slope should be about 3. Answers about whether or not the graph supports a student's conjecture in Q2 will vary.

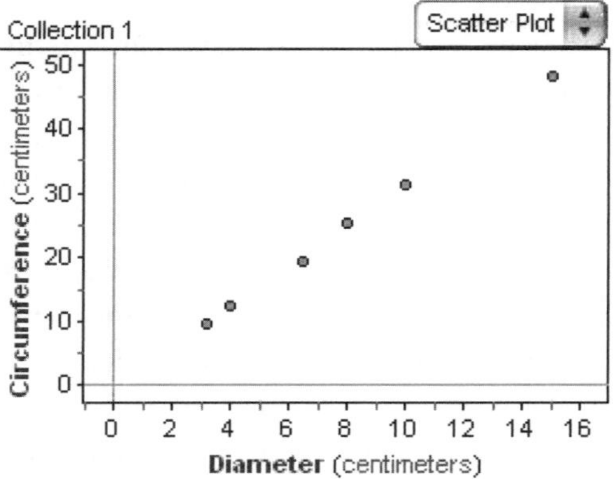

Q5 The pattern is linear, so a line would fit the points.

Q6 Yes, the line should go through (0, 0), because a circle with no diameter would have no circumference.

Q7 The linear equation should be approximately *Circumference* = 3.14*Diameter*. The number (coefficient) multiplied by *Diameter* represents the relationship between the diameter and the circumference. This number is represented by the physical slope of the line.

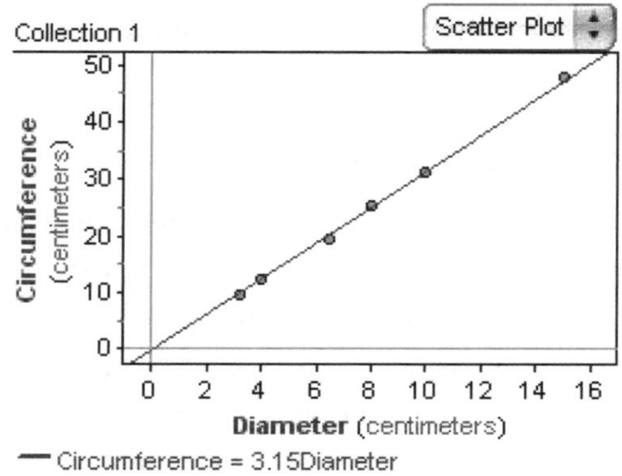

Q8 By definition, a measurement is an approximation, not an exact value. So, students' measurements are likely to vary a little from the actual relationship. Because the points are so close to being linear, students will likely guess that the relationship is truly linear.

Q9 The ratios should all be around 3.14. Compared to the rest of the activity, the ratios should be close to the mental math calculations in Q3 and the slope of the line in Q7. *Note:* You may want to have a class discussion about why *CircDiam* has no units.

	Diameter	Circumference	CircDiam
units	centimeters	centimeters	
1	4.0 cm	12.4 cm	3.1
2	8.0 cm	25.2 cm	3.15
3	6.5 cm	19.5 cm	3
4	10.0 cm	31.4 cm	3.14
5	3.2 cm	9.6 cm	3
6	15.0 cm	48.0 cm	3.2

Q10 The mean should be around 3.14.

CircDiam	3.0983333

S1 = mean ( )

Q11 The circumference is about 3.14 times the diameter, or $C = \pi d$. This may or may not be what students conjectured in Q1. Students should make some observation about the variability between the experimental measurements and the theoretical formula.

Q12 Although many students may know the formula $C = \pi d$, they may never have thought of it as a linear equation. So, seeing the points form a line with slope π may surprise some students.

EXPLORE MORE

1. Measuring diameter and circumference in inches makes no difference—the ratio will still be π. Measuring in different units technically introduces the ratio $\frac{2.54\text{ cm}}{1\text{ in.}}$. That is,

$$\textit{Circumference}\text{ (cm)} = 2.54\pi \cdot \textit{Diameter}\text{ (in.)}$$

$$\textit{Circumference}\text{ (in.)} = \frac{1}{2.54}\pi \cdot \textit{Diameter}\text{ (cm)}$$

However, because Fathom has built-in unit conversion, the equation for the line of fit will appear not to change, although the graphical slope of the line does. The following graph shows that the physical slope of the points increases to about 8 when *Diameter* is measured in inches. But, because Fathom does unit conversions, the values of the attribute *CircDiam* are still about 3.14 and the equation of the line of fit still shows a coefficient of 3.14.

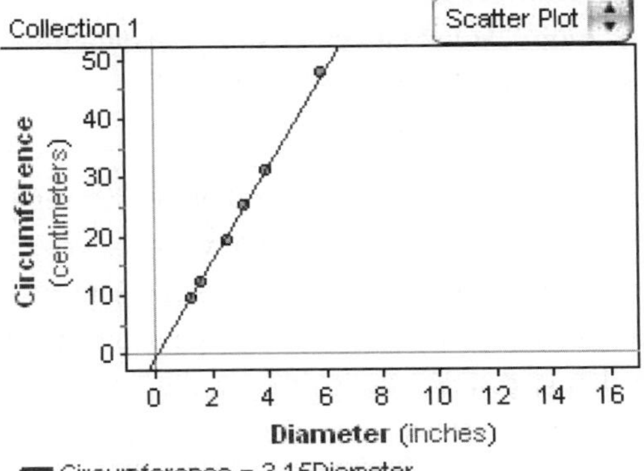

Collection 1

	Diameter	Circumference	CircDiam
units	inches	centimeters	
1	1.6 in	12.4 cm	3.1
2	3.1 in	25.2 cm	3.15
3	2.6 in	19.5 cm	3
4	3.9 in	31.4 cm	3.14
5	1.3 in	9.6 cm	3
6	5.9 in	48.0 cm	3.2

Some students might be confused why the graph shows a slope of about 8, yet the equation shows a slope of about 3.14. It's because the graph is dependent on the units used on the axes, while the equation shows a relationship between two distances that should have equal units. In other words, the equation shows that the relationship between circumference and diameter is always π, regardless of what units you use to measure.

2. Because students waste some amount of string while tying the knot, the relationship will not be the direct variation $Length = \pi \cdot Diameter$. If each knot requires 2 cm of string, then the relationship will be $Length - 2 = \pi \cdot Diameter$, or $Length = \pi \cdot Diameter + 2$. So, when students make a scatter plot and fit a line, the line will still have slope π, but will now have an intercept that represents the amount of string wasted by the knot. Because the relationship is not a direct variation, calculating the ratio *CircDiam* is meaningless in this scenario.

AREA AND PERIMETER (PAGE 29)

Activity Time: 40–55 minutes

Fathom Prerequisites: Students should be able to

- Create a collection by entering data into a case table
- Define attributes with formulas
- Make two-variable graphs (scatter plots)

Fathom Skills: Students will learn how to

- Add cases to a case table without adding data
- Use random numbers to simulate data
- Rerandomize data
- Make one-variable graphs (dot plots, histograms)
- Plot functions
- Create a slider and use its value as a parameter

Mathematics Prerequisites: Students should be able to calculate the area and perimeter of a rectangle; make a scatter plot of points; and graph linear and nonlinear functions.

Mathematics Skills: Students will learn how to simulate an experiment using technology; describe the distribution of one-variable data; fit curves (specifically, a parabola) to data; use algebra to mathematically explain a geometric situation; and see boundaries (limits) from a graph.

General Notes: In this activity, students simulate random rectangles and look for relationships between length, width, area, and perimeter. The activity takes students significantly deeper than the customary formulas $A = lw$ and $P = 2(l + w)$. It exposes students to statistics, algebraic modeling, and limits, and shows how these diverse areas of mathematics can be used to support each other. The activity also touches on the concept of optimization—How do you maximize area without maximizing perimeter?—which has many real-world applications, such as packaging design and manufacturing. That is, it illuminates the geometric concept that a square maximizes area for any perimeter.

As presented on the student worksheet, students use random numbers to simulate creating random rectangles. Before jumping into the Fathom activity, you may prefer to have students draw rectangles by hand, cut them out, and measure the lengths and widths. A quick way to do this is to give each student a piece of 8.5-by-11-inch paper and ask them to make three straight cuts to form three random rectangles. If you make a lot of rectangles as a class (say, 100 or more), you could enter your real data into Fathom and analyze the data in addition to or as a replacement for the computer simulation.

When students make the scatter plot of *Area* versus *Perimeter* in step 9, make sure that they understand what the position of each point represents in terms of a physical rectangle. Ask questions such as "What do rectangles in the lower-left look like?" (small in both dimensions) or "What do rectangles in the lower-right look like?" (long and skinny). Although the student worksheet eventually asks, "What type of rectangles are [along the curved boundary]?," it is worth asking this at step 9 as well, to make sure that students see them as squares.

A challenging discussion question is "Why do you suppose so many of the points are close to the curved boundary?" Large-area rectangles must be close to being squares; otherwise, they'd have a dimension larger than 10. For smaller-area rectangles, you can have a surprisingly large length-to-width ratio before the rectangle moves a long way from the border. Statistically speaking, you should get more squarish rectangles because the distribution of the quotient of two uniform random variables, larger to smaller, is greatly skewed toward 1. In this case, that means the majority of values for *Length* ÷ *Width* will be close to 1; so, the majority of rectangles will have about the same length as width, or be close to a square.

Although the context of this activity is geometric, it is also an excellent activity for algebra, probability, and statistics. Algebra and Precalculus students can practice creating scatter plots, fitting linear and quadratic functions, identifying limits, and algebraically proving why a particular function fits a set of data. Statistics students can practice using random numbers, performing simulations, comparing experimental versus theoretical probability, generating frequency distributions, and describing (and justifying) the shape and spread of distributions.

EXPERIMENT

Q1 The formula *random*(10) creates random numbers between 0 and 10; *random*(100) would create random numbers between 0 and 100; *random*( ) would create random numbers between 0 and 1. In general, the function *random* creates a random number between 0 and 1, which is then multiplied by the number in parentheses.

Q2 Technically these distributions are called *rectangular*. Because each random number between 0 and 10 has the same probability, stacks or bins of about the same height are created. (*Note:* Rather than making two separate graphs, students familiar with Fathom's ability to put multiple attributes on one axis might combine the dot plots or histograms, as shown in the third graph.)

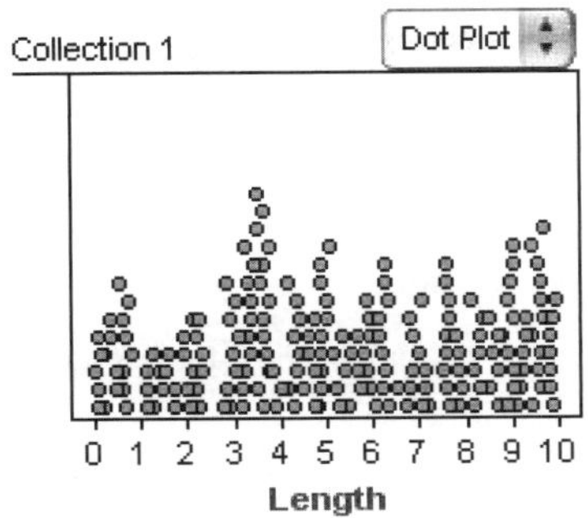

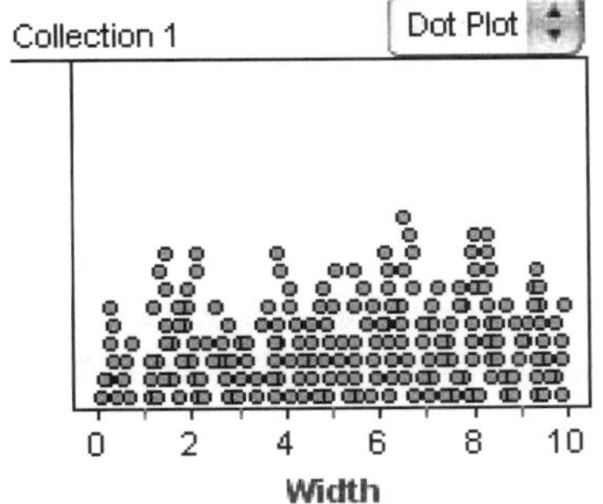

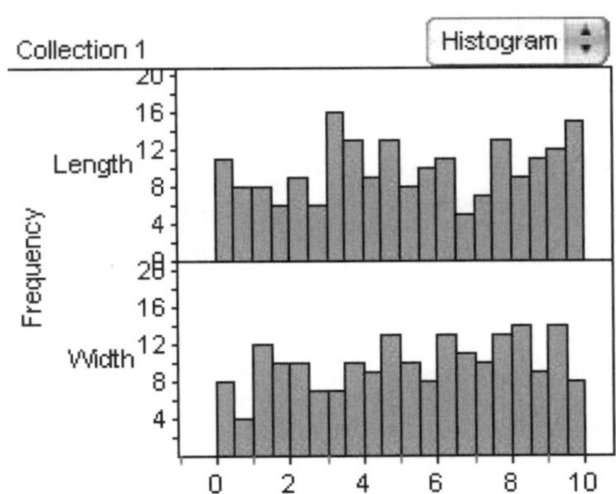

Q3 Students should somehow mention that the scatter plot is a random arrangement of points between (0, 0) and (10, 10).

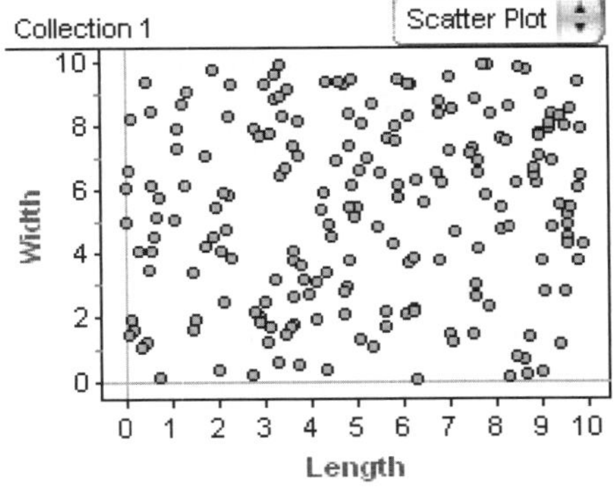

Q4 Students should use the formulas from the introduction to the worksheet: $Area = Length \cdot Width$ and $Perimeter = 2(Length + Width)$. Students should verify the formulas by showing hand calculations. For the first case in the table below, $9.42286 \cdot 5.50248 = 51.8491$ and $2(9.42286 + 5.50248) = 29.8507$.

	Length	Width	Area	Perimeter
1	9.42286	5.50248	51.8491	29.8507

MAKE A CONJECTURE

Q5 Answers will vary.

INVESTIGATE

Q6 The actual scatter plot has a curved upper boundary and a linear lower boundary, as shown on the next page. This probably is not what students expected, especially after having seen *Width* versus *Length,* which had no discernible shape. Students will probably be surprised to see that the points form such clear boundaries. Even seasoned geometry students who know that squares maximize area and who might expect the parabolic curve may be surprised by the linear lower boundary.

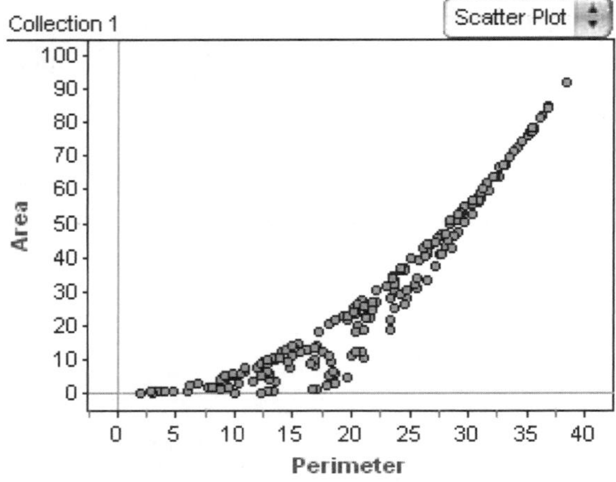

Q7 There are several ways to explain why there are no points in the upper-left region. An intuitive approach is to say that such a rectangle would have a big area and a small perimeter, which is impossible. For a given perimeter there's only so much area you can enclose (and some students may already know that a square maximizes area). For example, with a perimeter of 20 units, the most area you can enclose is a 5-by-5 square, or 25 square units. Therefore, the region above that limit is empty. Or, for a given area there's a minimum perimeter that encloses it. For example, with an area of 25 square units, 20 units is the smallest perimeter possible.

Q8 If students try a number between 0 and 1, the curve will get steeper, so they need to try larger numbers. If students try a number between 1 and 15, the curve will get shallower, but they'll still need to try a larger number. A few students might try 16, which will fit perfectly. If students try numbers greater than 16, they'll overshoot the boundary and will need to try smaller numbers. Students probably won't think to try negative numbers, but if they do, the graph will be reflected across the horizontal axis.

Q9 $V1 = 16$ makes a perfect fit.

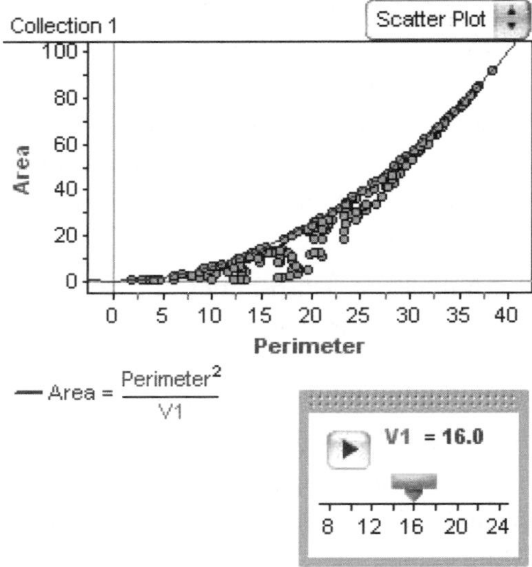

Q10 The rectangles near the boundary have (approximately) the same length and width, which means they are squares or almost squares. Squares form the upper boundary because squares maximize area for any given perimeter.

Note: You'll probably want to discuss how Q10 is directly related to Q7.

Q11 The area of a square is $Area = Length^2$. The perimeter of a square is $Perimeter = 4 \cdot Length$, or $Length = \frac{Perimeter}{4}$. Substituting for *Length* gives $Area = \left(\frac{Perimeter}{4}\right)^2$, or $Area = \frac{Perimeter^2}{16}$.

EXPLORE MORE

1. The empty region below the points exists because the maximum values of *Length* and *Width* limit the sizes of the rectangles. For example, if *Perimeter* were 30 units, then *Area* could not be 0 square units because then either *Length* or *Width* would have to be 15 units, yet the maximum for either is 10 units. This means there is a minimum area for any given perimeter. To minimize *Area* for a given *Perimeter,* two of the sides (say, *Length*) have to be as long as possible, 10 units each and 20 units combined, and the other two sides (say, *Width*) have to be as short as possible, or $Width = \frac{Perimeter - 20}{2}$. Then the

minimum area is *Area* = *Length* • *Width* = 10 • $\frac{Perimeter - 20}{2}$ = 5 • *Perimeter* − 100. Students could also find this linear equation by using a movable line:

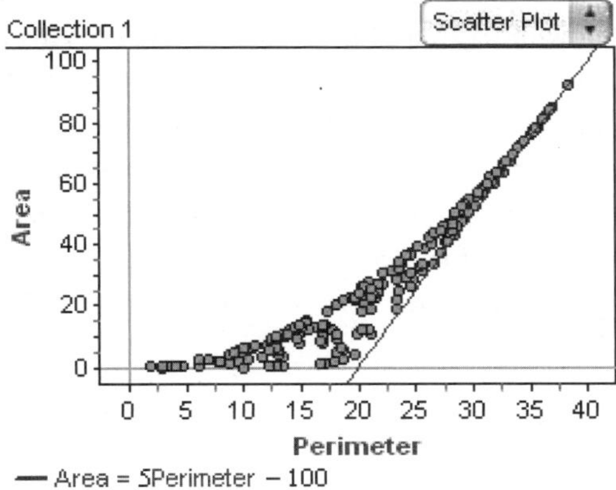

2. *Area* versus *Length* has one linear upper boundary: *Area* = 10 • *Length*. This maximum occurs when *Width* is as large as possible, or 10 units.

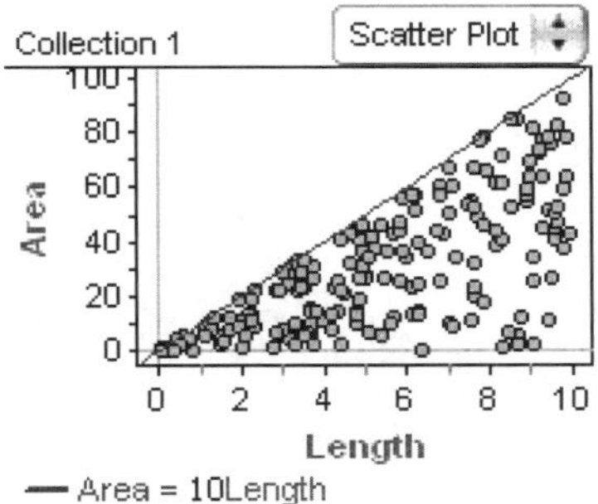

Perimeter versus *Length* has a linear upper boundary and a linear lower boundary: *Perimeter* = 2 • *Length* + 20 and *Perimeter* = 2 • *Length*. The maximum again occurs when *Width* is as large as possible, or 10 units. The minimum occurs when *Width* is as small as possible and can still make a rectangle, or very close to 0 units.

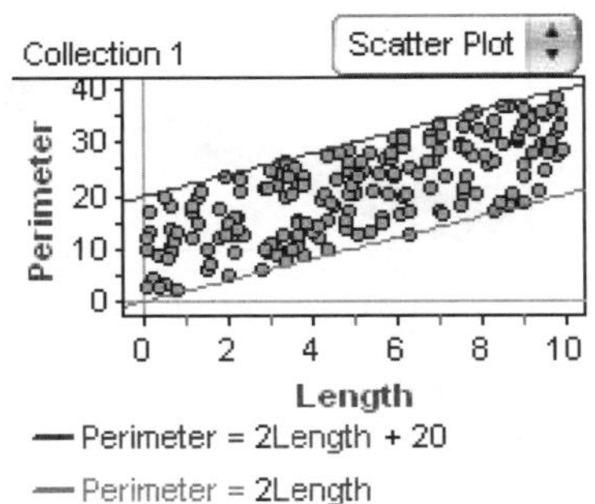

EXTENSIONS

1. Have students look at histograms of *Area* and *Perimeter*, describe the shape of these graphs, and explain why these shapes make sense. This is a particularly good extension for Statistics students.

   The graph of *Area* is skewed right, which means that smaller areas are more likely than larger areas. This makes sense because area is a product, and to get a large product you need two large factors; but because the length and width are randomly generated, it is less likely to get two large numbers paired together. As a simple example, imagine that length and width could each be 1 or 10. Then 1 • 1 = 1 (small), 1 • 10 = 10 (small), 10 • 1 = 10 (small), and 10 • 10 = 100 (large).

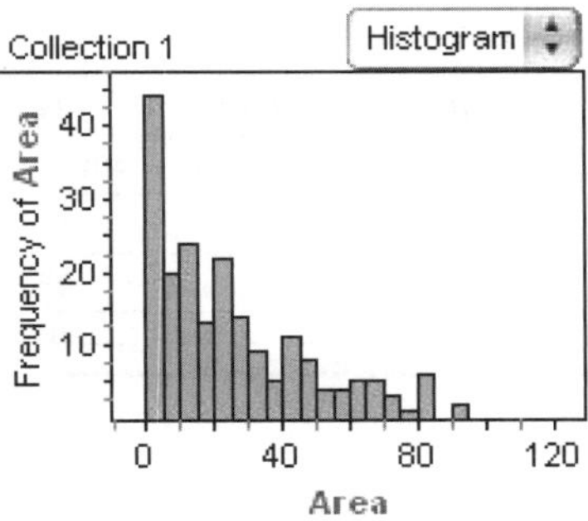

   The graph of *Perimeter* is triangular, which means that perimeters in the middle (between 15 and 25 units) are more likely than small or large perimeters. This makes sense because perimeter is a sum, and to get a small or large sum you need two small or large addends. Imagine the same simple example: 2(1 + 1) = 4 (small), 2(1 + 10) = 22 (medium), 2(10 + 1) = 22 (medium), and 2(10 + 10) = 40 (large).

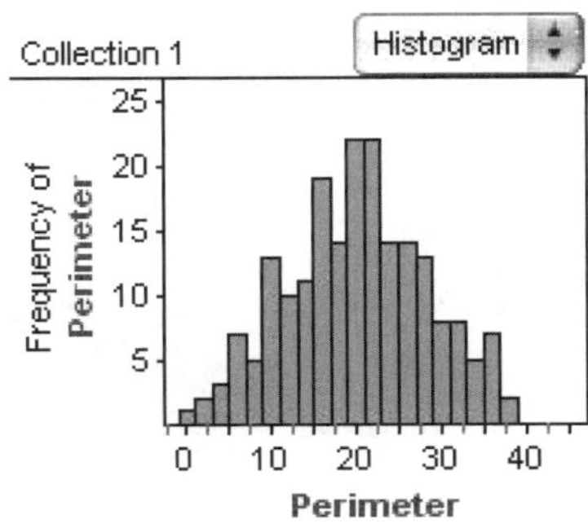

After students have created histograms of *Area* and *Perimeter,* have them select any one bin in either histogram. Have them observe where the points are in the scatter plots of *Length* versus *Width* and *Area* versus *Perimeter.* (If they did Explore More 2, also look at the location of points in *Area* versus *Length* and *Perimeter* versus *Length.*) Ask students to describe the patterns that they see as they gradually select consecutive bins in the histogram. Challenge them to explain why these patterns exist.

2. Have students explore what happens when they change the formulas for *Length* and *Width* to a different random number, say, *random*(5) or *random*(100), or what happens when they are different formulas, say, *Length* = *random*(10) and *Width* = *random*(5). Ask students to first predict how the scatter plot of *Area* versus *Perimeter* and its boundaries would change, then actually try it in Fathom. Challenge students to generalize the results to describe what happens for *Length* = *random*(*L*) and *Width* = *random*(*W*). This is a particularly good extension for Algebra students, because it involves generalizing functions for different parameters (see below).

Area and Perimeter, Extension 2

Collection 1

	Length	Width	Area	Perimeter
=	random (L)	random (W)	Length•Width	2(Length + Width)
1	19.7112	6.27622	123.712	51.9748
2	45.0115	1.90632	85.8064	93.8356
3	[illegible]	[illegible]	[illegible]	[illegible]

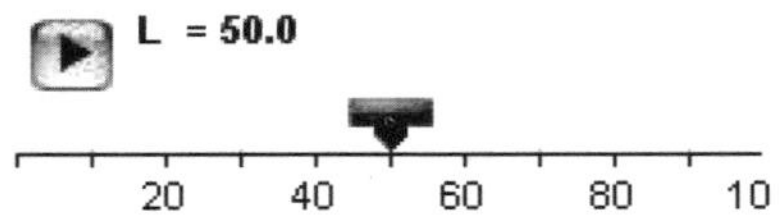

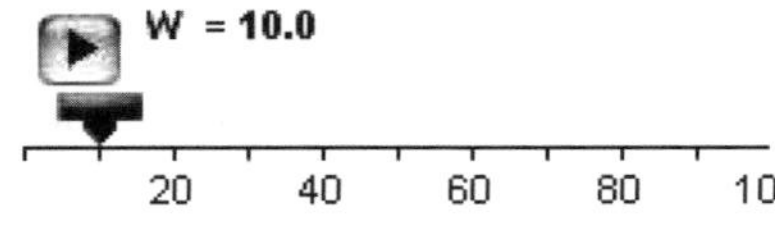

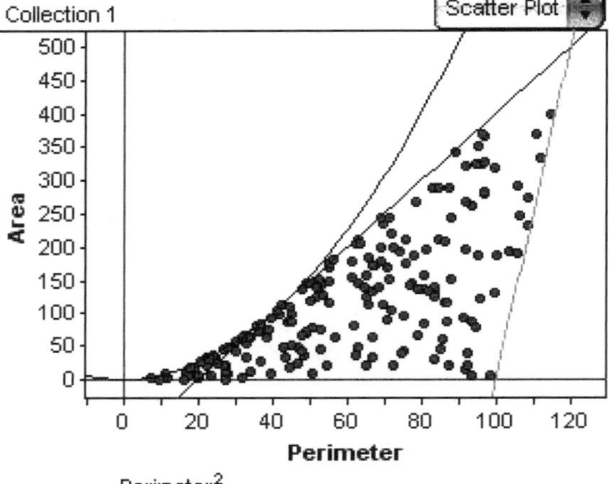

— $\text{Area} = \dfrac{\text{Perimeter}^2}{16}$

— $\text{Area} = \dfrac{\text{if}\ (L > W)\begin{cases}W\\L\end{cases}}{2}\ \text{Perimeter} - \text{if}\ (L > W)\begin{cases}W^2\\L\end{cases}$

— $\text{Area} = \dfrac{\text{if}\ (L > W)\begin{cases}L\\W\end{cases}}{2}\ \text{Perimeter} - \text{if}\ (L > W)\begin{cases}L^2\\W\end{cases}$

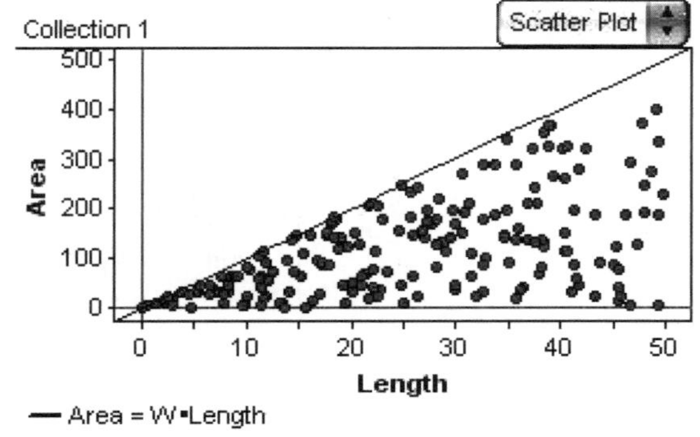

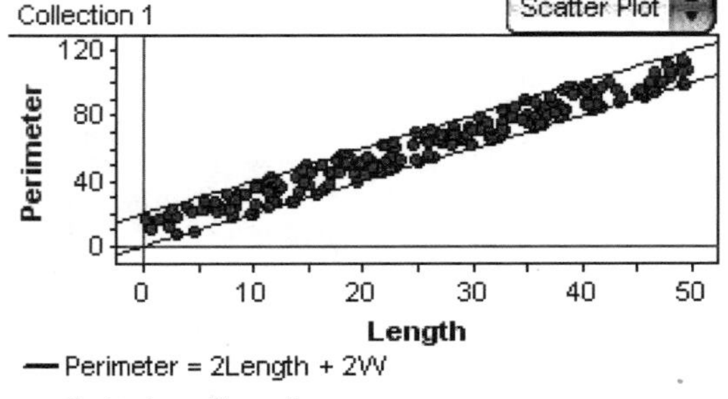

If $Length = random(L)$ and $Width = random(W)$, the results are similar to the results throughout this activity, except that many of the boundary functions are scaled accordingly. For the graph of *Area* versus *Perimeter*, part of the upper boundary is always $Area = \frac{Perimeter^2}{16}$ (and this is the only upper boundary if $L = W$). But if $L \neq W$, a second upper boundary comes into play: $Area = \left(\frac{\text{lesser of } L \text{ or } W}{2}\right) \cdot Perimeter - (\text{lesser of } L \text{ or } W)^2$. The lower boundary of *Area* versus *Perimeter* always depends on the greater of L or W:

$$Area = \frac{\text{greater of } L \text{ or } W}{2} \cdot Perimeter - (\text{greater of } L \text{ or } W)^2$$

Students might also notice that the upper boundary of the scatter plot of *Area* versus *Length* is always $Area = W \cdot Length$. For *Perimeter* versus *Length*, the boundaries are always $Perimeter = 2Length + 2W$ and $Perimeter = 2Length$.

Students can create sliders for L and W and confirm that their boundaries always work.

3. Statistics students can explore sample size by adding and deleting cases to see how the histograms and scatter plots compare for 10, 20, 50, 100, 200, 500, and 1000 cases. At what sample size can they begin to discern important patterns in the data? Are there pros and cons to using larger sample sizes? Students will probably find that they need at least 50 or 100 cases before they can describe patterns in the data. Even more cases, 500 or 1000, help "fill in" the patterns in the scatter plots, but don't help them see the pattern any better than smaller numbers.
4. For fun, show students how they can use the collection as a geometric representation of the rectangles. Drag the bottom corner of the collection to expand it. You'll see a gold ball for each rectangle. Double-click the collection to show the inspector and use the settings shown at right on the **Display** panel. The gold balls will change to rectangles.

If you asked the question "Why do you suppose so many of the points are close to the curved boundary?," students can now see that many of the rectangles are indeed close to being squares.

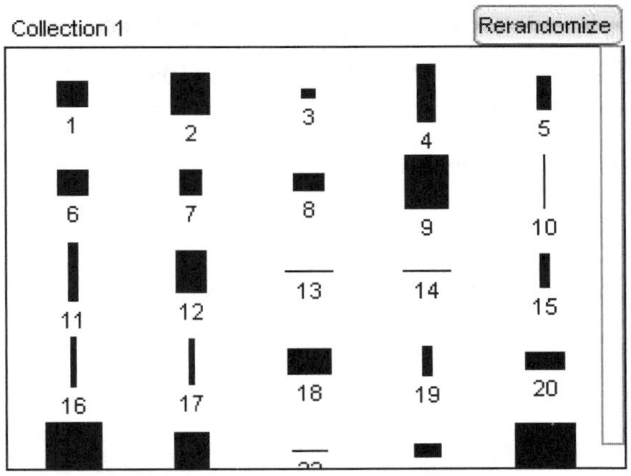

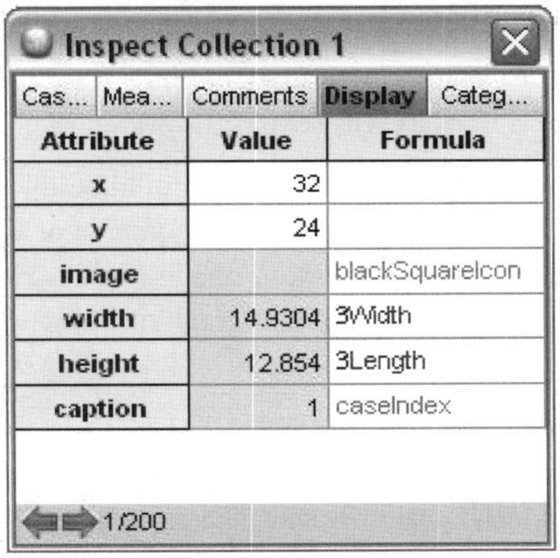

Collection 1 | Rerandomize

Inspect Collection 1

Cas... | Mea... | Comments | **Display** | Categ...

Attribute	Value	Formula
x	32	
y	24	
image		blackSquareIcon
width	14.9304	3Width
height	12.854	3Length
caption	1	caseIndex

1/200

MAUNA LOA (PAGE 35)

Activity Time: 45–55 minutes

Required Document: MaunaLoa2003.ftm

Optional Documents: GlobalCarbon2000.ftm and **RegionCarbon2000.ftm** contain additional data that can be used with the Extension.

Fathom Prerequisites: Students should be able to

- Open a document

Fathom Skills: Students will learn how to

- Work with case tables
- Define an attribute with a formula
- Create graphs (scatter plots)
- Graph lines of fit
- *Optional:* Create a summary table and create a collection from its cells (Explore More 2)

Mathematics Prerequisites: Students should be able to make a scatter plot of points, write the equation of a line in slope-intercept form, use the slope of a line to describe rate of change, and use the equation or graph of a function to extrapolate values.

Mathematics Skills: Students will learn how to recognize patterns in a scatter plot of points, fit lines (and possibly curves) to model data, informally determine how well a function model fits a graph of data, and identify periodic behavior.

General Notes: In this activity, students focus on time series data and look at repeated measurements of atmospheric carbon dioxide (CO_2) over time. They'll look at trends in the data, namely that the concentration of CO_2 in the Earth's atmosphere is increasing. Although students have probably heard about the effects of global warming, in day-to-day life they may not be aware of atmospheric changes and could be skeptical of global-warming claims. This activity uses famous CO_2 measurements taken near the summit of Mauna Loa on the island of Hawai'i—the longest and best series of such data in the world. When students graph the Mauna Loa data, the increase in CO_2 is alarmingly obvious and concerns about global warming are more tangible.

You might begin with a brief discussion about global warming. Have students explain the basics of the problem: that greenhouse gases such as carbon dioxide (CO_2) and methane (CH_4) occur naturally in the atmosphere, but scientists believe that the concentrations are increasing as a result of human activity. It is further believed that this increase will cause global climate change as these gases trap infrared radiation (heat) inside the atmosphere. Ask, "If we are skeptical, what would we have to know to be convinced that this is true?" Briefly make a list of things students would want to know. Some connections are difficult to prove, of course, but there are also very simple questions: "Do we really emit a lot of CO_2?" and "Are the concentrations of these gases really increasing?" The latter question is the focus of this activity. The idea of human emissions can be one direction of research for the Extension.

While there are "official" techniques and representations commonly used in time-series data analysis, such as Fourier series and control charts, this activity uses an informal exploration. It is assumed that all Algebra 2 students are familiar with using linear equations to model real-world data. They have probably used informal methods (drawing a line that seems to fit) since middle school and may have already learned formal methods (median-median lines or least-squares lines). But students may have had experience only with "textbook" data that look almost perfectly linear when graphed. The data in this activity may surprise many students. While the general pattern is almost linear, it does have a slight curvature. And if you look closely at the seasonal changes between months, you'll notice a periodic wave in the data. (*Note:* In step 8, you should give your students explicit instructions about which lines of fit to use, depending on which lines of fit you have studied in class. If you have not studied any lines of fit, you may want to use step 8 as an opportunity to explore all three and discuss pros, cons, similarities, and differences.)

If you have used other activities in this book, you may notice that the document **MaunaLoa2003.ftm** does not use units. Even though Fathom does recognize the unit parts per million (ppm), units have been omitted here to make it easier to do Explore More 1. If ppm were used for the CO_2 concentrations, creating nonlinear functions would become complicated because you would have to include units in the function equations.

The conclusion of this activity—the last two questions, the Explore More ideas, and the Extension—is purposefully left open-ended. This gives all students an opportunity to problem-solve with data, deciding which data and graphs will help them answer different questions. It also makes the activity appropriate for Precalculus or Statistics students, allowing them to go beyond linear models and apply exponential functions, polynomial functions, trigonometric functions, or advanced methods of regression analysis. (See Explore More 1 for ideas about using nonlinear functions.)

MAKE A CONJECTURE

Q1 Students are probably aware that the amount of CO_2 in our atmosphere is increasing.

Q2 Some students might predict that the increase is linear. Others might predict a curve, such as an exponential function or a quadratic function.

INVESTIGATE

Q3 326.93 ppm. You find this from Mauna Loa, Continuous by scrolling down to find the value of attribute *CarbonDioxide* for *Year* 1970 and *Month* 3 (case number 147). You find this from Mauna Loa, By Month by finding the value of attribute *March* for *Year* 1970 (case number 13).

Q4 From looking at the case table for Mauna Loa, Continuous, students might have trouble noticing a pattern because the continuous values fluctuate. From the case table for Mauna Loa, By Month, students can clearly see that the concentrations steadily increase for any one month, but that they fluctuate for any one year.

Q5 Although the graph forms a wide band of points, the general pattern is increasing.

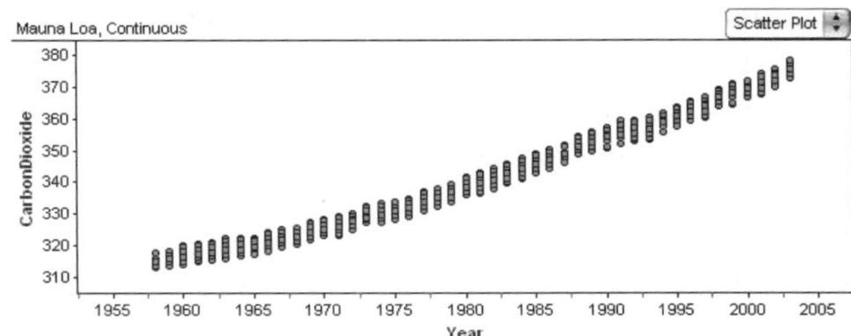

Q6 Students can use a variety of formulas for *YearAndMonth*. The simplest is $Year + \frac{Month}{12}$. Although this formula technically rounds December up to the next calendar year (for example, $1958 + \frac{12}{12} = 1959$), it is close enough for this informal analysis. You may want to ask students to share the different formulas that they used and to discuss the pros and cons of each.

Q7 Again, the general pattern is increasing. Students will likely mention the "wave" pattern formed by the data, which represents seasonal fluctuations in the CO_2 concentration.

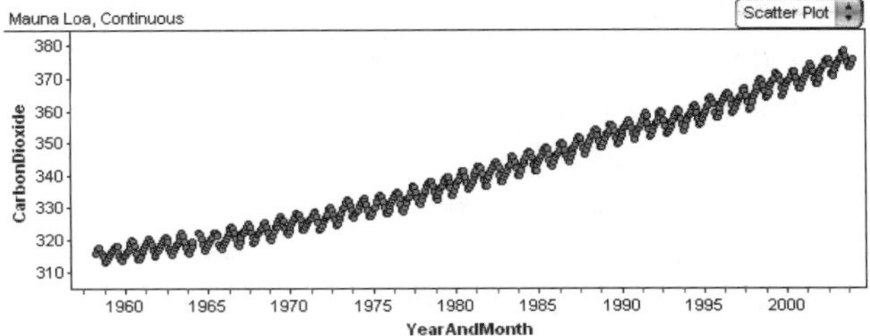

Q8 Some students may not be able to see beyond the periodic nature of the data and will describe the shape as a "wave"; some of those students may describe the shape as "periodic" or "sinusoidal." Other students may look beyond the periodic nature and focus on the overall shape; they might describe the shape as "linear" or "slightly curved." In general, the shape is probably more complex than what students predicted in Q2.

Q9 Students will probably say that the line does not fit well. The median-median line shown in the next graph fits well in the middle portion of the graph, but the data on either end are a little too far above the line. This implies that a curve, such as an exponential function or a polynomial function, might be a better fit for the general pattern. Again, some students may not be able to see past the periodic nature, so they might recommend a trigonometric function of some sort.

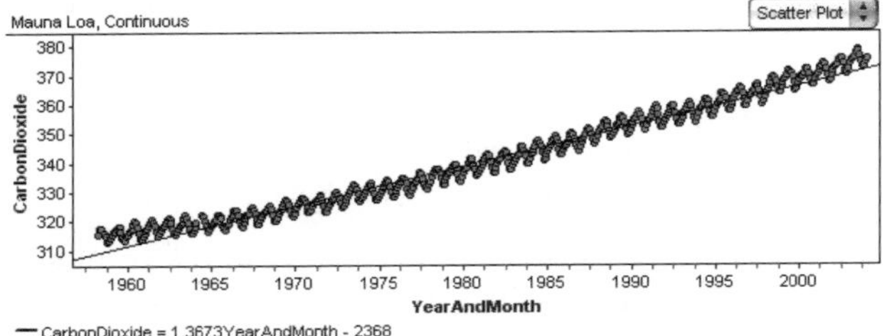

Q10 The graph above shows an increase of about 1.37 ppm per year. (*Note:* The units are per year, not month, because *YearAndMonth* is a decimal part of a year.) Students' answers may vary anywhere from 1.0 to 1.5, especially if they use a movable line.

Q11 Techniques (and the current year) will vary. One technique is to trace the median-median line or least-squares line from the graph in step 8. This technique requires that students pick one value from any fractional part of the year; students might pick the beginning of the year (2005.0), the very middle (2005.5), or the end (2006). Another technique is to use Mauna Loa, By Month and create a new attribute that calculates the average concentration for each year, then make a scatter plot of the averages over time, fit a line, and extrapolate the average concentration for the current year. (Technically, this method is slightly flawed because the monthly concentrations themselves are averages of continuous readings. Mathematically speaking, the average of several averages is an invalid statistic.)

Q12 Techniques (and birthdays) will vary. One technique is to trace the line of fit for all of the data. In order to do this accurately, students will need to calculate their birth month (or, more accurately, birth day) as a decimal part of a year, trace to that point on the line, and then estimate the amount of fluctuation above or below the line for that month (or day). Another technique is to use Mauna Loa, By Month and use a scatter plot of only the student's birth month. This technique is a nice way to determine the average CO_2 concentration for any given month, but it does not lend itself to predicting any particular day.

EXPLORE MORE

1. This question extends the activity into nonlinear models, specifically exponential, polynomial, or trigonometric. By combining the general curvature of the data and the periodic seasonal fluctuation, students could even be challenged to write and graph the sum of two functions. Fathom does not calculate nonlinear models, so students will need to use trial and error or transform the data by creating new attributes.

   By trial and error, students may find that a quadratic function best fits the general curvature of the data. Sliders can be used for the parameters to narrow in on an equation similar to $CarbonDioxide = 0.011544(YearAndMonth)^2 - 44.366\,YearAndMonth + 42{,}925$. Then, looking at the amplitude, period, and phase shift of the wave, and using sliders, students may be able to append the function with $+\ 3.4\sin(2\pi YearAndMonth - 0.5)$.

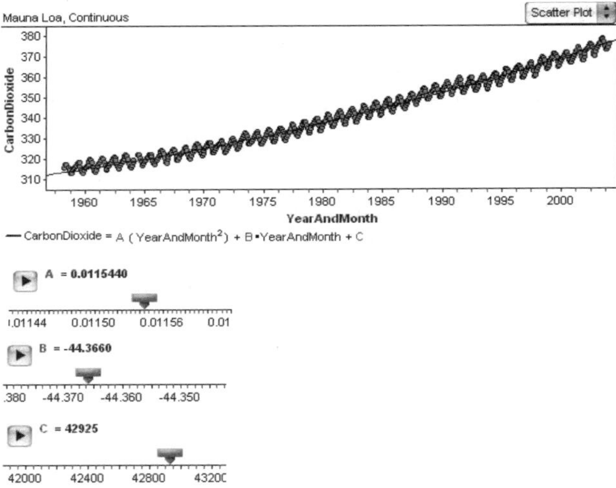

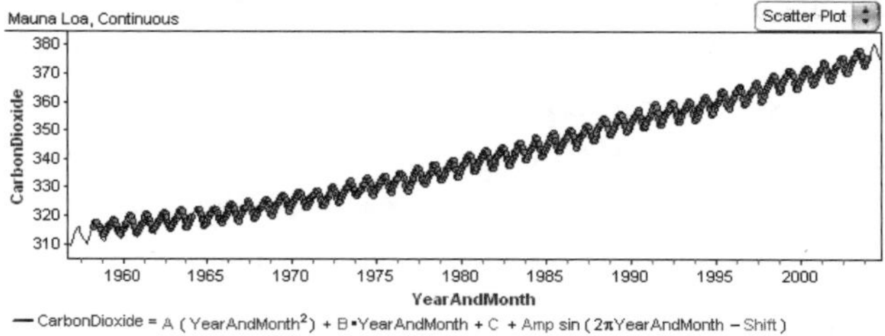

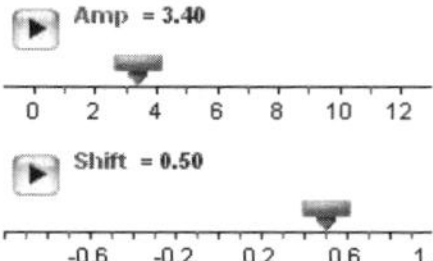

2. This might be a good time to reinforce (or introduce) terminology related to periodic behavior: *maximum* (crest), *minimum* (trough), *amplitude, period,* and so on. With very few exceptions, the maximum crests occur in May and the minimum troughs occur in September or October.

An interesting way to analyze the range of fluctuations is to create a summary table for Mauna Loa, Continuous that calculates the range of carbon dioxide concentrations for each year. You can then create a collection from the cells in the summary table (see Fathom Help: Create a Collection from the Cells of a Summary Table) and make a graph of the ranges over time. There is a great amount of variation in the ranges, but there is a slight, overall increasing pattern.

Mauna Loa, Continuous

1958	4.31
1959	4.95
1960	6.2
1961	5.59
1962	5.59
1963	6.25
1964	5.53
1965	4.86
1966	5.97
1967	5.74
1968	5.32
Column Summary	65.16

S1 = max(CarbonDioxide) – min(CarbonDioxide)

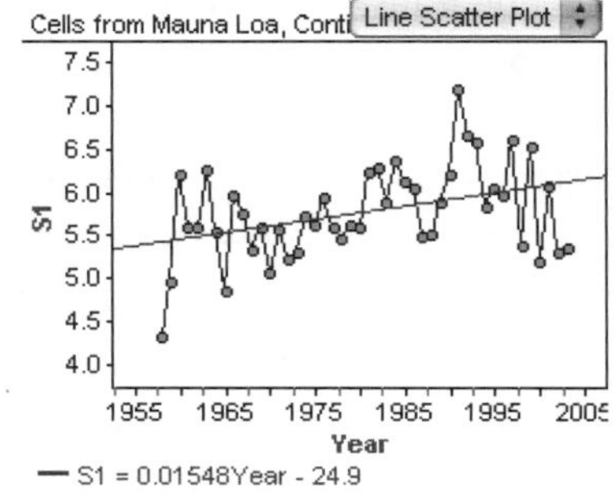

EXTENSION

Have students do additional research on carbon dioxide, other greenhouse gases, and global warming. Their research might take them in a variety of directions. Some students might want to do an essay or a paper on exactly what global warming is, why it is a concern, and what scientists and environmental agencies are doing to counteract it. Others might research scientists' current analysis of greenhouse gases and global warming and describe how their Fathom analysis of the Mauna Loa data is consistent with formal studies. Still others might find additional data on CO_2 (such as the amount of CO_2 that human activity contributes to the environment), analyze it, and explain how it fits with the Mauna Loa data. Or students might find data on other greenhouses gases, such as methane (CH_4). A good place to begin researching is the Carbon Dioxide Information Analysis Center (CDIAC), which you can find on the Internet at cdiac.esd.ornl.gov.

GlobalCarbon2000.ftm and **RegionCarbon2000.ftm** contain additional data gathered from the CDIAC Web site. These documents give carbon dioxide emissions—the amount humans put into the atmosphere, as opposed to the amount that is naturally part of the environment—from various sources around the world. Each file gives the total emissions in million metric tons of carbon and breaks down the total into component parts: *Gas* (e.g., natural gas), *Liquid* (e.g., petroleum), *Solid* (e.g., coal), *Cement* (carbon dioxide from cement production), and *Flaring* (the burning of gas at refineries and drilling sites). The documents also give *PerCapita* carbon dioxide production in metric tons per person per year. **GlobalCarbon2000.ftm** gives measurements for the whole world, while **RegionCarbon2000.ftm** breaks down the emissions by geographic regions.

FUNCTION TRANSFORMATIONS (PAGE 38)

Activity Time: 50–100 minutes

Required Document: FunctionTransformations.ftm

Optional Document: FuncTransformPRE.ftm

Fathom Prerequisites: Students should be able to

- Create attributes defined by formulas
- Make a scatter plot of two attributes

Fathom Skills: Students will learn how to

- Create sliders
- Plot functions
- Duplicate graphs
- Link graphs' axes

Mathematics Prerequisites: Students should be able to graph linear, quadratic, absolute value, exponential, square root, and inverse-variation functions; and identify the general shapes of linear, quadratic, absolute value, exponential, square root, and inverse-variation functions. (*Note:* If students know only a few of these functions, you can modify the activity so that they work only with the functions they know.)

Mathematics Skills: Students will learn how to transform data, transform functions, identify the transformation that results from different function parameters, and determine the function that fits data based on transformations.

General Notes: This activity is different from most Fathom activities. Instead of analyzing real-world data that have reasonable amounts of variability, this activity uses data generated by functions. This allows you to use Fathom as a tool for algebraic manipulation.

In this activity, students will transform a set of quadratic data (and possibly data generated by other functions) and see how the equation of the curve that fits the data changes. Students will learn how the parameters h and k (translations) and a and b (dilations) affect the graph of a function. This gives students in-depth experience with multiple representations of function: table, graph, and algebraic equation.

If you did the activity Slope-Intercept Form on pages 11–14, the format of this activity will be familiar. Or, if you make extensive use of graphing calculators in your algebra class, the structure of this activity may also seem familiar. Transforming the data by creating new attributes is very similar to creating lists on a graphing calculator.

Be aware that there is a subtle distinction between transforming data and transforming a function that might confuse some students. For example, consider that you have data in the form (x, y) from the parabola $y = x^2$. When you transform the data into the form $(x, y + 2)$ by translating each point 2 units up, the parabola that fits is now $y = x^2 + 2$. Some students may be puzzled because you add to the y-coordinate, yet the equation compensates by adding to the x-side of the equation. One explanation is that the equation must maintain the same equality as before the data were transformed, or $y = x^2$. So, if you add to the y-coordinate, the equation must add the same amount from the x-side—substituting $(x, y + 2)$ into $y = x^2 + 2$ gives $y + 2 = x^2 + 2$, or $y = x^2$. Another explanation is that the equation must undo the transformation in order to be consistent with the original data. For this explanation, rewrite the transformed equation as $y - 2 = x^2$; when you substitute $(x, y + 2)$, you get $y + 2 - 2 = x^2$, or $y = x^2$. The latter explanation is sounder because it helps explain a wider array of function transformations. In general, it explains why data in the form (x, y) from the function $y = f(x)$ can be transformed into $(x + h, y + k)$ and the function $y - k = f(x - h)$.

This activity encourages students to explore several function transformations (translations, reflections, and dilations) and several different functions (linear, quadratic, absolute value, exponential, square root, and inverse variation). To do all of the possible combinations will take seasoned Fathom users a long time; it will take novice Fathom users even longer to become comfortable with making attributes, sliders, and graphs. Hence, you should plan at least two days to complete the entire activity. One option is to have students explore one transformation for all functions on each day. That is, explore translations for all functions, and then explore dilations for all functions. If you want to do reflections or rotations, you can squeeze them in during the second day or use a third day of exploration. (The worksheet is already organized by different transformations to help you follow this option.) Another option is to explore all transformations for one function on each day. That is, explore translations and dilations (and possibly reflections and rotations) for just quadratic functions; then explore all transformations for just absolute value functions; and so on. This option is particularly useful if your students haven't learned about all of the different functions yet. You could even revisit the activity throughout the school year as you introduce each new function.

Part of the goal of this activity is to teach students how to use several of Fathom's features, such as sliders and duplicate graphs. If your students are already familiar with Fathom, or you want to save the time necessary to teach the software to novice students, you may prefer to use **FuncTransformPRE.ftm.** This "pre-made" document has the sliders and graphs prepared for you and your students. That way, students can complete the worksheet by answering only the questions beginning with Q1.

Understanding function transformations is frequently taught in Algebra 2, but a few curricula teach them or review them in Precalculus; and a few curricula introduce function transformations in Algebra 1. Therefore, depending on your curriculum, this activity could be successfully used in higher- or lower-level courses.

INVESTIGATE

Q1 Changing h makes the points move left (negative) or right (positive) by that number of units.

Q2 Changing k makes the points move down (negative) or up (positive) by that number of units.

Q3 a. The points will be moved right 3 units and up 5 units.

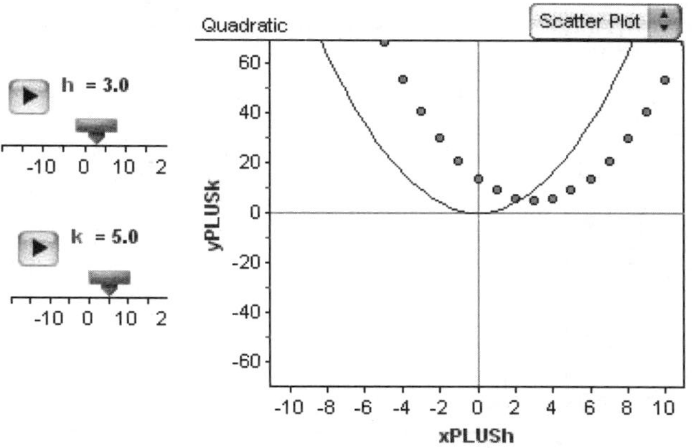

b. The points will be moved left 8 units.

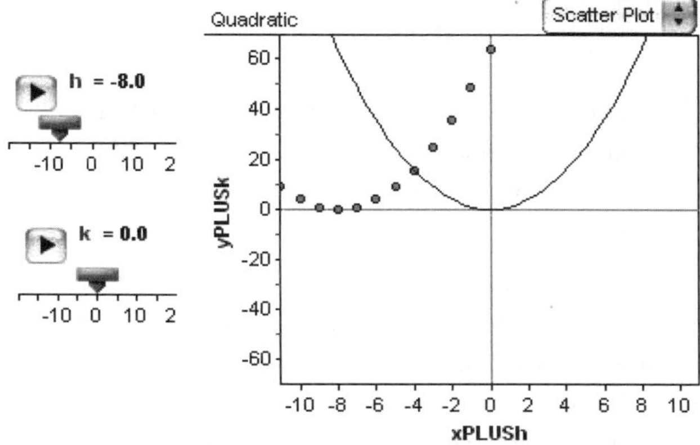

c. The points will be moved right 5 units and down 20 units.

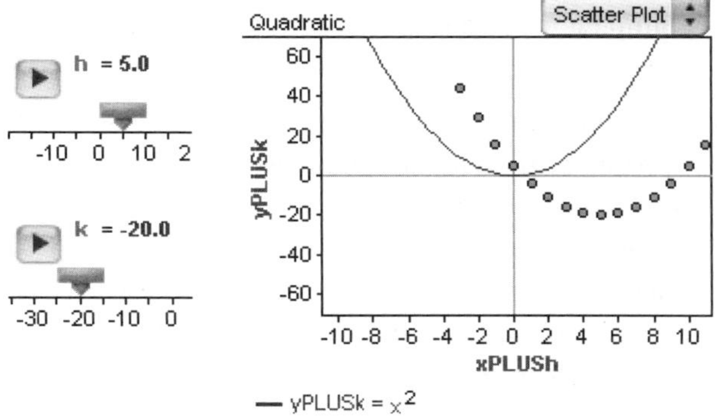

Q4 The coordinates of the vertex are (h, k).

Q5 $yPLUSk = (xPLUSh - h)^2 + k$

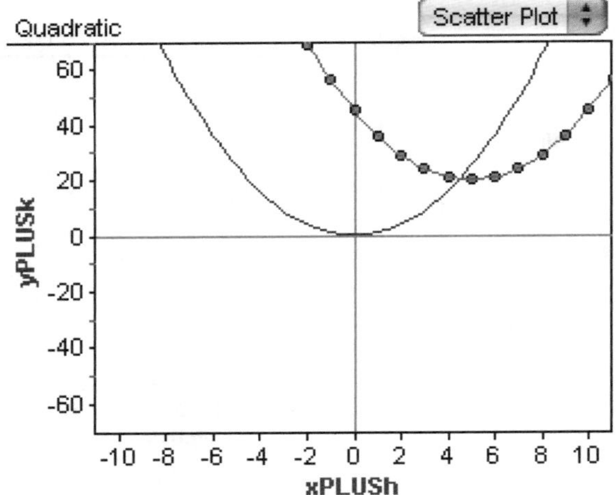

Q6 Students should find that the same translation rules apply to all functions. In general, h and k will transform $y = f(x)$ into $y = f(x - h) + k$, or $y - k = f(x - h)$.

Hint: Ask students to explain what point(s) they consider to be like the vertex of a parabola when answering Q4 for the other functions. For absolute value and square root functions, students may recognize an analogous vertex. However, the other functions require some ingenuity.

Note: To explore the other collections, students need to create case tables for the data in a collection. The simplest method is to select the collection and then drag a case table from the shelf.

Q7 At a minimum, students should mention that a shrinks or stretches the graph horizontally and b shrinks or stretches it vertically. Some students may give more detailed descriptions, describing what happens for values greater than 1, equal to 1, between 0 and 1, equal to 0, between 0 and -1, equal to -1, and less than -1.

Q8 $bTIMESy = b\left(\frac{xTIMESa}{a}\right)^2$

Q9 Answers will vary, but students should find that the same dilation rules apply to all functions. In general, a and b will transform $y = f(x)$ into $y = b \cdot f\left(\frac{x}{a}\right)$, or $\frac{y}{b} = f\left(\frac{x}{a}\right)$.

Q10 When $a = -1$, there is a reflection across the y-axis. When $b = -1$, there is a reflection across the x-axis.

Note: Because both quadratic and absolute value functions have the y-axis as a line of symmetry, suggest that students use other functions when exploring the effect of $a = -1$. They should then be able to explain why the transformation has no effect on those functions.

EXPLORE MORE

1. Students should find that dilations and translations work together the same way they do individually. In general, a, b, h, and k will transform $y = f(x)$ into $y = b \cdot f\left(\frac{x-h}{a}\right) + k$, or $\frac{y-k}{b} = f\left(\frac{x-h}{a}\right)$. The only thing that may challenge some students is realizing that a and b are the quotients for the entire translations.
2. $(-x, -y)$ creates a 180° rotation about the origin; $(-y, x)$ creates a 90° counterclockwise rotation about the origin; and $(y, -x)$ creates a 90° clockwise rotation about the origin. Students may find that rotations are different in at least two ways. First, some rotations require that the coordinates be switched. Second, the rotations that require switching coordinates are not always functions; under translations, dilations, and reflections, the image of a function is always a function.

MOORE'S LAW (PAGE 42)

Activity Time: 45–55 minutes

Required Document: MooresLaw2004.ftm

Fathom Prerequisites: Students should be able to

- Make a scatter plot of two attributes
- Plot functions
- Create sliders
- *Optional:* Create attributes defined by formulas

Fathom Skills: Students will learn how to

- Trace a function to extrapolate
- Make residual plots

Mathematics Prerequisites: Students should be able to graph exponential functions and transform functions.

Mathematics Skills: Students will learn how to fit an exponential function to real-world data by trial and error, interpret doubling time from an exponential function's parameters, and use residuals to judge how well a function fits data.

General Notes: This activity explores data about the exponential growth of the number of transistors that can be placed on a computer's central processing unit. The growth was originally observed by Gordon Moore in an article titled "Cramming More Components onto Integrated Circuits" (*Electronics*, vol. 38, no. 8, April 19, 1965). In his famous article, Moore predicted that the "number of components per integrated function" (frequently interpreted to mean "number of transistors") would double about every year. In subsequent years, Moore himself and others have revised the prediction to be a doubling about every 1.5 to 2 years. This activity gives students an opportunity to find their own function of best fit and either agree or disagree with Moore's prediction.

This activity is intended to closely follow the previous activity, Function Transformations (pages 38–41). Here students use sliders and transformations to adjust an exponential function in the form $f(x) = b \cdot 2^{(x-h)/a} + k$ until it fits the data. If you have not done Function Transformations, you may want to do it first. Otherwise, plan to give more detailed instructions for step 4 of the student worksheet.

In step 4, adjusting the exponential curve with sliders to get the "best" fit is an extremely open-ended and subjective process—there is no right answer. Encourage students to try different combinations of transformations. The process is also complicated by the range and vertical scale of the graph, which makes some points appear to fit the function when they are actually quite removed from it. Therefore, encourage students to zoom in to small portions of the graph, especially the first eight points, to see how well the function really fits. For example, if students try only a horizontal translation, it may look like the function fits eleven of the twelve points well. However, zooming in to the first eight points shows that the curvature isn't quite right. In order to fix the curvature, students need to incorporate dilations as well.

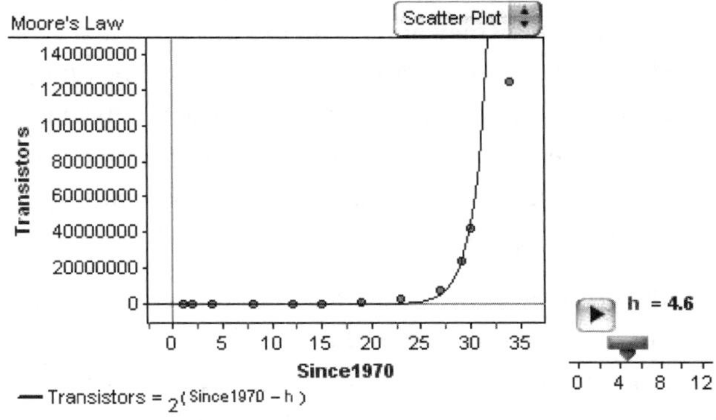

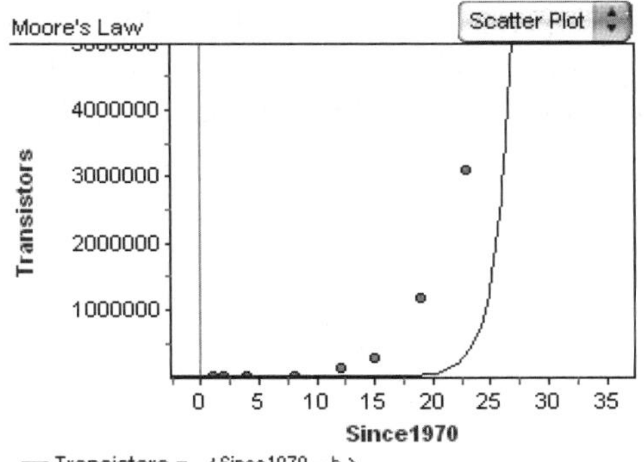

After students find a curve that fits, they need to be able to identify which parameter in the function represents doubling time. Pinpointing the doubling time allows students to compare their model to Moore's original prediction of doubling once every year. If your students have not studied doubling time or half-life, you can guide them toward the correct parameter by asking, "Which variable in the equation represents time?" and "What value of time would you need to get 2^1? 2^2? 2^3?" and "How many years are there between each multiple of 2?"

After finding a function of fit by trial and error with sliders, the activity introduces students to residual plots as a way to judge and refine the fit. This introduction is intended to be informal, giving Algebra 2 students the opportunity to explore how the residuals change as the function changes and helping them learn to identify points that fit relatively well versus those that don't. Again, the range and scale of the residual plot makes it look like the first five or six points always fit with a residual of zero, when actually they may not. If you use this activity with a Precalculus or Statistics class, you may want to encourage students to zoom in to the residuals of those points to get a clearer picture. Students in these classes might also benefit from showing the residual squares and trying to minimize the sum of the squares.

Precalculus or Statistics students can also benefit by doing a semi-log transformation of the data. Taking the logarithm of *Transistors* nicely linearizes the data. Students can use a least-squares line to extrapolate, or they can use powers and logarithms to rewrite the linear equation as an exponential function (with base 10 or base 2) that fits the original data. (See Explore More 2 for additional details.)

INVESTIGATE

Q1 Students may use a variety of verbal descriptions, hopefully including the word *exponential.* The graph implies that the rate at which the number of transistors is growing is increasing over time.

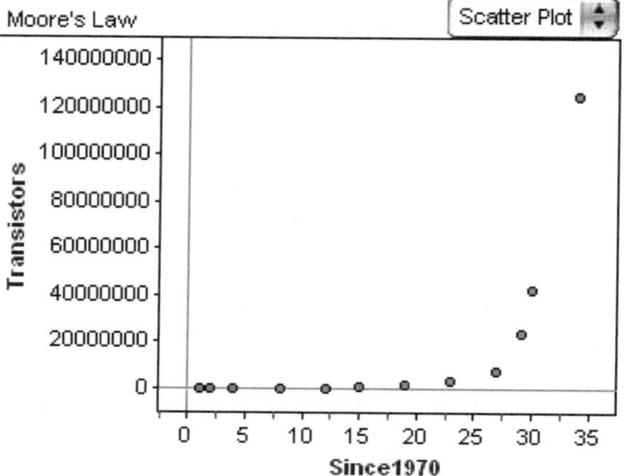

Q2 The function appears to fit the first seven points but definitely doesn't fit the last five points. If students zoom in to the first seven points, they will see that these points don't fit very well either. Students might think that a horizontal translation would improve the fit.

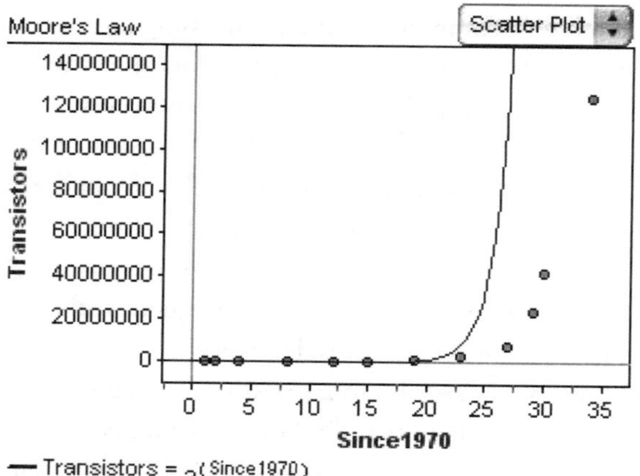

Q3 Some students may try only a horizontal translation. However, as explained in the general notes above, a translation misses the twelfth point and doesn't really fit the other points. Other students may find that a combination of dilations helps fit the data the best. Yet other students may try combining dilations and translations. Because the curve's upward bend is in the same direction as the points' upward bend, students will probably not try reflections.

Q4 The graph below shows the function $Transistors = 1594 \cdot 2^{(Since1970/2.1)}$, which is the result of two dilations.

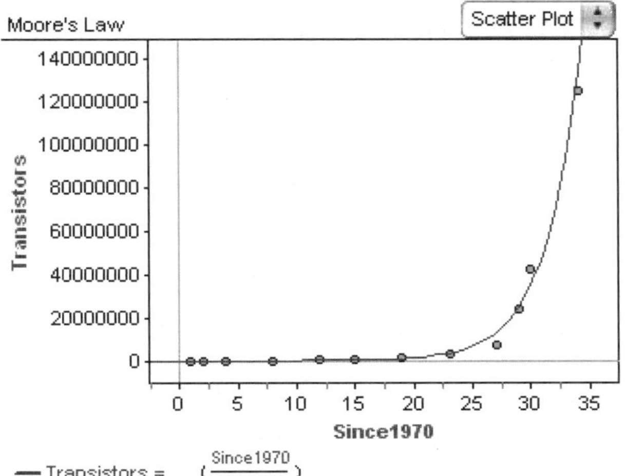

— Transistors = $b\,2^{\left(\frac{Since1970}{a}\right)}$

b = 1594

0 600 1200 1800

a = 2.1

0 2 4 6 8 10 12

Q5 Students should pick out the divisor of the exponent, or the parameter *a*, as the doubling time. For the example in Q4, the doubling time is 2.1 years. For students who use only a translation, the value of *a* is 1.

Q6 The exact answers the student gets depend on the method used to extrapolate. Direct substitution gives approximately 166 million transistors in 2005 (or 35 years since 1970) and approximately 864 million transistors in 2010 (or 40 years since 1970). If students trace the graph in Fathom, then the answers depend on the resolution used; the graph is not truly continuous, so not all values will show up. For the example in Q4, tracing gives approximately 188 million transistors for *Since1970* = 35 and over 1 billion transistors for *Since1970* = 40.

Note: Students may want to change the domain and range of the graph's axes so that they can adequately see the traced points.

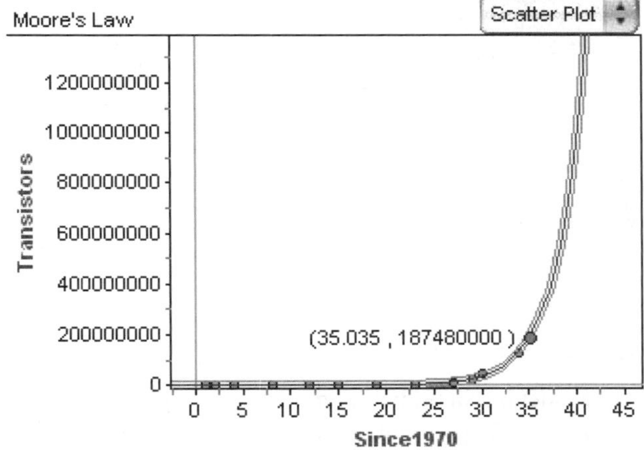

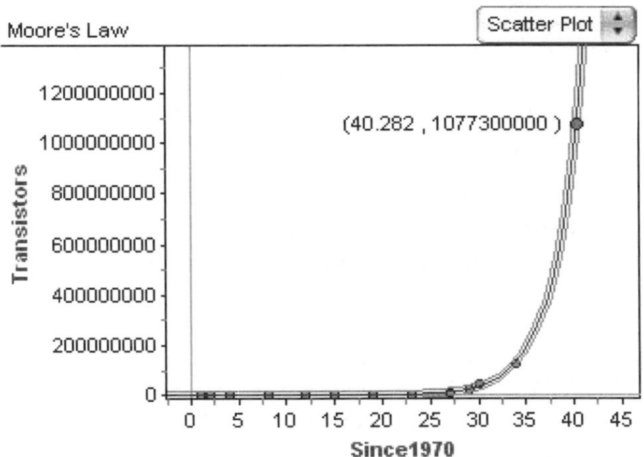

Q7 If the function passes through the data point, the residual point will be on the gray zero line. If the function doesn't pass through the data point, the residual point will be above or below the zero line. Students should notice that the residual grows larger as the function's fit worsens.

Q8 The points for the years 1997, 1999, 2000, and 2004 are the most problematic. As you adjust the function with the sliders, these residual points fluctuate wildly and it is very hard to make the function fit all of them well.

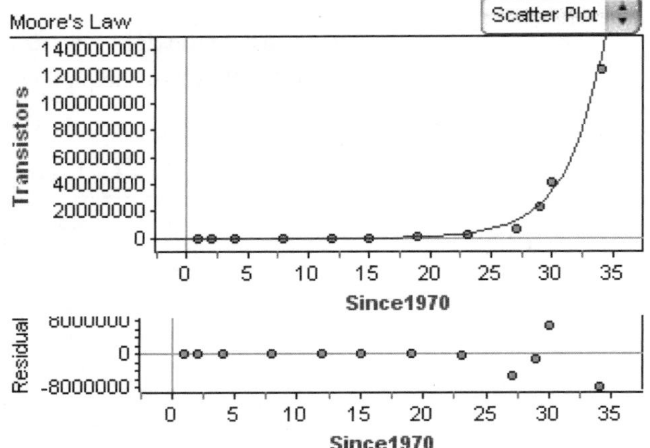

Q9 See the answer to Q4 for one possible function.

Q10 Students will probably agree that "complexity" varies exponentially. Doubling times and functions will vary.

Q11 Some students may be persuaded by the data in this activity and feel that if the number of transistors has grown exponentially for the last 35 years, then the trend is likely to continue. Other students may argue that the growth might reach a maximum and eventually taper off (similar to a logistic function). According to Intel Corporation's Web site, the company believes the trend will continue through at least 2010.

EXPLORE MORE

1. Suggest that students research Intel's Web site, www.intel.com/research/silicon/mooreslaw.htm, which was the original source for the data presented in the Fathom document **MooresLaw2004.ftm.** In September 2004 (after the Fathom document was compiled), Intel published data for the Itanium line of processors. The Itanium was released in 2002 with 220,000,000 transistors, and the Itanium 2 was released in 2003 with 410,000,000. Hence, these processors far exceed the exponential trend of the data used in this activity.

   Students can add the Itanium transistors, and any others that they research, to the Fathom document as new cases. They can then readjust the exponential function to obtain a better fit. Some students may find that no single function fits both the older and newer processors, so they might try to fit two or more exponential functions to create a piecewise-defined function.

2. Creating a semi-log graph of *logTransistors* and *Since1970* linearizes the data. Students can use a line of fit (least-squares line shown below) to model the data. The least-squares line can be traced to extrapolate, or students can convert to an exponential function. Using x and y, here's a conversion from the linear function to the exponential function:

$$\log(y) = 0.144x + 3.2$$
$$10^{\log(y)} = 10^{0.144x+3.2}$$
$$y = 10^{0.144x} \cdot 10^{3.2}$$
$$y = 2^{0.144/\log(2)} \cdot 1585$$
$$y = 1585 \cdot 2^{0.478x}$$
$$y = 1585 \cdot 2^{(x/2.09)}$$

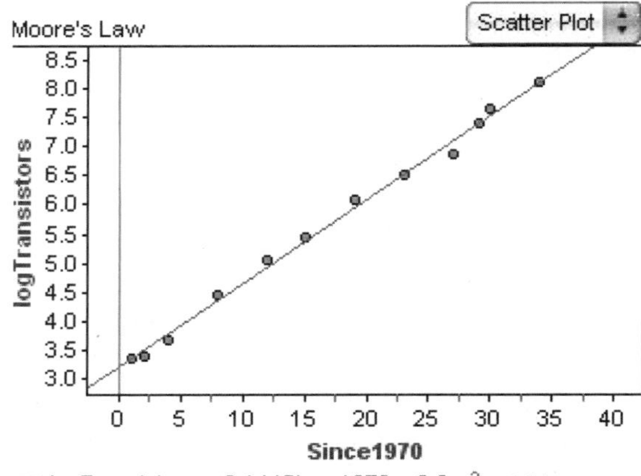

EXTENSION

As people living in the age of technology, students may take it for granted that computers are going to become more powerful every few years. Because of this, they may not realize how impressive the growth of computer technology is. To get a better perspective, have students do research on another type of technology, machinery, or industry and research its maximum performance or minimum cost in 1970. For example, they could research the maximum screen size of a television in 1970; or the price of a transcontinental flight in 1970; or another similar situation that would involve growth or decay. Apply Moore's Law (growth or decay version) to that technology, machinery, or industry. According to Moore's Law, what should the value be today? Then research the actual values today and compare.

At the time of this writing, Intel Corporation's Web site has a nice (if not lengthy) animated presentation about Moore's Law that includes an analogy to air travel. Visit www.intel.com/labs/eml/eml_demo/EML_demo.htm and jump to "An Analogy" to see this analogy. If you don't want to assign this extension as a short research project, you might be able to use this Internet presentation as a classroom demonstration instead.

After doing research, or after watching the Internet presentation, have a class discussion about whether students think it is legitimate to apply Moore's Law to other forms of technology, machinery, or industry. Some may argue that Moore's Law might apply to other areas if you didn't look at just 1970 to the present. For example, between the Wright Brothers' first flight (1903) to Howard Hughes' first worldwide flight (1938), the field of aviation developed at an impressive rate, too. Other students might argue that the speed at which computer technology develops does create pitfalls—for example, computer crashes and the consumer's cost of continually upgrading—that would be unacceptable in other products.

PRINTING PARAGRAPHS (PAGE 45)

Activity Time: 45–55 minutes

Materials:

- One copy of The Seven Paragraphs worksheet per group (page 49)
- Centimeter rulers

Optional Document: PrintingParagraphs.ftm

Fathom Prerequisites: Students should be able to

- Create a collection by starting a case table
- Make a scatter plot of two attributes
- Plot functions
- Make sliders

Fathom Skills: Students will learn how to

- Make a residual plot
- Use a residual plot to improve a function model

Mathematics Prerequisites: Students should be able to graph inverse-variation functions. *Optional:* Students should be able to use function transformations (dilations and translations) and fit an exponential function by trial and error.

Mathematics Skills: Students will learn how to fit an inverse-variation function to real-world data by trial and error, use residuals to judge how well a function fits data, and use residuals to improve the fit of a function.

General Notes: This activity has two main goals. First, it teaches a real-world application of inverse-variation functions. Specifically, it looks at the inverse relationship between paragraph width (horizontal) and length (vertical) assuming that the amount of text, or the area, remains the same. Second, it introduces residual plots (or re-introduces, if you did Moore's Law) as a means of judging how well a function fits data and how you might be able to adjust the function model to improve the fit.

For the first goal, students need to first recognize that the data follow an inverse variation. Even very experienced students, when seeing how *Length* decreases with *Width* to form a curve, will say, "It must be exponential." To overcome this misconception, the worksheet encourages students to think about the geometric relationship (*Length* • *Width* = Area) and then directs them to the function $Length = \frac{Area}{Width}$. By using a slider for the parameter *Area,* students can use the same curve-fitting methods that they used in Function Transformations and Moore's Law.

You may want to formally introduce the term *parameter* and fully distinguish it from a *variable* (or *attribute,* in Fathom's lingo). Although students will use a slider to *vary* the parameter *Area,* it is not a *variable.* Technically they are trying to find the best value of a *constant,* so *Area* is a *parameter.*

Please be aware that some students, especially English-as-a-second-language students, may get confused by the multiple uses of *length* in this activity. In the context of the activity, the length of the paragraph (the attribute *Length*) is how long the paragraph is when measured vertically. However, the attribute *Width* is also measuring a length—line length. For this reason, the worksheet avoids the phrase *line length,* even though it is a widely used term in the publishing industry. Despite any potential confusion, using *Length* and *Width* will help students recognize the connection to the area formula for rectangles, which is fundamental to the activity.

For the second goal, this activity intends to informally introduce residual plots. Residual plots show how far the data points in a scatter plot are from some function. By adjusting the slider(s) in this activity, students should get a feel for what a residual plot looks like for a good fit (most residuals close to zero) and what it looks like for a bad fit; what it means if all of the residuals are positive versus negative; and possibly what it means if you recognize a pattern in the residuals. Looking at residuals can tell you at least two things: whether your model is missing something and how accurately your model predicts the data. (The former concept is tackled when students add *White* to their function in Explore More 1.) In addition, just playing with Fathom's dynamic residual plots will give Algebra students more intuition about functions and how they're put together.

You may want to explain to students that there are two fundamental sources for residuals: errors and mistakes. Without getting too deeply into formal statistical definitions, the difference is that errors are unavoidable. In data analysis, you want to minimize and measure error and to avoid mistakes. In the context of this activity, measuring the paragraphs to the nearest tenth of a centimeter means that you will have unavoidable variability from the exact measurement—that's an error. On the contrary, modeling your data with a function that doesn't consider the ragged right margins means that your model is inherently wrong—that's a mistake. Sometimes it is hard (or even pointless) to tell the difference between an error and a mistake. But more often, distinguishing between these categories and their causes will help you make better sense of your data. For this activity, recognizing the mistake (omitting the ragged right) allows you to improve the function and find a better fit.

Another source of variability in this activity is how students measure the width of the paragraphs. Some students may measure the longest line; some may measure the shortest line; and some may try to approximate a median width for each paragraph. If you prescribe that certain groups use a particular method, you can pool the entire class's data into a single Fathom document and see how the data points and function models compare.

If time is a factor, you may prefer to have students use the pre-made document **PrintingParagraphs.ftm** instead of making their own measurements. This document already has measurements for *Width* and *Length* entered into a case table. By using this document, you can have students skip the Experiment section of the worksheet.

If you plan to use this activity with Precalculus or Statistics students, do not overlook Extension 2, in which students are challenged to find ways to straighten the data, find a linear model for the transformed data, and then convert the linear equation back into a nonlinear function for the original data.

MAKE A CONJECTURE

Q1 Students might say the graph will "decrease" and/or that it will "curve." Some students who visualize a curve might describe it as "exponential" or "decay." Depending on how recently you studied this type of function, a few students might say that it will be an "inverse variation."

Q2 Each paragraph is approximately a rectangle.

Q3 $Length \cdot Width = Area$, or $Length = \frac{Area}{Width}$

Q4 If students think of the area as consisting of only the text itself, they will say "yes" because each paragraph contains the same text. Some students may think of the area as the area of the rectangle that fits around the text, so they will say "no" because some rectangles have more white space in the right margin than others.

EXPERIMENT

Q5 Answers will vary, especially for measuring width. Some students will measure width with the longest line; some with the shortest line; and some with a median ("average") line.

INVESTIGATE

Q6 Here's a sample graph based on measuring the longest line for *Width*. Answers to "How does it compare?" will vary.

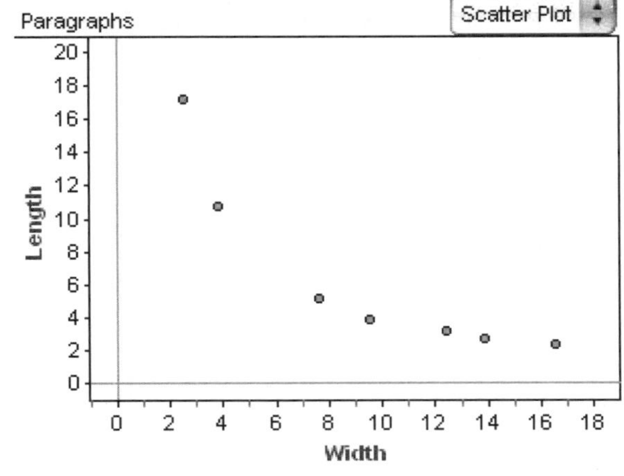

Q7 Hopefully some students will notice that smaller values of *Area* are required to fit the right-most points (the paragraphs with greater *Width*) and larger values of *Area* are required to fit the left-most points (the paragraphs with smaller *Width*). In terms of the printed paragraphs, this pattern exists because the narrower paragraphs have more words that wrap to the next line, so they end up being disproportionately longer and taking up a larger area.

Q8 No, the paragraphs do not have exactly the same area because no one value of *Area* fits all of the points. Yes, the areas are approximately the same because it is easy to make the curve fit very closely (not exactly) to each point.

Q9 Values around 40 are reasonable. Explanations might include that most of the points are close to the curve or that if you multiply any pair of *Length* and *Width* measurements you'll get a value around 40.

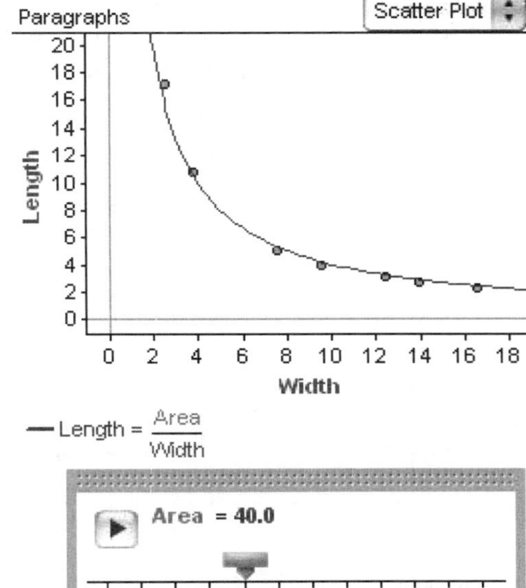

Q10 Ranges between 37 and 41 are reasonable.

Q11 The values of A show that the paragraphs' areas do increase as their widths decrease. They also show a range of 37 to 43.

	Width	Length	A
1	16.5	2.3	37.95
2	13.9	2.7	37.53
3	12.4	3.1	38.44
4	9.5	3.9	37.05
5	7.6	5.1	38.76
6	3.8	10.8	41.04
7	2.5	17.2	43

Q12 Students will probably find that the best value is somewhere in the middle of the range of A. However, it probably isn't equivalent to the median or mean of the values.

Q13 A value around 38 is reasonable because, although it leaves the first two points high, the majority of points are very close to zero. Students may say that if the majority of points are on one side of the curve, it can't be right. Others may reason that the two narrowest paragraphs (the left-hand points) look funny anyway, so you consider them outliers and make residuals as close to zero for the other five.

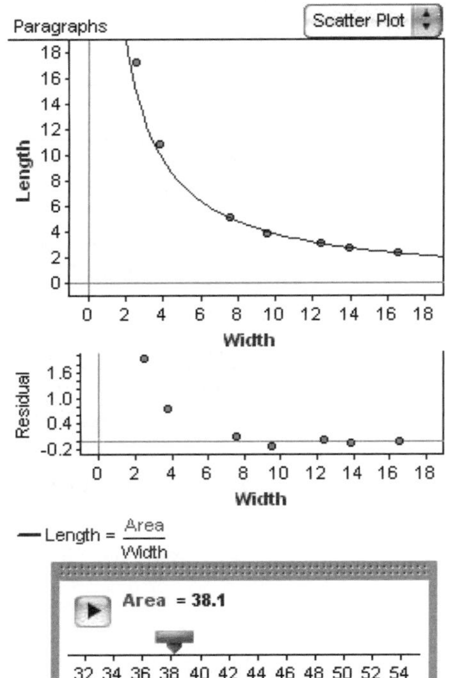

Q14 When focusing on the residual plot, many students will have a smaller value of *Area* than before.

Q15 Because the worksheet introduces (or reviews) the term *inverse variation,* many students will try to use that to describe the relationship between *Length* and *Width.* Many will also mention that *Area* is a key factor. However, based on the fact that *Area* increases as *Width* decreases or based on the imperfect residual plot, most students will say that the model is not the best possible. Some students may realize that the white space at the end of each line needs to be considered in order to improve the model.

EXPLORE MORE

1. As shown in the following sample graph, using the parameter *White* significantly reduces the residuals. The residuals for the two left-most points are impacted the most. These points represent the two paragraphs with the smallest *Width* and also the paragraphs in which words more frequently had to wrap to the next line. So, it makes sense that white space has more impact on these paragraphs. Students should also find that the value for *Area* is smaller after incorporating *White.* The reason is that by subtracting the white space from the right edge, you decrease the overall width of the paragraph. So, the area also needs to decrease in order to maintain the proportion. *Note:* Students who measured *Width* based on the smallest line should have a negative value for *White.* Students who used an average line should have a very small value for *White.*

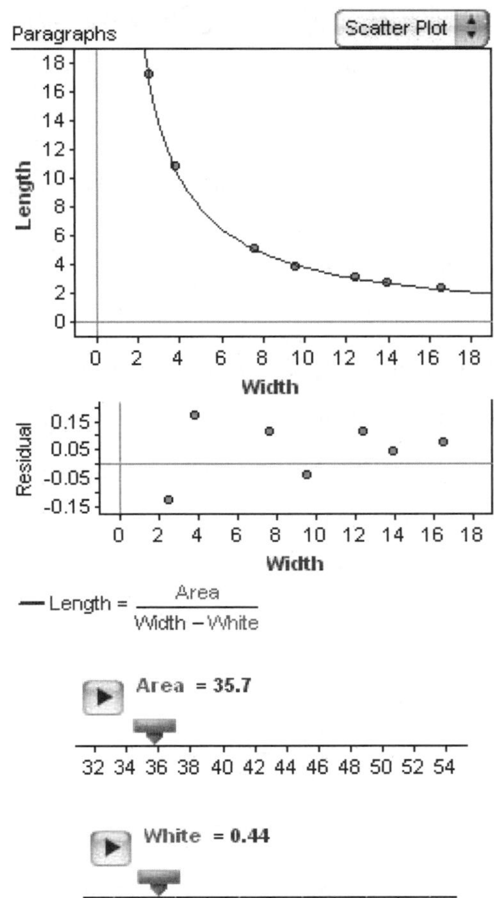

2. Mathematically speaking, *Area* dilates the curve toward the origin (both horizontally and vertically) and *White* translates the curve horizontally. For the residual plot, *Area* dilates toward the zero line with about proportionate changes in each residual and *White* also dilates but with a greater influence on the first two points (the outliers).

3. The geometric relationship is not exponential, so obviously students will have trouble fitting an exponential curve as well as the inverse-variation curve. Notably, students should find that the curvature is never quite right. The graph below shows one possible fit.

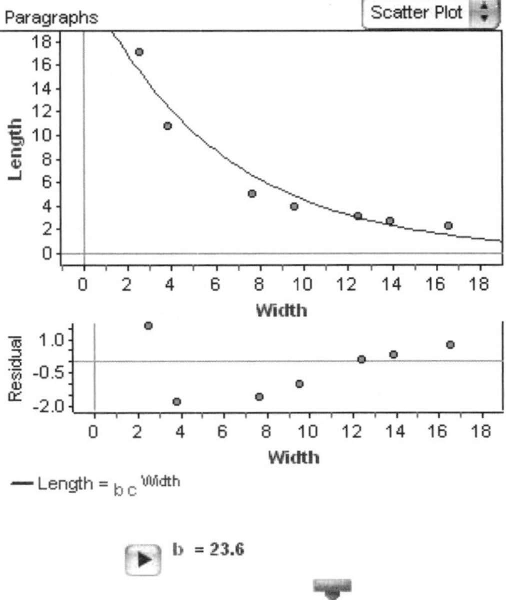

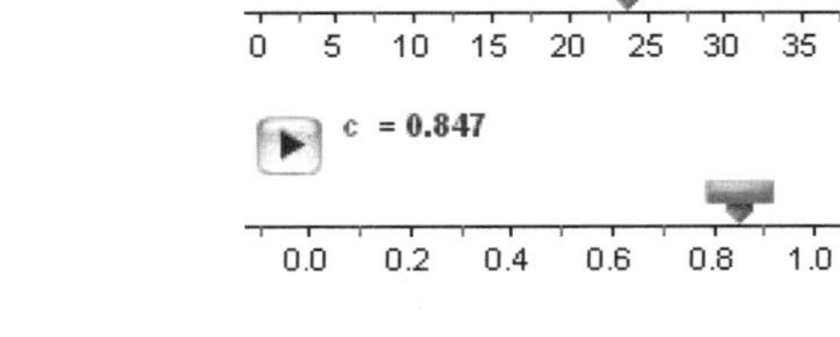

EXTENSIONS

1. Why would anyone ever need to predict the length of a paragraph? Hold a class discussion or have students do research on professional careers that might be concerned about the size of printed paragraphs. People who set type care about lengths of text—for example, newspaper layout people, advertisers, book publishers, magazine editors, and so on. Other aspects routinely considered in those fields are font size, general page layout (including artwork and photos), and readability.

2. Have students try transforming the data to get a linear pattern. Specifically, create an attribute *recipLength* (the reciprocal of *Length*) and graph *recipLength* versus *Width*. Talk about why this data transformation creates a linear pattern. Add a least-squares line to the graph and challenge students to algebraically transform the linear function into a

nonlinear function for the original data. For example, the linear function in the graph below could be transformed as follows:

$$\frac{1}{Length} = 0.0270\,Width - 0.0084$$

$$\frac{1}{Length} = 0.0270(Width - 0.3111)$$

$$Length = \frac{1}{0.0270(Width - 0.3111)}$$

$$Length = \frac{37.0370}{(Width - 0.3111)}$$

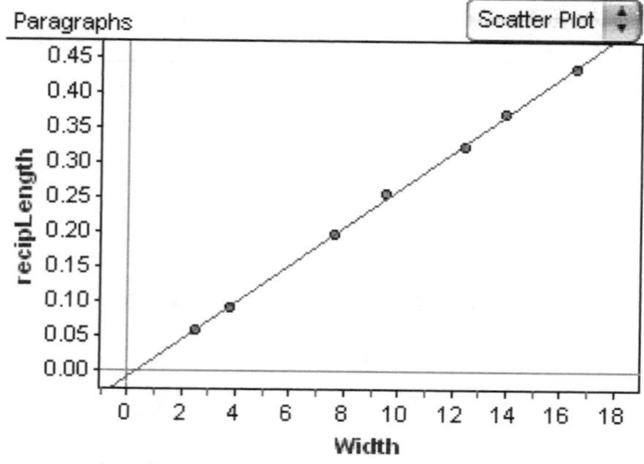

HOW MUCH PAPER IS LEFT? (PAGE 50)

Activity Time: 45–55 minutes

Materials:

- One new roll of adding-machine paper for each group
- Millimeter rulers
- Metersticks

Optional Document: HowMuchPaper.ftm

Fathom Prerequisites: Students should be able to

- Create a collection by starting a case table
- Work with units
- Create attributes defined by a formula
- Make a scatter plot of two attributes
- Graph a least-squares line
- Make a residual plot

Fathom Skills: Students will learn how to

- Use a residual plot to recognize a better function model

Mathematics Prerequisites: Students should be able to transform data and straighten data; use a linear equation in slope-intercept form (specifically, a least-squares line); interpret the coefficient of variation (r^2) for a least-squares line; use residuals to judge how well a function fits data; and recognize problem situations that result in quadratic functions.

Mathematics Skills: Students will learn how to use residuals to recognize a better function model and find a linear model that fits transformed data, and work backward to find a nonlinear model that fits the original data.

General Notes: This activity is about finding a model for nonlinear—specifically quadratic—data. However, unlike Moore's Law and Printing Paragraphs, both of which used sliders to improve a curved function with the original data, this activity looks for ways to straighten the data and then uses a least-squares line with the transformed data. This activity also extends students' understanding of residual plots. In the previous two activities, students used residual plots to improve function models that were apparently not perfect. Conversely, in this activity, the first model (a linear model) looks almost perfect when you graph it—it even has $r^2 = 1.00$—but when you look at the residuals, you know something is not quite right.

The task, basically, is to figure out how to use the diameter of a roll of adding-machine paper to tell how much paper is on the roll. Students do this by pulling off some paper and finding a relationship between the diameter and how much is pulled off. Once they find this relationship, they can calculate how much paper was on the roll by assuming the diameter is reduced to the core of the roll. The function is nonlinear because you use up more diameter per meter of paper as you get closer to the core—you go around more times. Furthermore, the function is quadratic because you're dealing with the area of an annulus. (See Extension 2 for a full explanation.)

Careful and precise measurements are imperative to the success of this activity. Students should be particularly careful measuring the diameter in millimeters, even going to the extent of approximating half- or quarter-millimeters. With careless measurements, the original data may not show the requisite bowing effect. If students do not clearly see the bowing in their own residual plot, point them to the sample graph on the student worksheet and/or have them work with the sample document **HowMuchPaper.ftm.** This document has sample diameter and length measurements from a 130-foot roll (approximately 39.6 meters) with a 22-millimeter core. (The sample answers that follow are based on the data in this document.) However, you are strongly encouraged to let students collect their own measurements and learn from their mistakes. If you can spare the time, you may prefer to use poorly collected data as a lesson in the necessity for precise measurement and then allow students to repeat the data collection with new rolls.

This activity is most appropriate for students in Algebra 2 (and preferably students who have had a Geometry course) because the function is quadratic and is based on the area formula of an annulus. However, you can successfully use it with Algebra 1 students because they don't have to understand the algebra and geometry of the situation to get good math out of the activity. Students in Algebra 2, Geometry, Precalculus, and Statistics can all be challenged by looking at the algebraic derivation of the relationship (Extension 2) and/or how to go from the linear function for the straightened data to a quadratic function for the original data (Explore More 2).

MAKE A CONJECTURE

Q1 Students usually agree that the function will curve, but they disagree about which way it will curve. All students should make a sketch that is decreasing—as diameter increases, length should decrease.

INVESTIGATE

Q2 Some students might feel that the least-squares line is a good fit because the residuals are very close to zero. Others might feel that it is not a good fit because of the bowing.

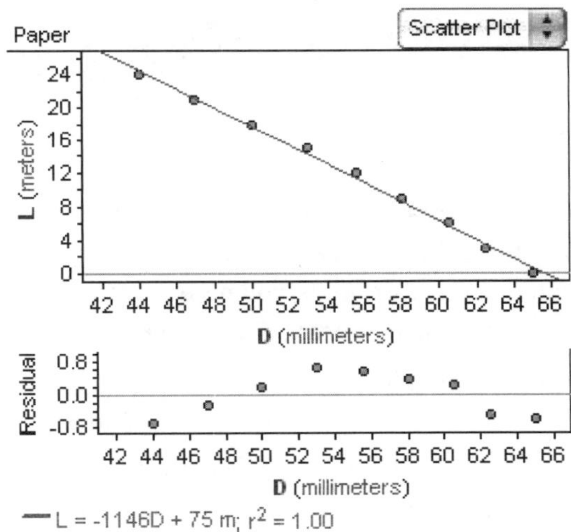

Q3 Students are likely to say that the decreasing slope of the least-squares line meets their expectations—that as diameter increases, length decreases. On the other hand, students are likely to say that the least-squares line contradicts their expectations because they predicted something curved.

Q4 The best graph is *L* versus *DD*, because the residuals have no pattern (or at least no prominent pattern) and they have the smallest magnitudes.

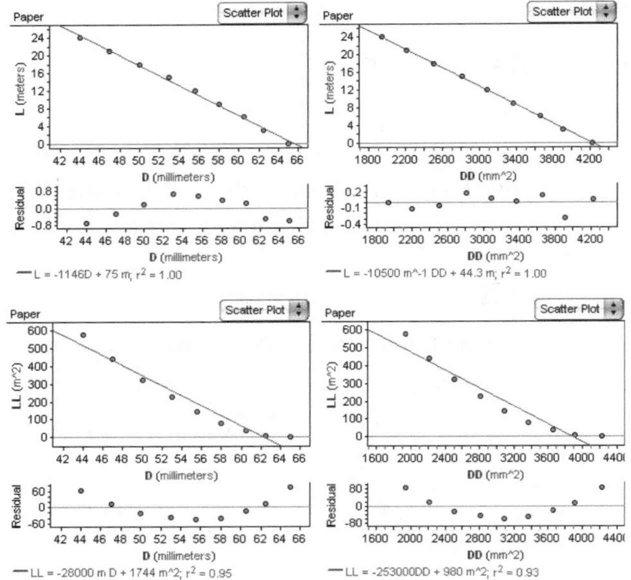

Q5 $L = -10500\text{ m}^{-1}\ DD + 44.3\text{ m}$

Q6 For these sample data, the core was $D = 22$ mm. To substitute this into the equation in Q5, which is stated with meters as the units, you need to square and convert to square meters: $DD = 0.000484\text{ m}^2$.

Q7 For these sample data:
$L = -10500\text{ m}^{-1}(0.000484\text{ m}^2) + 44.3\text{ m} =$
$-5.082\text{ m} + 44.3\text{ m} \approx 39.2\text{ m}.$

Note: Rather than substituting into the function, students could trace the graph to find the value of *L* when *DD* is approximately 484 mm^2. (Students probably won't be able to trace to exactly 484 mm^2.) That way, students don't need to do a unit conversion from square millimeters to square meters, although they still need to square the diameter of the core. This also gives a value around 39.2 m.

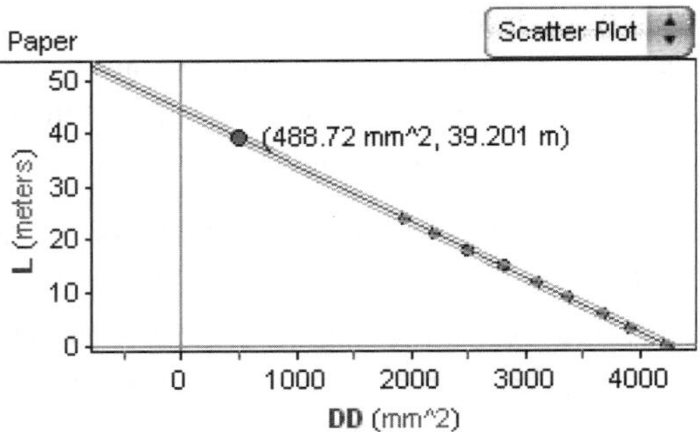

Q8 The roll used for the sample answers was advertised as 130 ft. Converting 39.2 m to feet gives approximately 129 ft. Conversely, if the roll had a full 130 ft, the answer to Q7 should have been about 39.6 m. So, the prediction in Q7 was pretty good.

Q9 The reason that the data looked fairly linear is a matter of perspective. If you zoom in close enough, any curve can begin to look straight. In terms of this geometric situation, a few meters of paper wraps around the roll only a few times when the roll is full, so the diameter changes only a little. However, if you had collected more data and gotten closer to the core, you would notice the curvature more prominently. That is, when you are near the core, the same few meters of paper will wrap around the roll several times and the diameter will change a lot.

EXPLORE MORE

1. The roll used for the sample answers had a red band at diameter $D = 25$ mm, or $DD = 0.000625\text{ m}^2$. This means that $L = -10500\text{ m}^{-1}(0.000625\text{ m}^2) + 44.3\text{ m}$, or approximately 37.7 m have been removed. So there are 39.2 – 37.7, or about 1.5 m left.
2. Transforming the linear function into a quadratic function is fairly simple—just replace *DD* with D^2. Getting a quadratic function makes sense because removing paper changes the area of the circle, and the area of a circle is found by squaring the diameter. If students plot the quadratic function, it will fit the points better than the linear function in step 6 and

will give the same residual plot that the transformed data gave in step 9. To plot the function, students must include units on the coefficient and constant.

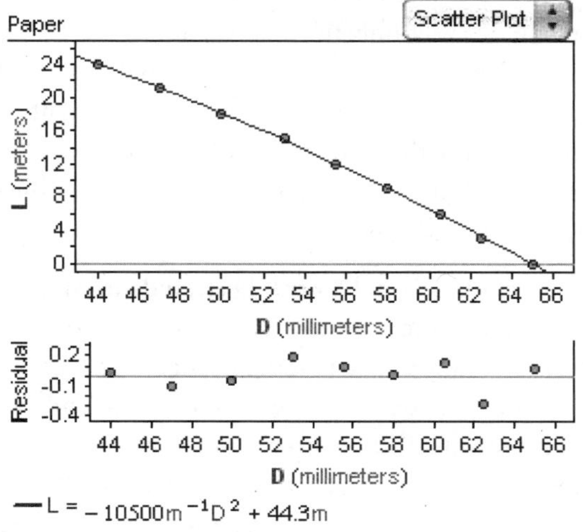

EXTENSIONS

1. Have students repeat the activity with a roll of toilet paper and come up with a way to determine the number of squares left on the roll as a function of its diameter. Toilet paper is "squishier" than adding-machine paper and therefore has more variability, so more experience and care are needed to get the activity to work. Students will need to devise creative ways to measure the diameter and length carefully and precisely.

2. Have students use algebra and geometry to derive the theoretical relationship between diameter and length. They can find a formula for either cumulative length pulled off as a function of diameter, or the length *remaining* on the roll as a function of diameter. The two formulas are closely related.

   The length of paper remaining on the roll (p) is proportional to the cross-sectional area of the roll. Because the roll has a core in the middle, that shape is an annulus. The area of an annulus is the area of the outside circle (with diameter d) minus the area of the core (with diameter c). If you let the constant of proportionality be K—which means the thickness of the paper is $\frac{1}{K}$—you start with the formula

$$p = KA_{\text{annulus}} = K\left[\pi\left(\frac{d}{2}\right)^2 - \pi\left(\frac{c}{2}\right)^2\right] = \frac{K\pi}{4}d^2 - \frac{K\pi}{4}c^2$$

Because the core does not change, the only independent variable in this function is d. Hence, the function is a quadratic function in the form $p = Ad^2 - B$. If you graph it as a parabola, it opens up with a vertex at $(0, -B)$, or $\left(0, \frac{K\pi}{4}c^2\right)$, and it crosses the horizontal axis where $\frac{K\pi}{4}d^2 - \frac{K\pi}{4}c^2 = 0$, or $d = c$.

In this activity, however, you don't know p, the paper remaining on the roll; you know ℓ, the amount you have pulled off. However, the sum of the amount remaining on the roll and the amount pulled off equals the constant total length that was originally on the roll, or $\ell + p = T$. Substituting $T - \ell$ for p and solving gives the formula

$$\ell = -Ad^2 + (B + T) \text{ or } \ell = -\frac{K\pi}{4}d^2 + \left(\frac{K\pi}{4}c^2 + T\right)$$

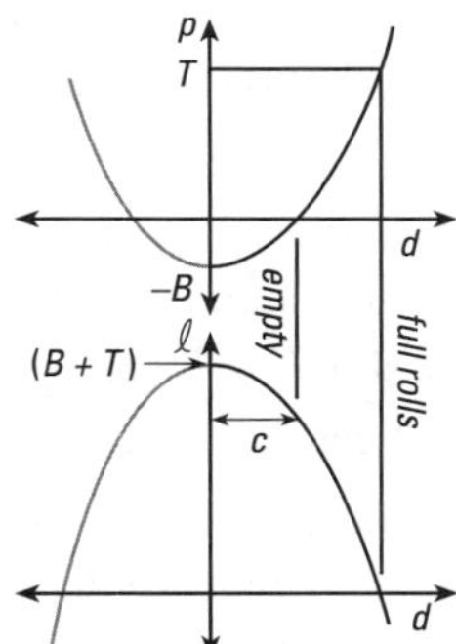

If you plot ℓ as a function of d^2 instead of as a function of d, you can see from the last equation that you'll get a straight line with $-A$, or $-\frac{K\pi}{4}$, as the slope and $(B + T)$, or $\left(\frac{K\pi}{4}c^2 + T\right)$, as the intercept. That's exactly what happened when you used a least-squares line on the transformed data of L versus DD.

It's worth noting that B, or $\frac{K\pi}{4}c^2$, is the amount of paper that could fill the core if the paper were wound down to zero radius.

COMPOUND INTEREST (PAGE 53)

Activity Time: 30–60 minutes

Required Document: CompoundInterest.ftm

Fathom Prerequisites: Students should be able to

- Adjust a slider (by dragging it and setting it to a specific value)
- Read cases from a case table

Fathom Skills: Students will learn how to

- *Optional:* Create a collection of measures (see Explore More 3)
- *Optional:* Add cases to a case table (see problem g on the next page)

Mathematics Prerequisites: Students should be able to use exponential functions for growth and decay problems. *Optional:* Students should be able to calculate simple and/or compound interest.

Mathematics Skills: Students will learn how to recognize how parameters affect a function.

General Notes: Compound interest is a pervasive feature of our society. Savings accounts, investments, retirement accounts, credit cards, mortgages, and automobile loans are all governed by the rules of compound interest. This activity uses a pre-made document that models compound interest. Students use sliders to set the parameters, and the case table and graph dynamically show how the account grows or decays. You can use this activity to introduce compound interest, supplement your textbook's discussion of this topic, and to teach valuable life skills.

Because everything in **CompoundInterest.ftm** is pre-made, the "feel" of this activity is somewhat different from the other activities in this book. The pre-made document also makes this an ideal activity to do as a teacher-led demonstration, especially if you do not have time to take the entire class to the computer lab. To save time, either as a student activity or as a class demonstration, don't forget that you can set the value of a slider by dragging it or by double-clicking the value of the slider and typing a specific value.

Within the document, a slider called *Principal* is used to represent only the amount of the original investment or loan. The case table then uses an attribute called *Balance* to represent the amount in the account at any subsequent time. In this way, only the first balance is based on the principal; each subsequent balance is compounded from the previous balance. Please note that accountants sometimes use the word *principal* to mean not only the original amount but also the current balance at the start of any compounding period.

For question Q5 on the worksheet, students might struggle with selecting the right case(s) to answer the question(s). The key to fully understanding the data in the case table is being able to understand the attributes *Year* and *Period*. *Year* represents the total number of years that have *elapsed*—notice that it starts with 0; likewise, *Period* is the total number of compounding periods that have elapsed. Hence, if students need to find the balance at the end of the 2nd compounding period of the 4th year, they would look for *Year* = 3 and *Period* = 2. That means 3 years have elapsed (you are now in the 4th year) and 2 whole compounding periods have elapsed. Similarly, if students need to find information for the end of 2 years, they should look for *Year* = 2, *Period* = 0, which means that 2 whole years have elapsed. Because of the potential confusion, it may be worthwhile to pause before Q5 and spot-check students' understanding of the attributes.

For brevity, question Q5 has only four options. The concept of each problem is slightly different and they are in order of increasing difficulty. If you would like to have students model more problems, here are three additional scenarios. You could also have students solve any compound interest problem from your current textbook.

e. You put $100 in a savings account with an annual rate of 6%, compounded monthly. You make no additional payments to the account. What is the balance of the account after 2 years? [Answer: $112.72]

f. You want to buy a used motorcycle for $3500. Your aunt gives you $500 to start, and you find a savings account that earns 9%, compounded monthly. How much will you need to add to the account each month in order to reach your goal by the end of 2 years? How much would you need to pay each month if your aunt had not given you $500? [Answer: With aunt's gift: $111 (or $110.81 if *PaymentPerPeriod* is not restricted to integers); without aunt's gift: $134 (or $133.65)]

g. At age 25, Ben invests $1000 in a retirement account. The account earns 5.5% interest, compounded quarterly. He plans to contribute another $50 each quarter. Assuming the interest rate doesn't change, how much will he have if he retires at age 65? At 67? At 70? Do you think Ben will be able to retire "comfortably"? [Answer: At 65: $37,584.42; at 67: $42,343.02; at 70: $50,530.49. None of these amounts would be enough to live "comfortably." *Note:* Students will need to add new cases to solve this problem.]

Because compound interest is an important application of exponents and exponential functions, some curricula introduce it as early as Prealgebra and the topic continues through Precalculus and Calculus. Hence, this activity can be used at a variety of grade levels, and the complexity of the activity can be varied for students with different levels of experience with the topic.

INVESTIGATE

Q1 Most importantly, *Principal* moves the vertical intercept of the graph to the value of *Principal*, regardless of the other sliders. The other points move too, but the amount by which they move depends on the settings of the sliders. Some students might describe the transformation due to *Principal* as a "translation" because the points appear to slide. However, because *Principal* is a constant factor, the transformation is actually a vertical dilation relative to the horizontal axis.

Q2 As *InterestRate* increases in the positive direction, the curve is stretched vertically and the steepness increases—the function grows more quickly. For negative values of *InterestRate*, the graph curves downward. A negative interest rate is equivalent to decay or depreciation. One real-world example is the depreciating value of a new automobile. Some students might describe the transformation due to *InterestRate* as a "dilation." However, because *InterestRate* is not a factor of the function, the transformation is not that simple. Furthermore, it is not a simple dilation because negative values of *InterestRate* do not create mirror images of similar positive values.

Q3 For positive interest rates, as *PeriodsPerYear* increases the points get closer together and the curve appears to get steeper—the function grows more quickly. For negative interest rates, as *PeriodsPerYear* increases the points get closer together and the curve appears to get flatter—the function decays more slowly.

Q4 As *PaymentPerPeriod* increases in the positive direction, the curve is stretched vertically and the steepness increases. For negative values of *PaymentPerPeriod*, depending on the value of *InterestRate*, the curve may be reflected and stretched across the line *Balance* = *Principal*. A negative payment means that you are taking money out of a savings account or that you are making a payment on a loan.

Q5 a. $3377.02. Set *Principal* = 3000, *InterestRate* = 2.5, *PeriodsPerYear* = 4, and *PaymentPerPeriod* = 0. Find case 20, which represents the state of the investment after 4 full years and 3 quarters, or the 3rd quarter in the 5th year. *Note:* Many students may incorrectly find case 24 (*Year* = 5, *Period* = 3), but that actually represents the state of the investment after 5 full years, which is actually in the 6th year.

Interest

	Year	Period	TimeInYears	Balance	Interest	Payment
13	3	0	3	3232.90	20.21	0.00
14	3	1	3.25	3253.10	20.33	0.00
15	3	2	3.5	3273.44	20.46	0.00
16	3	3	3.75	3293.89	20.59	0.00
17	4	0	4	3314.48	20.72	0.00
18	4	1	4.25	3335.20	20.84	0.00
19	4	2	4.5	3356.04	20.98	0.00
20	4	3	4.75	3377.02	21.11	0.00
21	5	0	5	3398.12	21.24	0.00
22	5	1	5.25	3419.36	21.37	0.00
23	5	2	5.5	3440.73	21.50	0.00
24	5	3	5.75	3462.24	21.64	0.00
25	6	0	6	3483.88	21.77	0.00

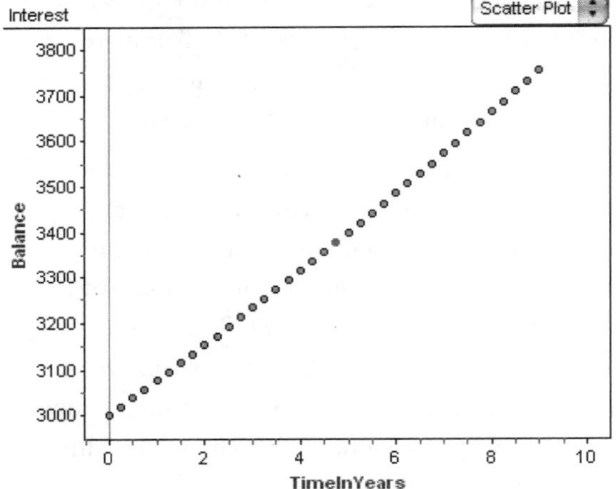

b. $2683.08. Set *Principal* = 0, *InterestRate* = 7, *PeriodsPerYear* = 12, and *PaymentPerPeriod* = 100. Find case 26, which represents the state of the investment for the 25th paycheck. *Note:* Many students may incorrectly set *Principal* = 100, but you start with nothing until the first paycheck deducts something.

c. $36 (or $35.70 if *PaymentPerPeriod* is not restricted to integers). Set *Principal* = 1200, *InterestRate* = 4.5, and *PeriodsPerYear* = 12. Adjust the slider for *PaymentPerPeriod* into the negative range until case 37 is 0. *Note:* In order for the balance to decrease, *PaymentPerPeriod* must be negative. That's what the hint on the student worksheet is suggesting.

d. The balance will be fully paid off with the 94th payment, or after 7 years 10 months; Kelly will have paid 94 • 40, or $3760. Set *Principal* = 2000, *InterestRate* = 18, *PeriodsPerYear* = 12, and *PaymentPerPeriod* = −40. Add at least 58 cases to the collection. Skim the case table or graph to find when *Principal* first passes 0. *Note:* Because the last payment actually makes the principal negative, in the real world Kelly's last payment would not be a full $40; rather she would pay just the $4.41 remaining on the previous bill.

Interest

	Year	Period	TimeInYears	Balance	Interest	Payment
84	6	11	6.91667	372.68	5.59	-40.00
85	7	0	7	338.27	5.07	-40.00
86	7	1	7.08333	303.35	4.55	-40.00
87	7	2	7.16667	267.90	4.02	-40.00
88	7	3	7.25	231.92	3.48	-40.00
89	7	4	7.33333	195.40	2.93	-40.00
90	7	5	7.41667	158.33	2.37	-40.00
91	7	6	7.5	120.70	1.81	-40.00
92	7	7	7.58333	82.51	1.24	-40.00
93	7	8	7.66667	43.75	0.66	-40.00
94	7	9	7.75	4.41	0.07	-40.00
95	7	10	7.83333	-35.53	-0.53	-40.00
96	7	11	7.91667	-76.06	-1.14	-40.00

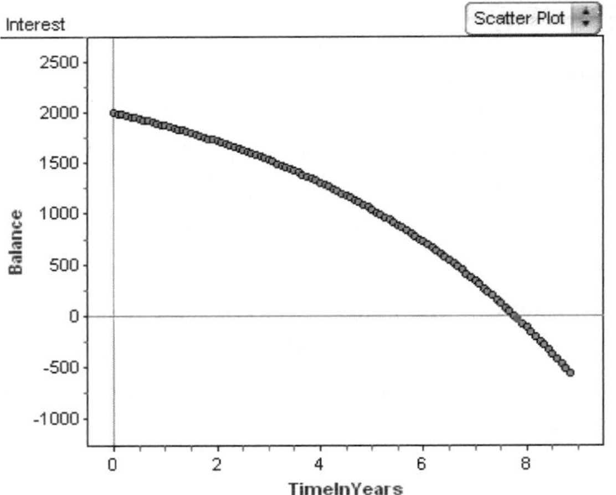

EXPLORE MORE

1. In the long run, if your interest is compounded more frequently, your balance will be greater. Students may have noticed this from the steepness of the curve as they explored the effect of *PeriodsPerYear* for question Q3. Or they might actually set specific values for *Principal* and *InterestRate* and see what the balance is after, say, 1 full year of compounding under each scenario.

   Students may be surprised by the results of this extension. Before using Fathom to explore the situation, students might incorrectly assume that compounding once a year with an interest rate and compounding twelve times a year with one-twelfth the same interest rate should be equivalent, but they are not.

   You might want to introduce *annual percentage yield,* which is a banking term for the percent interest that actually accrues over one year when the interest rate is compounded more frequently than once a year.

2. At the least, students should recognize that the doubling time will decrease as the interest rate increases, because a higher interest rate means that you'll earn more money more quickly.

   If students collect coordinate pairs in the form (*interest rate, doubling time*), they may see that the general shape is similar to an inverse-variation function. You can also challenge students to do one or both of the mathematical derivations of the relationship, where P represents the principal in dollars, r represents the annual interest rate compounded c times per year, and t represents the number of periods required for doubling. If students have learned about inverses, you could discuss how and why the functions for interest rate and for doubling time are inverses of each other.

   Doubling time as a function of interest rate:

$$P\left(1+\frac{r}{c}\right)^t = 2P$$
$$\left(1+\frac{r}{c}\right)^t = 2$$
$$\log\left(1+\frac{r}{c}\right)^t = \log 2$$
$$t\log\left(1+\frac{r}{c}\right) = \log 2$$
$$t = \frac{\log 2}{\log\left(1+\frac{r}{c}\right)}$$

   Interest rate as a function of doubling time:

$$P\left(1+\frac{r}{c}\right)^t = 2P$$
$$\left(1+\frac{r}{c}\right)^t = 2$$
$$1+\frac{r}{c} = 2^{1/t}$$
$$\frac{r}{c} = 2^{1/t} - 1$$
$$r = c(2^{1/t} - 1)$$

3. At the least, students should be able to manually record coordinate pairs for the value of *PaymentPerPeriod* beside the resulting value of *Balance* after 3 years (when *Year* = 3 and *Period* = 0). By looking at the table of coordinate pairs, or by creating a case table in Fathom and making a scatter plot, they should see that the relationship is perfectly linear.

   If you choose, this exploration can be used to introduce Fathom's ability to create a collection of measures. The pairs of values that you need to explore are any value of *PaymentPerPeriod* and *Balance* when *Year* = 3 and *Period* = 0. Show the collection inspector for *Interest* (double-click the collection) and go to the **Measures** panel. Create two attributes, *Payment* and *Balance3Years,* defined by the formulas *PaymentPerPeriod* and *lookupValueByIndex* ("Interest," "Balance," *PeriodsPerYear* • 3 + 1), respectively. These measures tell you the payment and balance after 3 years for any particular setting of *PaymentPerPeriod.*

Close the inspector, select the collection, and choose **Collect Measures** from the **Collection** menu. A derived collection called Measures from Interest is created; by creating a case table, you'll see that it contains 5 identical cases for *Payment* and *Balance3Years.* Show the collection inspector for this new collection and go to the **Collect Measures** panel. Choose the settings shown below.

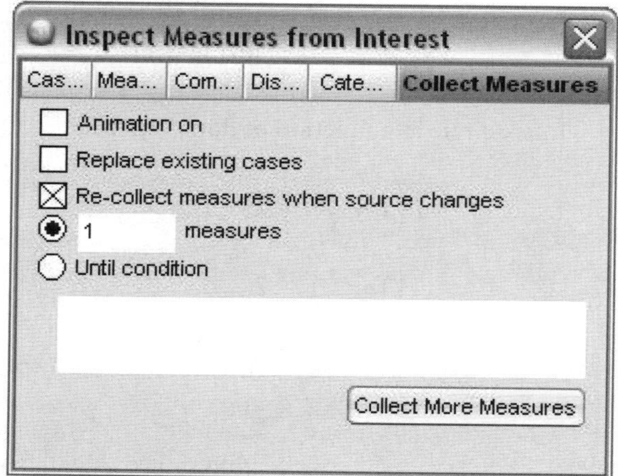

Now drag the slider for *PaymentPerPeriod* and watch Fathom populate the case table. Make a scatter plot of *Balance3Years* versus *Payment* to see that there is a perfect linear relationship. (The graph below is for *Principal* = 100, *InterestRate* = 20, and *PeriodsPerYear* = 4.)

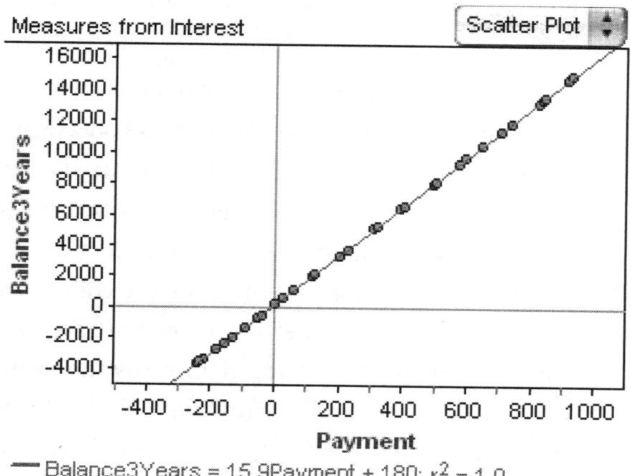

In an attempt to be completely quantitative, have students write down the equation of the least-squares line and values of all the parameters and then repeat for new settings of *Principal, InterestRate,* and/or *PeriodsPerYear.* (The easiest way to start over is to adjust the sliders, select all of the cases in the derived collection and delete them, and then start dragging *PaymentPerPeriod.*) Challenge students to find where the linear equation's slope and intercept come from. The vertical intercept of the linear relationship is the easiest to determine. Because the intercept occurs when *Payment* = 0, the balance after 3 years is simply $P\left(1+\frac{r}{c}\right)^{3c}$, where P is the principal, r is the interest rate, and c is the number of compoundings per year.

The slope, however, requires knowledge about recursion and geometric series. Because the payment occurs after the principal has accrued interest, the balance after t periods looks like

$$\left[\left[\left[\left[P\left(1+\frac{r}{c}\right)+\mathit{Payment}\right]\left(1+\frac{r}{c}\right)+\mathit{Payment}\right]\left(1+\frac{r}{c}\right)+\mathit{Payment}\right]\cdots\left(1+\frac{r}{c}\right)+\mathit{Payment}\right]$$

or

$$P\left(1+\frac{r}{c}\right)^{3c}+\mathit{Payment}\left(1+\frac{r}{c}\right)^{3c-1}+\mathit{Payment}\left(1+\frac{r}{c}\right)^{3c-2}+\cdots+\mathit{Payment}$$

or

$$P\left(1+\frac{r}{c}\right)^{3c}+\mathit{Payment}\left[\left(1+\frac{r}{c}\right)^{3c-1}+\left(1+\frac{r}{c}\right)^{3c-2}+\cdots+1\right]$$

The last expression is a linear expression in the form $A + Bx$. You'll notice that the constant term, $P\left(1+\frac{r}{c}\right)^{3c}$, is the same vertical intercept found

previously. Because payment is the independent variable in the function, $\left[\left(1 + \frac{r}{c}\right)^{3c-1} + \left(1 + \frac{r}{c}\right)^{3c-2} + \cdots + 1\right]$ is the slope. This, however, is a geometric series with first term 1, ratio $\left(1 + \frac{r}{c}\right)$, and $3c$ terms, so it could be rewritten

$$\frac{1 - \left(1 + \frac{r}{c}\right)^{3c}}{1 - \left(1 + \frac{r}{c}\right)}$$

So, for any principal P and interest rate r compounded c times per year, the relationship between payment and balance after 3 years is

$$Balance3Years = \frac{1 - \left(1 + \frac{r}{c}\right)^{3c}}{1 - \left(1 + \frac{r}{c}\right)} \cdot Payment + P\left(1 + \frac{r}{c}\right)^{3c}$$

You can now confirm the linear function in the preceding graph, using *Principal* = 100, *InterestRate* = 20, and *PeriodsPerYear* = 4:

$$Balance3Years = \frac{1 - \left(1 + \frac{0.20}{4}\right)^{3.4}}{1 - \left(1 + \frac{0.20}{4}\right)} \cdot Payment +$$

$$100\left(1 + \frac{0.20}{4}\right)^{3.4} \approx 15.9 \cdot Payment + 180$$

Some students may recognize that the function can be further generalized for t years:

$$Balance3Years = \frac{1 - \left(1 + \frac{r}{c}\right)^{tc}}{1 - \left(1 + \frac{r}{c}\right)} \cdot Payment + P\left(1 + \frac{r}{c}\right)^{tc}$$

JUPITER'S MOONS (PAGE 59)

Activity Time: 30–45 minutes

Required Document: JupiterMoons.ftm

Fathom Prerequisites: Students should be able to

- Open a document
- Create attributes defined by formula
- Create graphs of two attributes
- Create a slider

Fathom Skills: Students will learn how to

- Rescale a graph by using the pop-up menu to choose the graph type again
- Highlight points in graphs by selecting them in the case table
- Find the coordinates of a particular point in a graph
- Plot a function in a graph

Mathematics Prerequisites: Students should be able to write the equation for a translated and dilated periodic function.

Mathematics Skills: Students will learn how to transform data to improve a model; create a formula for the phase of a periodic function; write a periodic function to model data; and vary the period, phase, and amplitude of a periodic function to model data.

General Notes: This activity is about accuracy. How accurately can you determine how long it takes one of the moons of Jupiter to go around that planet? Students will propose one period and overlay the waves to see whether they line up. This requires a good understanding of the *phase* of a periodic function. Below left is a diagram of the path of a moon, with a proposed period—but the period is too short. If we overlay the periods, it looks like the diagram below right.

As students get the period closer and closer to being correct, the segments line up better and better. The nearer periods will line up first; the faraway ones need a very accurate period to line up, because even a tiny error is multiplied by the total number of periods. The concept of overlaying the cycles, once grasped, is powerful. And while the arithmetic is easy—and common in data processing—many advanced students have never come across a calculation like it.

Besides going over the questions on the student worksheet, ask students why the formula for *phase* works—and why it is needed. If your data cover a small range in *x* but their absolute values are large, then differences in slope (in a linear fit) create errors in the model that can overwhelm you, because tiny errors are magnified over that long distance from the *y*-axis. One solution is to translate the data back to the vertical axis.

INVESTIGATE

Q1 The points appear to be part of a trigonometric function. The period appears to be somewhere between 3 and 4 days. Estimates will be very rough at this stage.

Q2 The formula for *phase* should be

$$mjd - period \cdot floor\left(\frac{mjd}{period}\right)$$

Students may need help with this. If *mjd* were 163.5 and the period were 4.00, the *phase* would be 3.5, since 160.0 is exactly 40 cycles. Fathom uses *floor* for the next-lowest whole number, so *floor*(163.5 / 4.00) gives 40 for the number of whole cycles. Multiply the number of whole cycles by the period, then subtract from the current *mjd* to get the *phase*.

Q3 The behavior is very sporadic. It's hard to distinguish what is really happening. Students will learn how to modify *mjd* in step 6.

Q4 If students happen to adjust the slider to an integer multiple of the period, the points will also line up. Discuss this with students and make sure they look for the smallest value that lines up the points. It corresponds to January 1, 2000.

Q5 Students should get values within 0.3 day of those in Q6.

Q6 The estimates change slightly. *Io:* 1.771; *Europa:* 3.558; *Ganymede:* 7.169; *Callisto:* 16.839.

These estimates probably changed because there were more data to give the estimation more accuracy. Also, the new data points are far from the old points on the *x*-axis. This makes them more sensitive to small changes in the slider, improving the accuracy.

Q7 $\frac{\max(Europa) - \min(Europa)}{2}$

This function uses the maximum and minimum values of the data taken for *Europa* to get a value of 199.12. The data taken have gaps between values, so you can't be sure of the accuracy—the true min or max might lie in one of the gaps.

14. You may want to remind students about translation and dilation of a trigonometric function.

Q8 Sample answers:

$$Io = 126.73\sin\left(\frac{2\pi}{1.771}(phase - 0.55)\right)$$

$$Europa = -199.70\sin\left(\frac{2\pi}{3.558}(phase - 0.45)\right)$$

$$Ganymede = -310.5\sin\left(\frac{2\pi}{7.169}(phase - 0.24)\right)$$

$$Callisto = 548.7\sin\left(\frac{2\pi}{16.839}(phase + 2.17)\right)$$

Some students may have used cosine or used a different amplitude and displacement. This is a good opportunity for reviewing properties of periodic functions.

EXPLORE MORE

1. Students will need to rescale the graph to see the function clearly. The function should fit, because all that is changing is the unit of time.
2. Answers will vary. Check to make sure students calculated the date correctly.
3. Callisto has the longest orbital period, taking more than 16 days to get around Jupiter. Io has the shortest, just under 2 days.

POPULATION GROWTH (PAGE 63)

Activity Time: 50 minutes

Required Document: PopulationGrowth.ftm

Fathom Prerequisites: Students should be able to

- Open a document
- Create attributes defined by formula
- Create graphs of two attributes

Fathom Skills: Students will learn how to

- Create new cases
- Create and name sliders
- Plot a function
- Change slider bounds
- Change the scale of the graph

Mathematics Prerequisites: Students should be familiar with exponential and logistic functions. (This activity can also serve as an introduction to logistic functions.)

Mathematics Skills: Students will learn how to model population with an exponential function and modify the function to take limiting factors into account, creating a logistic model.

General Notes: In this activity, students take a simple model for population, and gradually modify it to reflect various types of changes in the population. They fit a function to the data, making sure that the function fits the data at several scales. This activity could also be appropriate for Algebra 2 students studying exponential models.

EXPERIMENT

Q1 *year* represents the number of years after you moved to Chelmsdale. *new* represents the number of new people that have come to live in Chelmsdale that year. *pop* represents the total number of people in Chelmsdale.

Q2 The population is 4882.81. The quick rise in population could be due to any number of occurrences. For example, a large corporation may have moved to town, bringing many jobs; families may be having more children; or there may have been recent housing development in town.

Q3 Exponential function. (Some students may mistake this for a power function.)

Q4 After 24 years, this population would be 423,516 according to our model. It does not seem reasonable for the town to be this large after barely one generation. This is the first hint of the limiting factors students will explore later in the activity.

INVESTIGATE

Q5 As you increase A, the function becomes steeper (the population increases more rapidly). When $A = 0$, the function is a horizontal line at $pop = 0$. When A is negative, the function is below the x-axis.

Q6 As you increase B when $B > 1$, the function becomes steeper (the population increases more rapidly). When $B = 1$ or $B = 0$, the function is flat. When $B < 0$, the function is undefined. When $0 < B < 1$, the function grows as *year* becomes more *negative*, indicating that for this model to represent growth, B must be greater than 1.

Q7 $A = 2000$, the initial population of Chelmsdale. $B = 1.25$, the rate of population growth. (Students should understand that B must be greater than 1 to have the population increase.)

Q8 You must change 0.25 to 0.27. This is because there must be more new people coming into the community than the original model expressed.

Q9 The new formula subtracts the deaths of the previous year and should read

$$\text{if}\ (caseindex = 1)\begin{cases} 2000 \\ prev(pop) + prev(new) - prev(deaths) \end{cases}$$

The exponential equation for *pop* still fits.

Q10 $pop = A(1 + newrate - deathrate)^{year}$

Q11 As the population grows, the rate of death also grows. (This question hints at the concept of derivative.) Students may notice that the graph points are "clumping" as the population gets close to its limit.

Q12 As time goes on, the population seems to be stabilizing at a specific number, which appears to be 13,500.

Q13 When *newrate* = 0.28, the population appears to approach 14,000. When *newrate* = 0.29, the population appears to approach 14,500. For each percentage point increase, the population limit appears to increase by 500 people.

EXPLORE MORE

Assuming students use 13,500 for c, the values are $a = 5.75$ and $b \approx 1.29$, giving

$$pop = \frac{13{,}500}{1 + 5.75(1.29)^{-year}}$$

This function should be a good model for their data.

EXTENSION

Have students pick two cities, research their growth, and model the data using Fathom.

RATES OF CHANGE (PAGE 67)

Activity Time: 30 minutes

Required Document: RatesOfChange.ftm

Fathom Prerequisites: Students should be able to

- Open a document
- Work with sliders and formulas
- Create graphs

Fathom Skills: Students will learn how to

- Enter formulas for attributes in case tables and graphs
- Manipulate sliders and graphs

Mathematics Prerequisites: Students should be familiar with slopes (rates of change) of functions and have been introduced to the concepts of derivative and instantaneous rate of change.

Mathematics Skills: Students will get a better understanding of the derivative by comparison of the average and instantaneous rates of change.

General Notes: Students will explore the difference between the average and instantaneous rate of change both numerically and graphically. The activity concentrates on power functions.

EXPERIMENT

Q1 a is the derivative. You could describe this kind of motion as a racecar, initially at rest, that picks up speed and accelerates faster as time passes.

Q2 v is an increasing linear function; a is a horizontal line at $a = 1$.

INVESTIGATE

Q3 As x increases, the difference between a and *Ave_Rate* gets larger. $x = 5$, Difference = 14; $x = 20$, Difference = 59; $x = 35$, Difference = 104.

Q4 Difference = 7.25. The difference will continue to decrease as n decreases.

Q5 $x = 5$, $a = 75$

n	*Ave_Rate*	$a -$ *Ave_Rate*
1	61	14
0.5	67.75	7.25
0.2	72.04	2.96
0.01	73.51	1.49
0.05	74.25	0.75
0.01	74.85	0.15

Q6 The instantaneous rate of change at $x = 5$ is the limit of the average rate of change at $x = 5$ as the interval approaches 0.

Q7 The *Ave_Rate* curve gets closer and closer to the actual derivative as n gets smaller.

$n = 0.5$

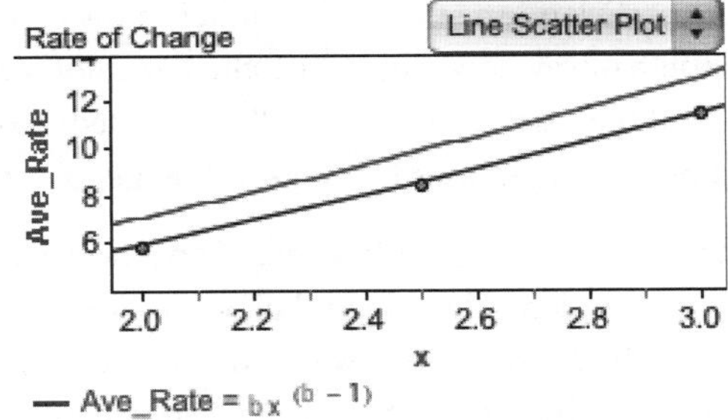

$n = 0.1$

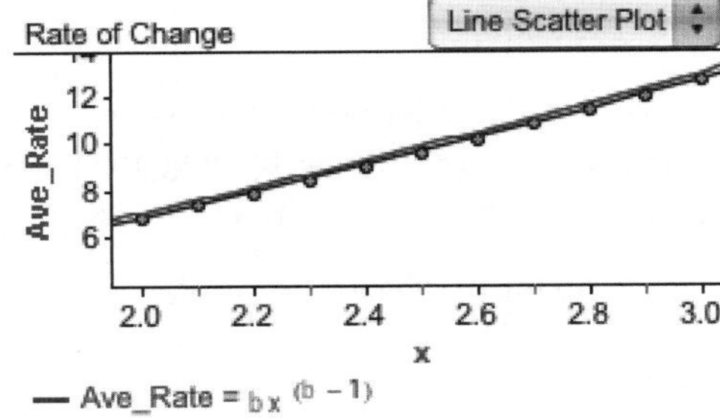

$n = 0.05$

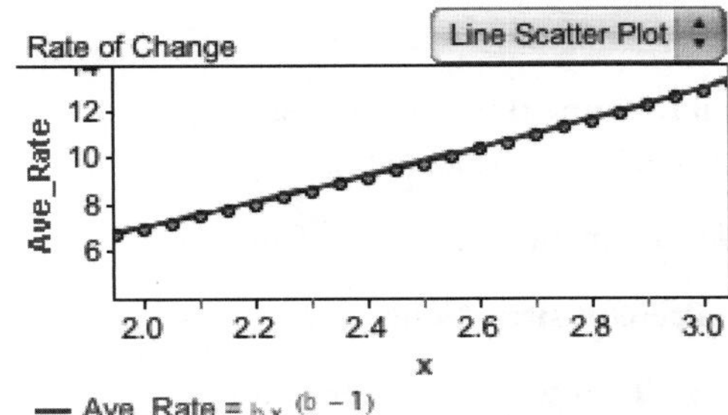

$n = 0.01$

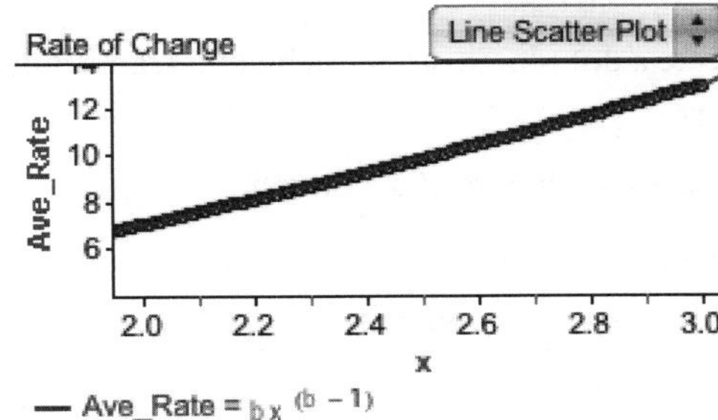

Q8 $f(x) = v$; In questions Q3–Q6, $c = 5$. In Q7, c is any of the points on the *Ave_Rate* graph. The derivative is the limit of the average rate of change over the interval from c to x as x approaches c.

U.S. CENSUS DATA (PAGE 73)

Activity Time: 45 minutes

Required Document: A census data file (called **CensusData.ftm** in the activity)

Example Document: CensusTex.ftm

Fathom Prerequisites: None

Fathom Skills: Students will learn how to

- Open a document
- Create a case table
- Create a dot plot, histogram, box plot, and ribbon chart
- Rescale the bin size of a histogram
- Plot a value on a graph
- Create new attributes
- Create formulas
- Create and modify a filter

Mathematics Prerequisites: Students should be able to understand one-variable graphs (dot plot, histogram, box plot) and work with the mean and the median.

Mathematics Skills: Students will look at different representations of data, such as tables, histograms, and box plots; examine differences and similarities between groups; consider the difference between mean and median as measures of center; and observe the effect of filtering out a particular group from a population.

General Notes: This activity uses census microdata to explore and compare one-variable graphs and measures of center. Students use selection to see where cases in one graph are located in another graph. It is appropriate for any class studying one-variable statistics.

You can use any sample of census data in this activity. The census file you use should include the following attributes: *Age, Sex, Marital_status, Total_personal_income,* and *Wage_and_salary_income.* Here is a view of the collection in **CensusTex.ftm:**

Texas Census 2000

	Census...	State_Fl...	Age	Sex	Race_G...	Marital_...	Total_p...	Wage_a...
1	2000	Texas	62	Female	White	Divorced	3000	0
2	2000	Texas	86	Female	White	Married_...	3800	0
3	2000	Texas	40	Female	White	Divorced	7700	7700
4	2000	Texas	22	Male	Other ra...	Married_...	0	0
5	2000	Texas	14	Male	Other ra...	Never m...		
6	2000	Texas	19	Male	White	Married_...	1800	1800
7	2000	Texas	66	Male	White	Married_...	35600	12000
8	2000	Texas	58	Female	White	Married_...	0	0
9	2000	Texas	8	Male	White	Never m...		

Try the activity with the file you plan to use *on a school machine* before giving it to your students. The file **CensusTex.ftm** has about 500 cases. Depending on the speed of your machines, that may be too many. If it's too slow, select about half the cases and delete them. To select many cases, click on the first row number in the case table. Then scroll halfway down and Shift-click on another row number. All the cases in between will be selected. To delete them, choose **Delete Cases** from the **Table** menu.

If you have time and a good Internet connection, you may want to have students download their own samples of census data. To do this, in a new document choose **File | Import | U.S. Census Data.** Select attributes and cases by expanding the lists. Make sure students request the attributes listed above. Click **Download Data** to import the data into Fathom.

If students need help getting started with axes, you might tell them they can change the scale by dragging parts of the axes. The cursor changes to give a hint.

Answers given are for the Texas Census file.

EXPERIMENT

Q1 Students can make the table larger by dragging one corner. They can drag the edges of the columns to better see the attribute names. In the file provided, the attributes are *Census_year, State_FIPS_code* (state), *Age, Sex, Race_general, Marital_status, Total_personal_income, Wage_and_salary_income.*

INVESTIGATE

Q2 In the Texas Census file, the data are slightly skewed right. There are clumps of people at ages 3–4, 25, 39, and 46.

Q3 There are 37 people between 15 and 20 years old. Students may have difficulty lining up the bin widths exactly. The idea is for them to experiment with changing the scale of the axes and changing the bin widths and to see that if they select cases in the graph, they will be given information about the cases in the bottom-left corner of their window.

Q4 The oldest person is 89. A dot plot makes it easier to view individual cases.

Q5 The median age is 30.5. A box plot will show the median.

Q6 The median age for males is 29.5. The median age for females is 31.

Q7 The mean age for males appears to be a little under 32. The mean age for females appears to be a little under 33. The mean age of 32.382 shown at the bottom of the graph is the mean age for the entire population.

Q8 The population has a longer tail on the right. The high ages affect the mean more than the median.

Q9 Not surprisingly, the children in the population have never been married. The never-married cases make up about 41.8%. In this sample there are some older women who have never married, but no older men.

Q10 209, or 41.8%, fall into the *married_spouse present* category. Another 16, or 3.2%, are *married_spouse absent.*

Q11 The richest people are mostly middle-aged males, married or divorced. Students will differ on how many people they select.

Q12 For the formula shown, anyone making over $50,000 will be considered rich. Anyone making $50,000 or less will be considered poor. Students will choose different category names and cutoff points.

Q13

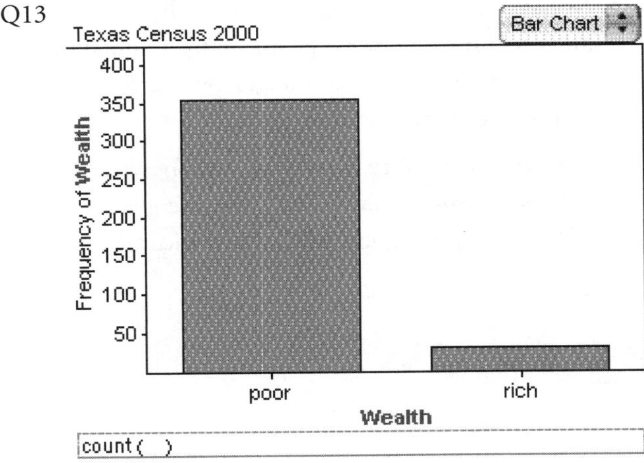

Q14 29 cases, or 7.59%. Click the "rich" bar to see the count.

Q15 Students may prefer either the height comparison of the bar chart or the width comparison of the ribbon chart.

Q16 The mean *Wage_and_salary_income* is about 18,729.9; the median is about 12,000.

Q17 Filtering out the retired people reduces the number of people with wages of 0. The new mean is 19,938.9; the new median is 14,450.

EXPLORE MORE

Encourage students to view different types of graphs and experiment with the other Fathom techniques they have learned.

1. Sample formula for *wealth* using *switch:*

```
Formula for Wealth
Wealth =  switch (Wealth) { (Wage_and_salary_income > 100000) : "rich"
                          { (Wage_and_salary_income > 50000)  : "upper-middle"
                          { (Wage_and_salary_income > 20000)  : "lower-middle"
                          { else                              : "poor"
```

2. Students could use the filter *inRange*(*Age*,13,19) to view only the teenagers.

3. Notice that *Total_personal_income* includes wages and other income. Some people in the population may have no income from wages, but a great deal of income from other sources.
4. Students may realize that it makes more sense to look at *Total_personal_income* for elderly people, as many of them are retired and will have no income from wages.

RANDOM WALK (PAGE 77)

Activity Time: 30–45 minutes

Fathom Prerequisites: None

Fathom Skills: Students will learn how to

- Open a new document
- Create a case table
- Create graphs (line graph, histogram)
- Create a derived collection
- Use the inspector to create a measure
- Collect measures

Mathematics Prerequisites: Students should be familiar with absolute value and average.

Mathematics Skills: Students will simulate a random-walk situation and interpret the meaning of an average in different contexts.

General Notes: The random walk is a basic situation for the theoretical study of spread. It's actually a binomial problem—the populations at the various positions after *n* steps follow the distribution in the *n*th row of Pascal's triangle. With enough steps, the distribution approaches normality, and (of vital importance) the size of the standard deviation increases proportionally to the square root of *n*.

Here, students explore a less sophisticated question: What is the average distance you've gone after a random walk of 10 steps?

This activity gives students some experience with which to underpin the random-walk situation.

Students should learn that what we mean by *average* varies with context. The activity develops Fathom skills that will help students simulate the theoretical results.

This activity introduces *derived collections*. Students create what is called a *measures collection*—a collection whose job is to collect summary values from another collection. Those values are statistics—measures of that "source" collection. In the case of our random walk, they're the final position of the walk. This table compares the two collections:

Random-Walk (Source) Collection	Measures Collection
Each case is a step.	Each case represents one andom walk.
The whole collection is one random walk: a collection of steps.	The collection summarizes many random walks (10 by default).
The final position is a single number (a statistic, a measure) that summarizes the whole walk.	Each case contains the final position of one walk, so the collection has many "final positions."
You can't calculate the mean distance from the origin here, because this collection is only one example.	You can calculate the mean distance from the origin in this collection—by averaging the final positions.

MAKE A CONJECTURE

Q1 Predictions will vary. It might be useful to have students do a random walk before doing this activity. Ask what the greatest and least possible ending values are for each number of steps (for example, after 5 steps, the maximum possible value is 5, the minimum possible value is −5).

EXPERIMENT

Q2 Students should have the idea that the next position equals the previous position plus *randomPick*(−1,1).

Q3 The numbers will change. Students should do this enough times to see a variety of results. The starting value will always be 1 or −1, and the final value will usually be between −6 and 6.

Q4 Students will have 20 values. One would expect the average to be 0, but answers will vary.

Q5 The average of the absolute values will be higher. The first average represents the average ending location on the number line for 20 walks. The second average represents the average distance of the final point from the starting point of 0.

INVESTIGATE

Q6 The bars represent the number of times the walk ended at each of those values. The line represents the mean of those end values.

Q7 The mean of the absolute values will be larger, except in the unlikely case that both are 0, because the student is averaging positive numbers (and 0).

Q8 It makes sense to have a value close to 0 for the average of *final*. For the mean of the absolute value of *final*, it seems to be close to 2.5.

EXPLORE MORE

1. The theoretical mean of the absolute value will not change for 400 or for 40 trials, since each walk consists of 10 steps. The observed mean will probably be closer to the theoretical value with 400 trials than with only 40.

2. If the walk were 40 steps instead of 10, there would be four times as many steps, so you would be likely to be twice as far away—about 5 units. The exact answer is

$$expectedvalue = 4 \cdot (0.5)^n \sum_{i=1}^{n/2} i \cdot \binom{n}{\frac{n}{2} - i} \approx 5.015$$

where n, the number of steps, is 40.

3. Here is an approach using Pascal's triangle. Each additional row represents the possibilities after an additional step. After 10 steps, we have 11 numbers, representing the possibilities from −10 to 10 (even numbers only). Looking at only that row of Pascal's triangle, we see

Pascal	1	10	45	120	210	252	210	120	45	10	1
Location	−10	−8	−6	−4	−2	0	2	4	6	8	10

Each of the Pascal numbers is the number of ways you can get to that location. There are 10 steps, so there are $2^{10} = 1024$ possible routes—and that is the sum of the Pascal row.

To find the expected absolute value, find the mean of the absolute value of Location, weighted by the number of routes. So, add the absolute values of the products of the top and bottom rows of that table:

$$10 + 80 + 270 + 480 + 420 + 0 + 420 + 480 + 270 + 80 + 10 = 2520$$

That's the total distance for all the "walks," so divide by the number of walks, 1024. The expected value is $\frac{2520}{1024} = 2.461$.

EXPLORING SAMPLING (PAGE 81)

Activity Time: 30–45 minutes

Required Document: DeckOfCards.ftm

Fathom Prerequisites: Students should be able to

- Open files
- Create a case table
- Create a new attribute
- Use the formula editor

Fathom Skills: Students will learn how to

- Sample cases with and without replacement
- Change the properties of a sample, such as the sample size
- Use an inspector to create a measure
- Create a collection of measures

Mathematics Prerequisites: Students should be familiar with basic probability concepts.

Mathematics Skills: Students will create a simulation using sampling, understand the difference between sampling with and without replacement, and calculate an empirical probability from sampling data.

General Notes: Sampling is a central idea in statistics. This activity introduces the mechanics of sampling with Fathom and then uses sampling to investigate probability. Students explore the distinction between sampling with replacement and without it.

In question Q15, students are asked to find out how many pairs were drawn in all the samples from the entire class. You will need to facilitate this data collection in any way that is practical. We do this to increase the number of samples and thereby to decrease the sampling error of the probability we get.

The handout doesn't tell students how to make the formula for *pair*—the Boolean formula that assesses whether or not the two cards in the sample are a pair. Any formula that accomplishes the task is acceptable. Here are two possibilities:

Straightforward *first*(*number*) = *last*(*number*)

Subtle *uniqueValues*(*number*) = 1

Students are more likely to come up with the first formula, which works nicely. If they go on to the Explore More section, you should introduce them to the second formula. For the question on getting a pair in a five-card sample, the formula is *uniqueValues*(*number*) = 4. (The equals sign—as opposed to ≤—is correct. If *uniqueValues*(*number*) = 3, for example, that means the hand has two pair or three of a kind.)

MAKE A CONJECTURE

Q1 The teacher will write down 10 names, but the names may repeat. It is possible, but not likely, that the teacher will pick the same name 10 times in a row.

Q2 The teacher will write down 10 different names. It is not possible for the same student to be picked twice, because the names are not replaced after being picked.

Q3 If the teacher is sampling with replacement, she can theoretically continue picking students forever. If she is sampling without replacement, she can pick only 30 names.

EXPERIMENT

Q4 There are 10 names in the case table. It is sampling with replacement. This is evident because there are only 8 names, but 10 names in the sample. Some are repeating.

Q5 Each time the **Sample More Cases** button is clicked, a new set of 5 names appears in the case table. They may repeat.

Q6 Student results will vary. You can gather results from the class to show the spread of results.

Q7 No, the same name will never appear twice in the sample. If the sample size is changed to 8, all 8 names will come up every time (but the order will change).

Q8 All 8 names come up every time.

Q9 When **Sample More Cases** is clicked, the inspector changes the number of cases to 8. This is the maximum number of cases for sampling without replacement.

Q10 There are 52 cases in the collection. The attributes are *suit, number,* and *name.* The collection represents a deck of cards.

Q11 Clicking **Sample More Cases** brings up 10 new cards. Cards may repeat.

INVESTIGATE

Q12 One possibility is *first*(*number*) = *last*(*number*). Another possibility is *uniqueValues*(*number*) = 1.

Q13 This collection has attributes *cardSize* and *pair.* There should be 5 cases if the sample size is set to its default of 5. Have students click the arrow to view different cases.

Q14 Sample answer: 15 cases true, 185 false. Students can use the graph to find the number of trues and verify that the bar counts add up to 200.

Q15 Make sure that you have recorded class values before moving on. The next part of the activity will wipe out the previous data.

Q16 Hopefully, there will be fewer trues—perhaps 12 out of 200.

Q17 Make sure students know that empirical probability is the same as experimental probability. Use the class results to calculate these answers. Sample answer: The probability would be $\frac{15}{200}$, or 0.08, for the pair with replacement, and $\frac{12}{200}$, or 0.06, for the pair without replacement.

EXPLORE MORE

1. You can have a more general discussion of the principles if students have not studied probability. Think about only the second card. With replacement, the chances are $\frac{4}{52}$ that you will draw a card of the same number. Without replacement, the probability is only $\frac{3}{52}$.
2. Note that the value of *number* for an ace is 1. You need to test the first and the last (second) card in the sample to see whether it is an ace or a ten card. (Face cards have a value of ten.) One way to do this is to create new measures in the original collection with these formulas:

$hasAce = (first(number) = 1)$ or $(last(number) = 1)$

$hasTen = (first(number) > 9)$ or $(last(number) > 9)$

$blackjack = hasAce$ and $hasTen$

The theoretical probability for getting blackjack without replacement is

$$\frac{4}{52} \cdot \frac{16}{51} + \frac{16}{52} \cdot \frac{4}{52} \approx 0.048$$

With replacement, the probability is

$$\frac{4}{52} \cdot \frac{16}{52} + \frac{16}{52} \cdot \frac{4}{52} \approx 0.047$$

3. Change the number of cases for the sample collection to be 5. To get a formula for the pair, use $uniqueValues(number) = 4$. This will return the cases where there are only four unique numbers, indicating that two cards must match.

ROLLING DICE (PAGE 85)

Activity Time: 30–45 minutes

Required Document: RollingDice.ftm

Materials: None (you may want to introduce the activity using a 6-sided die)

Fathom Prerequisites: Students should be able to

- Open files
- Create a case table
- Create a histogram
- Use an inspector
- Make collection attributes
- Create formulas

Fathom Skills: Students will learn how to

- Sample until a condition is true
- Graph a mean value
- Create an attribute for a measures collection

Mathematics Prerequisites: Students should be familiar with basic probability concepts.

Mathematics Skills: Students will differentiate between mode and mean, find a mode from a histogram, and relate the probability of an event to the expected number of trials to get a success.

General Notes: This activity explores how many trials it will take to achieve a particular result.

If the probability of an event is p, the expected number of trials you need to get a success is $\frac{1}{p}$. In this case, the probability of rolling a 6 is $\frac{1}{6}$, so the expected number of trials is 6.

Sampling does not necessarily involve choosing the size of the sample ahead of time. However, if it does not, you must be specific about the conditions under which sampling ceases. In the case of Fathom, you can control sampling with a Boolean expression.

It is possible (though unlikely, we hope) for some sampling situations to go on forever. If your sampling seems to go on forever, you can press the Escape key to stop it.

This situation gives rise to a distribution that starts off big and tails off. With this kind of distribution, mean > median > mode.

MAKE A CONJECTURE

Q1 Many students may give the correct answer of 6.

EXPERIMENT

Q2 As the sample is collected, the number of cases in the case table increases or decreases to accommodate the number of rolls. The last number in the case table is always 6.

Q3 Any bar may be the tallest. The bars probably (but not necessarily) decrease in size moving to the right (it is a geometric distribution).

Q4 Sample graph:

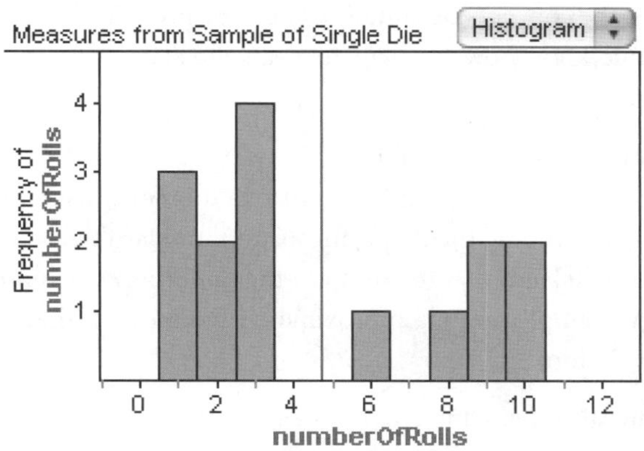

The number being plotted is the answer to our question: the average number of rolls to get a 6.

Q5 Hopefully, students will collect a large number of measures, and the mean will be approximately 6. The histogram should look smoother and the distribution more geometric.

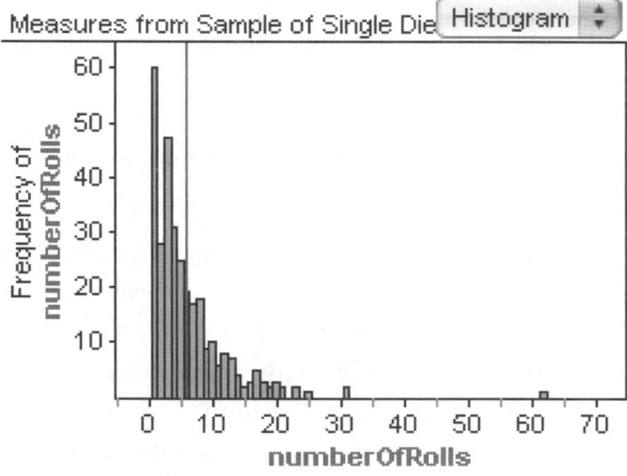

Q6 The most likely number of rolls to get a six is the mode, which is 1. This should be the tallest bar in the histogram.

Q7 The mode is at one end of the distribution. The long tail of higher numbers of rolls pulls the mean to the right.

EXPLORE MORE

1. The median number is 4 rolls to get a six. Students can plot this value on their graph, or they can view the graph as a box plot to see the median.
2. The mean number of rolls would go down, because there wouldn't be any repeated numbers. It would become impossible for the number of rolls to be greater than 6.
3. In one experiment, the average number of trials to get a five and a six was 4.7, and the average number of trials to get a five or a six was 2.4. A statement with *or* in it is more likely than a statement with *and.* The probability is greater that one of the two conditions will be met before both are met (especially if they can't both occur at the same time).

EXTENSIONS

1. Use the Fathom random-number function *randomExponential*$\left(\frac{1}{6}\right)$, where $p = \frac{1}{6}$ is the probability of an event, to model this situation more quickly and get a *lot* of cases.
2. Pose this problem: Suppose you roll two six-sided dice. How many rolls will you need, on the average, to get a seven or an eleven? Have students predict first, based on this activity, then design the simulation and carry it out.

   A good guess would be between 4 and 5 rolls, because there are 8 ways to get a seven or an eleven out of the 36 total outcomes (6 on the first die times 6 on the second die). Theoretically, the mean is the reciprocal of the probability (4.5). The simulation can be carried out by sampling with replacement. One set of 100 trials gave a mean of 4.5 and a median of 3 rolls.

POCKET PENNIES (PAGE 87)

Activity Time: 45 minutes

Optional Document: PocketPennies.ftm

Materials: 25 pennies per student, if using class data

Fathom Prerequisites: Students should be able to

- Take samples and collect measures
- Create histograms and graph values and functions

Fathom Skills: Students will learn how to

- Collect and combine measures for different sample sizes
- Split a graph by using an attribute as a category
- Differentiate between a collection, samples from the collection, and measures of samples from the collection
- *Optional:* Graph a normal curve (Explore More 1)

Mathematics Prerequisites: Students should be familiar with the concepts of sampling and measures. Students should know how to calculate mean and standard deviation.

Mathematics Skills: In this activity, students will discover the properties of the sampling distribution of the sample mean, including the shape, mean, and standard deviation. They will learn that the mean of the sampling distribution of the sample mean is approximately the mean of the population.

General Notes: This activity is an introduction to the Central Limit Theorem. The sampling distribution of the sample mean approaches the normal distribution as the sample size increases, regardless of the shape of the original population distribution.

The pre-made file **PocketPennies.ftm** contains the dates for a collection of 648 pennies. You can compile these data yourself using pennies that your students record. There is also a file on the Fathom Reource Center called **648pennies.ftm.** Note that in **648pennies.ftm,** *Penny_Age* is given, and *Year* is calculated from that with a formula.

Students may get confused about the difference between the mean calculated from the original collection and the graph of *MeanAge* for the samples. Question Q7 addresses this, but it may be helpful to discuss it earlier.

INVESTIGATE

Q1 Students may predict a bell-shaped curve. The actual curve is roughly geometric.

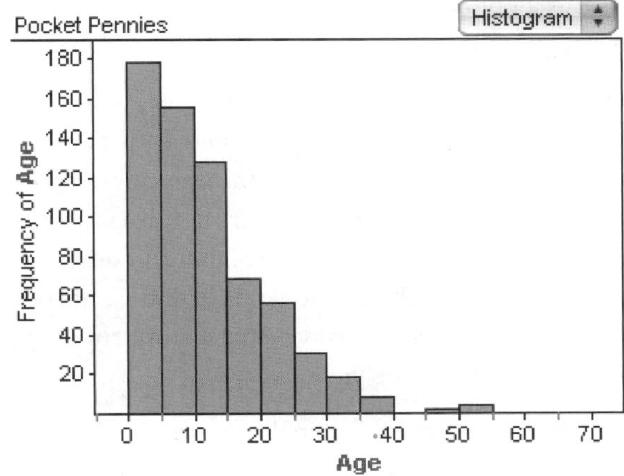

Q2 Students should reflect on what assumptions they made in their prediction and what the actual distribution shows. Estimates will vary.

Q3 Sample answer: The mean is about 10.4 and the standard deviation is about 9.2.

Q4 The mean for one sample was 14.8. At this point, means may vary widely. Students may not be able to make a valid prediction yet.

Q5 The value for mean should be close to the value of mean for the original collection. The standard deviation should be smaller. Sample results: a mean of 10.3 and a standard deviation of 4.2.

Q6–Q7 As the sample size increases, the shape of the histogram should look more like a normal curve. The mean for the sampling distributions should be approximately equal to the mean for the population of all pennies, but the standard deviation should decrease as the sample size increases. The standard deviation of the sampling distributions should approximately equal the standard deviation of the population divided by the square root of the sample size.

Q8 Discuss this question with the entire class. One case in Pocket Pennies represents one penny. One case in Sample of Pocket Pennies represents a penny selected randomly from the original collection. One case in Measures from Sample of Pocket Pennies represents a measure of the *MeanAge* and *SampleSize* from one sample.

EXPLORE MORE

1. Students will need to enter the following formula to see the normal distribution scaled to fit their graphs: 100 • *normalDensity*(*x*, *mean*, 1).
2. Students should make a new graph with *MeanAge* on the vertical axis. They can split by *SampleSize* on the horizontal axis. The normal quantile plot is an option in the graph pop-up menu. The closer the data are to normal, the more they will lie on a straight line. (This graph plots the data against the *z*-score associated with the percentile of each case if the data were normally distributed. Therefore, if the data are normal, the plot should show a straight line. The line in the plot corresponds to quantiles of a normal distribution whose mean and standard deviation are the same as the mean and standard deviation of the data. The intercept of the line is the mean of the data, the slope is the standard deviation.)

ORBITAL EXPRESS (PAGE 90)

Activity Time: 60–120 minutes

Required Document: OrbEx.ftm

Materials:

- Two kinds of paper with different weights, such as copier paper and paper towels. One sheet of each kind per group.
- 3 × 5 cards, cut into small, identically-sized pieces (e.g., quarters). 20 pieces per group
- One tape measure at least 5 feet long per group
- A small marker, one per group (a coin will work)
- A roll of masking tape, one per group
- Paper and pencil for recording data

Fathom Prerequisites: Students should be able to

- Enter data
- Make graphs
- Write a formula
- Use the inspector

Fathom Skills: Students will learn how to

- Use scrambling
- Collect measures
- Compare their test statistic to the distribution

Mathematics Prerequisites: Students should be familiar with mean and median.

Mathematics Skills: Students develop a statistic that measures how much better one design is than the other. They come to understand that this statistic could result from chance variation; they also see that many genuinely random patterns look quite skewed. Students shuffle the data between the designs repeatedly to assess how likely it is that any difference they see is due to chance.

General Notes: This activity is about hypothesis testing. Students test two competing designs for orbital re-entry vehicles by dropping wads of paper. The null hypothesis is that there is no difference between the designs; the analysis will see if we can reject that hypothesis. The first part of the activity is offline. You can use the student worksheets provided or just give verbal instructions to the students.

In the second part of the activity, students create a distribution of a statistic given the null hypothesis. That is, in order to see whether their statistic would likely arise by chance, they artificially make the two variables—*distance* and *paper*—independent. Their association is broken through randomization (by scrambling the values of one of the attributes).

Preparation: Paper towels and copier paper are so different that you may want to try materials that are more similar. Cheap, flimsy binder paper or scratch newsprint works well when contrasted with a crisp, strong copier paper. Ideally, some groups will get significant differences, but not so gross that there is no point in doing statistics. (You may, if you wish, ask students to brainstorm *briefly* how they plan to analyze their data.)

Find a place (indoors or sheltered from wind) where students can drop wads of paper. Standing and dropping is okay, but not as much fun as using stairwells or balconies. If you use outdoor bleachers, you'll need different re-entry vehicles to account for the wind.

Make sure to take time to discuss the development of the students' statistic. Discuss the way the procedures for calculating statistics do or do not fit the small/large rule (see step 4). One of the points of this activity is that random variation is more varied than we expect. Consider recording these informal "critical values" so that you can compare them to the distribution later.

Overview of Scrambling: Scrambling was probably not part of your statistics education as an instructor, but it is a recognized nonparametric technique. It's called a *randomized permutation test.* Your students will do it with concrete materials—cards on a tape measure—as well as with Fathom.

This section gives you additional background on the procedure and how it works in Fathom.

There are two attributes, *paper* and *distance.* The values of *paper* will be (for example) "copier" and "towel," so *paper* is a categorical attribute. The distances will be numeric, measured in centimeters. Each case (each row in the table) will be *only one measurement.* Students should not put the two kinds of paper in the same row. Each collection will have 14 cases. That's the *source* collection.

Here's the key: If one design (towel, say) is really better than the other, there will be a relationship between the two attributes. For example, the median distance may be smaller for "towel" than it is for "copier". Put another way, knowing what kind of paper is being used helps you predict the distance.

On the other hand, if there is no difference between the two designs, the two attributes are independent. Knowing the kind of paper doesn't help you predict distance. That's our *null hypothesis.* Even under the null hypothesis, though, one median will be smaller in a given sample of 14 drops. But that's because of chance variation, not because one design is really better.

Now suppose that the median distance for "towel" is 12 cm less than for "copier." How do we figure out whether our data could be due to chance variation? We make the null hypothesis real and generate the data many times to make a distribution. In this case, we make the null hypothesis real by forcing the two attributes to be independent—by shuffling (or *scrambling*) one of them. When an attribute is randomly shuffled, *there is no relationship between its values and those of any other attribute.* There will still be chance variation, but that's what we want. By computing our measure (e.g., the difference of medians) for a slew of null-hypothesis situations, we can see how much the measure is likely to vary by chance.

To do this in Fathom requires three collections. See the screen shot at the bottom of the page for what a document might look like near the end of the activity.

The original data are on the left. In the middle, you can see the same data with the first attribute, *paper,* scrambled. The scrambled collection itself is on the top in the middle.

At the right, you see the measures collection, Measures from Scrambled Drop Data. It has 100 values of *myMeasure,* which is the difference of medians. We defined *myMeasure* as a measure in the original Drop Data collection. Then every time we scramble, the scrambled collection calculates its value for *myMeasure* and passes it on to the measures collection, which graphs it.

Overview of Scrambling

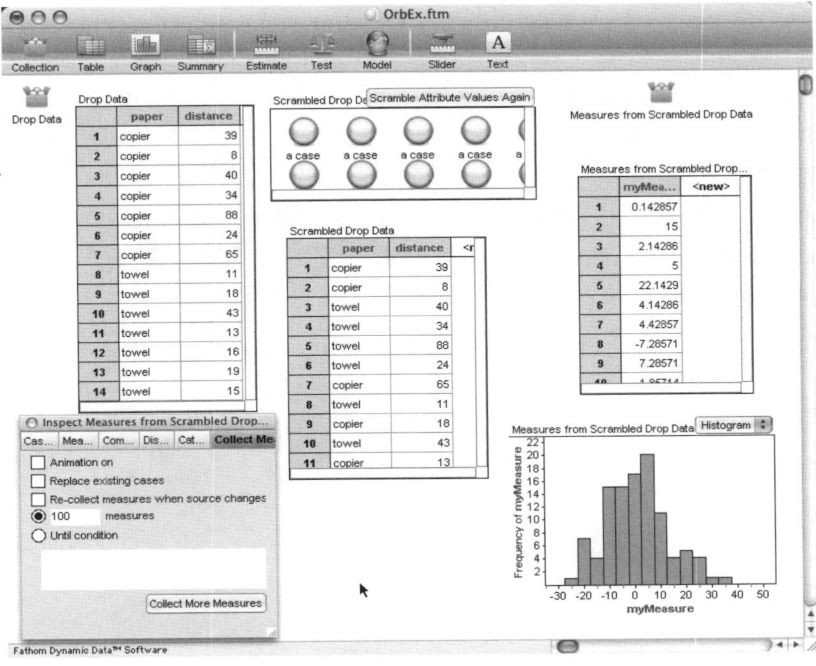

Students will need help writing formulas. Listen carefully to their ideas and see if you can explain things in terms of the ideas they already have. Let them try their formulas and see what happens. Say "Fathom won't understand that" instead of "That's wrong."

For example, when you ask what number they will use to describe how much better one is than the other, some students answer, "The mean." If you ask, "The mean of what?" they answer, "The mean of *distance*." Let them try it. The formula would be *mean*(*distance*).

With that formula, every scramble gets the same statistic! What they really want is the *difference* of means:
mean(*distance*, *paper* = "*copier*") −
mean(*distance*, *paper* = "*towel*").

Of course, we'd like to see many different formulas in the class. Here are some other ideas: difference of medians; ratio of medians; ratio of means; the mean of the copier paper only; and the number of copier measurements that are larger than the overall mean.

For most groups, it will look as if the paper towel is better than the copier paper. Nevertheless, when you do the test, you will probably get a *P*-value above the orthodox 5%; that is, it will look somewhat unlikely—but still plausible—that the difference could have arisen by chance. One solution is to get more samples.

Here are additional issues you might raise:

- Why do you suppose the directions always say "at least as extreme" instead of "more extreme"? That is, why do ties count for the null hypothesis?
- What makes a formula easy or hard to describe in Fathom? Does anyone have ideas for ways to express a hard formula more easily?
- Besides scrambling, how else could you test whether the two papers were different? How is that method similar to the one we used here? What are the important differences between the two techniques?
- Shouldn't we be using a two-tailed test? (Probably.) How would you do that in Fathom?

INVESTIGATE (BY HAND)

Q1 Depending on how different the two types of paper are, students may have a lot of evidence or a little evidence that one design is better than the other.

Q2 Give students a lot of support in developing and testing their statistic. Ideas are given in the general notes.

Q3 Student answers will vary.

Q4 Some groups may find that the values for their statistic are always larger from the shuffles. Have groups compare their results.

Q5 Wind, distance dropped from, irregularities on the landing surface, and other factors can affect how close to the target the vehicle lands.

Q6 You may want to discuss measurement accuracy and significant figures with students.

Q7 Make sure that students understand the reason for shuffling. They are now creating a random division of the measurements and observing whether or not there seems to be a measurable difference. They may be surprised by the distribution of their shuffled cases.

Q8 The null hypothesis is that there is no difference between the two designs.

INVESTIGATE (WITH FATHOM)

Q9 This answer should match student responses from their offline experiment (Q1). Here are some sample data:

Drop Data

	paper	distance
1	copier	39
2	copier	8
3	copier	40
4	copier	34
5	copier	88
6	copier	24
7	copier	65
8	towel	11
9	towel	18
10	towel	43
11	towel	13
12	towel	16
13	towel	19
14	towel	15

Q10 Check that students have correctly entered their statistic into *myMeasure.* Here is one version:

Inspect drop data

Cases | Measures | Comments | Display | Categories

Measure	Value	Formula
myMeasure	23.2857	mean(distance, paper = "copier") − mean(distance, paper = "towel")
<new>		

Q11 Make sure that students are checking the value of *myMeasure* in the scrambled collection.

Q12 The first collection is the data from the original drops. This keeps the values from the student experiment and separates them by paper (design) type. The second collection is the scrambled data, and this will be used to discover if the measure is due to chance or shows a real difference in the paper quality. The third collection is recording a large number of scrambles so that we can find out if the *myMeasure* value tells us the answer to this question.

Q13 In one trial, 4 cases out of 105, or 3.8%, were selected.

Q14 Students can increase the number of measures to collect. They may notice a difference if they collect a very large number of measures, such as 1000.

Q15 In a typical class, only half or fewer get a significant difference at the 5% level.

EXTENSION

Have students try to design a re-entry vehicle that's better than the existing designs. They should make a prototype and test it against the best "wad" design. They might also consider having a different researcher conduct the test.

CREATING ERROR (PAGE 95)

Activity Time: 60 minutes

Fathom Prerequisites: Students should be able to

- Create a case table
- Create an attribute and give it a formula
- Create a graph
- Create and name a slider

Fathom Skills: Students will learn how to

- Create a residual plot
- Rerandomize a collection
- Set the range for a slider

Mathematics Prerequisites: Students should be familiar with linear and quadratic graphs and equations, normal distributions, and random numbers.

Mathematics Skills: Students will learn how error affects analysis by controlling the amount of error in their data and observing what features are visible in the data with different amounts of error.

General Notes: In the Experiment section, students create a simple linear relationship that they then cloud up by introducing error. The activity makes explicit a common construction in statistics: that the observations consist of a signal plus an error term. Adding error reduces the correlation coefficient. If the errors are much larger than the scale of the function, r^2 can appear to go to 0. Horizontal errors reduce the slope of the least-squares line, but vertical errors do not change it. This is because the residuals we look at to make the least-squares line are vertical. You can think of the least-squares line as trying to go through the mean value in each vertical stripe. That mean will be the same no matter how much error is added in.

Some items you may wish to address with students: Why is the correlation coefficient *r* the same no matter which attribute is on which axis? It's fundamentally different from the slope of the least-squares line. It's a measure of association between the attributes, not an analysis of how one depends on the other. The formula for the correlation coefficient is completely symmetrical.

When you see the two graphs and the two least-squares lines, do the lines go through the same points? Here are two strategies for finding out: One is to select points in one graph and see that, for example, points on the line in one graph are off the line in the other; the second is to do the algebra on the two equations and show that when you solve for effect they are not the same.

The Investigate section explores two issues: the use of residual plots to identify underlying shape in a distribution, and the way measurement error can obscure a model. Students first create data that lie along a parabola, then add variable amounts of error and observe the changes in the graph and the residual plot.

Students should see that random error can make it impossible to see an effect; in other words, they will completely lose the shape of the original curve when the error is too great. Students will test the effect of error by simulating it. That is, after the activity, they will see that to detect the curvature in the data, they will need to measure to within about 0.1.

Sample Graphs: Following are three graphs like the ones students should produce. All three have the same data—the function $y = x^2$—but each has a different amount of error added. The standard deviation (*SD*) of the first graph's error is 1.0, and the curvature is completely washed out. In the second, *SD* is only 0.15, and you can detect the curvature if you have a good imagination. Finally, at *SD* = 0.04—amazingly small—the curvature is obvious, especially in the residual plot. Notice the vertical scales on these plots.

SD = 1.00

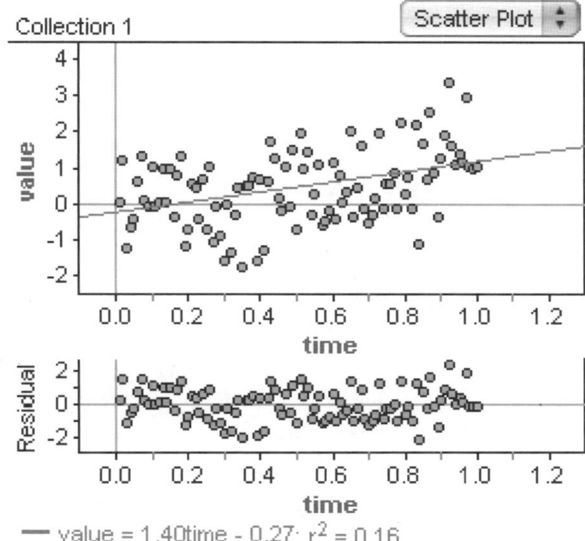

SD = 0.04

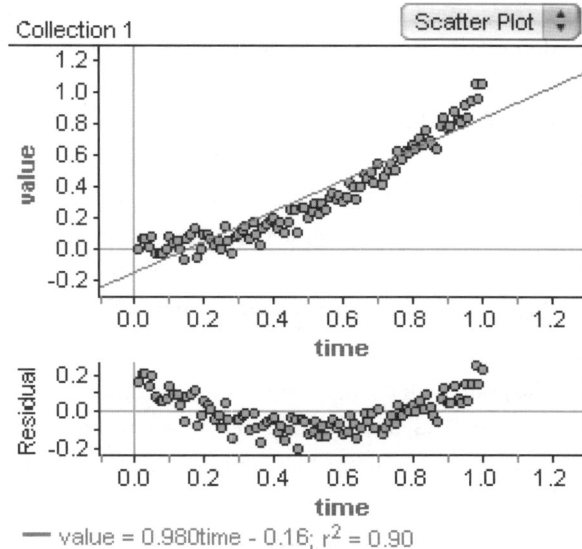

SD = 0.15

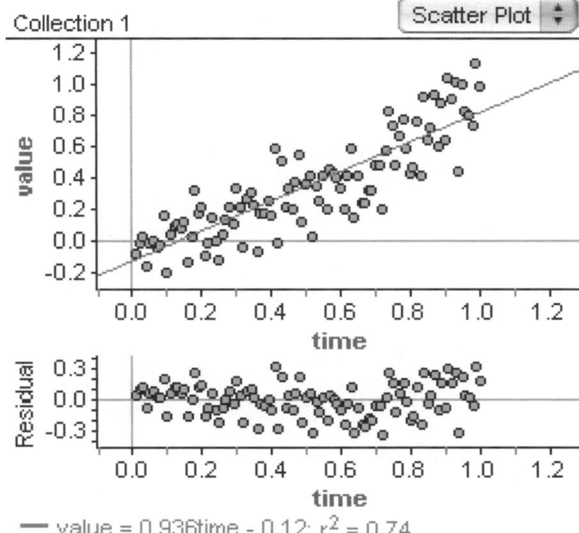

EXPERIMENT

Q1 The slope of the least-squares line is 1. The value of r^2 is 1.00. This is what you expect, because the graph is $y = x$ (*effect* = *cause*).

Q2 When *SD* is near 0, the data are nearer the line $y = x$.

Q3 As *SD* gets larger, the error increases and points become more scattered about the original line, decreasing the r^2 value. The slope varies more because of sampling variation, but the values remain the same on the average. On any given vertical swath of the graph, the mean value of *effect* is the same.

Q4 The slope and r^2 both go to 0 as *SD* increases. The correlation coefficient is symmetrical, but the least-squares line is not. As *SD* increases, the mean value for *cause* in a vertical swath where *effect* is low increases. The reverse happens for large values of *effect,* lowering the slope of the regression line.

INVESTIGATE

Q5 Between *time* = 0 and *time* = 0.5, the function is increasing, but the residual plot is decreasing. This is because the points are decreasing relative to the least-squares line—they start out above it and end up below it.

Q6 When *SD* is very close to 0, the graph and the residual plot will show the curve. Students must get the slider extremely close to 0 (less than 0.05) to see this. If they do not get the slider very close, they may see the curve as they adjust the slider, but lose it when they rescale the graph. This is a good opportunity to discuss the effects of scale on models of data. See Explore More 1 for more on this idea.

Q7 Students may be able to see the curve at values of *SD* from 0.04 to 0.10. Students may have higher values at this step, but after rerandomizing they will need to lower their values.

Q8 The graph will change shape as the student rerandomizes. Some graphs may now appear flat and random, and students may need to adjust their values from Q7.

Q9 From 0.04 to 0.15, depending on the person viewing the graph.

EXPLORE MORE

1. The scale of the graph changes, so the range of *y*-values is now 100 to 121, whereas the earlier graph had *y*-values from 0 to 1. The graph looks straight, but the residual plot will look similar.
2. Students can use the formula *random*() for *time.* It shouldn't make any difference in the *SD* value.
3. By adding more cases, the curve can endure more error. The value for *SD* can be increased and the curvature will still be visible.
4. Including more cases can help reduce the effect of error on the curve. If you suspect curvature, increasing the range of the independent variable is very effective.

Comment Form

Please take a moment to provide us with feedback about this book. We are eager to read any comments or suggestions you may have. Once you've filled out this form, simply fold it along the dotted lines and drop it in the mail. We'll pay the postage. Thank you!

Your Name ______________________________

School ______________________________

School Address ______________________________

City/State/Zip ______________________________

Phone ______________________________

Book Title ______________________________

Please list any comments you have about this book.

____

____

____

____

____

____

____

____

____

____

Do you have any suggestions for improving the student or teacher material?

____

____

____

____

____

____

____

Please detach page, fold on lines and tape edge.

NO POSTAGE
NECESSARY
IF MAILED
IN THE
UNITED STATES

BUSINESS REPLY MAIL
FIRST CLASS PERMIT NO. 338 OAKLAND, CA

POSTAGE WILL BE PAID BY ADDRESSEE

KEY CURRICULUM PRESS
1150 65TH STREET
EMERYVILLE CA 94608-9740
ATTN: EDITORIAL